ONE HUNDRED YEARS OF ARMY NURSING

ONE HUNDRED YEARS
OF ARMY NURSING

The Story of the British Army Nursing Services
from the time of Florence Nightingale
to the present day

by IAN HAY
(Major-General John Hay Beith, C.B.E., M.C.)

CASSELL & COMPANY LIMITED

LONDON

CASSELL & CO. LTD.
37/38 St. Andrew's Hill
Queen Victoria Street
London, E.C.4

and at

210 Queen Street, Melbourne
26/30 Clarence Street, Sydney
Haddon Hall, City Road, Auckland, N.Z.
1068 Broadview Avenue, Toronto 6
122 East 55th Street, New York 22
Avenida 9 de Julho 1138, São Paulo
Galeria Güemes, Escritorio 518/520 Florida 165, Buenos Aires
Haroon Chambers, South Napier Road, Karachi
15 Graham Road, Ballard Estate, Bombay 1
17 Central Avenue P.O. Dharamtala, Calcutta
P.O. Box 275, Cape Town
P.O. Box 1386, Salisbury, S. Rhodesia
P.O. Box 959, Accra, Gold Coast
Calçada Do Carma 55/2°, Lisbon
25 rue Henri Barbusse, Paris 5e
Islands Brygge 5, Copenhagen

First published 1953

Printed in Great Britain by
Wyman and Sons, Ltd., London, Fakenham and Reading
F. 1252

"One Hundred Years of Army Nursing"
is a memorial to the work achieved since the
leadership of Florence Nightingale.

This book should be a source of pride
to Queen Alexandra's Imperial Military Nursing
Service and an inspiration to Queen Alexandra's
Royal Army Nursing Corps.

I send them all my good wishes and
the assurance of my confidence that they will
uphold the traditions of the Corps of which I
am proud to be Colonel-in-Chief.

Mary R

October, 1952.

DEDICATED

To the Members of the Army Nursing Service who gave their Lives in the Second World War, 1939–1945.

QUEEN ALEXANDRA'S IMPERIAL MILITARY NURSING SERVICE

Principal Matron: V. M. E. Jones

Matrons

A. Cheyne
E. M. E. Ievers

L. C. Moir
S. G. Richardson
W. Russell

D. M. Smith
C. L. M. West

Sisters

E. K. Carroll
L. Coward
M. Davies
D. A. Field
M. R. Finlay
M. H. T. Fowler

M. A. Hodgson
E. Kelly
B. Le Blanc-Smith
A. C. Mills
H. L. Montgomery
M. O'Shea
M. L. A. Painter

E. D. Pedlow
M. E. Reed
V. V. Spedding
E. M. Thomson
D. H. Tombs
B. I. Wells

QUEEN ALEXANDRA'S IMPERIAL MILITARY NURSING SERVICE RESERVE

Sisters

F. Airey
J. K. Atkin
E. N. Ayers
A. M. C. Balfour
E. M. Bateman
E. E. Bevis
H. C. M. Bishop
C. F. Black
A. M. Blackman
G. G. E. Boehmer
E. Boundy
D. Bowyer
S. C. Boyd-Roberts
D. J. Brady
M. Brand
A. Brown
I. Burrows
S. Butler
N. M. Clement
C. H. Clewett
D. M. Cole

M. Cooper
J. Coulter
C. M. Cribb
M. K. Cruikshank
J. S. A. Curran
E. A. Dalgarno
L. Dalton
E. D. Dann
J. Darnell
E. F. Davidson
J. M. Davidson
S. Davidson
M. E. Davies
G. Dervan
A. W. Dewar
R. H. Dickson
S. E. Dixon
T. Doran
B. O. Dowling
D. Dunlop
R. N. Essex

M. E. Evans
M. Evershed
M. Farrelly
M. E. E. Farthing
C. M. FitzGerald
M. Florence
E. Foskett
A. M. Gardener
D. Garn
P. Gibson
H. M. Glazebrook
D. Groom
E. Hadridge
M. J. Haffenden
B. L. Hall
W. A. E. Harrison
G. W. Harvey
V. F. Hastings
F. E. Hennin
A. J. Hervey-Murray
E. Hollis

iii

Q. A. I. M. N. S. R. *Sisters—continued*

M. A. Hood
J. M. Houston
M. C. Humphrey
M. L. Hunt
W. M. James
M. Jarman
M. D. Job
M. F. Johnston
A. M. Kearon
M. J. Kells
W. E. Kells
E. F. Kirby
B. Kitt
G. L. Knight
E. A. Ladkin
A. Lamb
M. E. Leckey
B. E. Leech
M. J. Littleton
H. Lowbridge
K. D. McBryde
M. T. McCay
A. M. D. McClelland
M. D. McGregor
D. Machin
J. N. McLaren
M. C. McMillan
E. McMillin
E. MacPhail
F. L. Maddison
J. Malcolm
C. D. Manfield
H. I. Martin
E. M. Mawston

M. Maxwell
G. E. F. Miles
F. A. Millar
A. R. Mitchell
B. R. Moore
I. Moore
I. B. Morgan
M. Morgan
S. Morgan
D. M. Morris
A. W. Muir
C. M. Nichol
C. M. Nicholson
M. Nolan
P. Nuttal
A. M. O'Loughlin
C. L. O'Loughlin
M. O'Shea
B. A. O'Sullivan
M. M. O'Sullivan
B. Pirrie
J. Pitt
H. Porterfield
J. S. Portingale
M. N. Price
C. S. Pringle
E. W. Quin
E. E. Rhoden
P. G. Roberts
H. M. Robertson
M. Satchell
E. J. M. Schluter
D. E. Senior
C. M. Sharpe

H. K. Slann
M. Smith
E. M. Spellen
I. Spence
N. Sullivan
B. M. Sutherland
L. S. Symonds
K. M. M. Taylor
J. M. G. Thomas
M. I. Tonge
K. Toohey
G. C. Toon
H. A. Tudor
M. A. R. Urquhart
S. H. Vian
K. H. Walker
R. A. Warwick
G. Waters
E. H. Watson
L. M. E. Wheelock
M. S. Whitaker
G. M. White
K. F. M. White
A. A. Willis
M. M. I. Wilson
A. R. Wingate
W. M. F. Wood
M. Woodhead
C. D. M. Wort
P. Wren
I. Wright
J. B. Wright
E. J. Young

TERRITORIAL ARMY NURSING SERVICE

Sisters

M. A. Alton
L. A. Atkins
M. Baker
M. Bembridge
U. Cameron
E. Carter
A. M. Davies
E. English
M. E. Gale
D. E. George

H. F. M. Home
A. A. Ingham
A. Jobling
M. L. Johnson
M. Lea
A. Macgregor
M. M. M. MacKay
J. M. McRae
I. H. I. Main
N. Matthews

K. V. Peach
C. Rogers
E. Strachan
D. M. Stratford
L. S. Truman
J. Walters
M. Whitehead
H. B. Wills
E. M. Wilson
M. Woodhouse

CONTENTS

A*   v

Part Four

RETURN TO NORMAL

APPENDICES

MAPS

LIST OF ILLUSTRATIONS

FOREWORD

THIS book, in tracing the history of the Army Nursing Service from its beginning in the Crimea to the present day, shows what a long and weary road it has traversed from Florence Nightingale and the Institute of Protestant Deaconesses at Kaiserwerth to the Advanced Operating Centres of the last war and the Depot and Training Establishment of the Queen Alexandra's Royal Army Nursing Corps; from poke bonnets and long full skirts to steel helmets and battle-dress.

There were many factors to make that progress slow of which the most potent was the status of women in a society completely dominated by men. Hence the passion and prejudice engendered in many occupying high places in the medical and military professions at the intrusion of women into their domain. These old, long-drawn-out disputes are rightly dismissed summarily in this book, for the issues now seem so obvious that one is left wondering what it was all about—'so much as there is of passion so much there is of nothing to the purpose.'

The milestones on the road were the Commissions of Enquiry into the inadequacy of the medical services which were set up with monotonous regularity after every campaign, the Crimea, South Africa, Dardanelles, Mesopotamia. They make sad and sorrowful if salutary reading, and their lesson was learnt so very slowly.

Much of the progress of medicine is also implicit in these pages, for the story starts before anæsthetics were in general use, before Lister had paved the way for modern surgery, when hospitals were hotbeds of infection, when pain and death held sway. And so to the days of blood transfusion, modern anæsthesia, penicillin, highly-trained nurses, the conquest of pain and death and, in the 1939–45 war, the recovery of ninety-four per cent of all wounded who reached the medical services alive. In every phase of this progress the nursing service played an important part. After the South African War, the advance became more rapid. In 1902 the Queen Alexandra's Imperial Military Nursing Service was established and, in 1908, the Territorial Army Nursing Service. Then came the 1914–18 war in which over 10,000 trained nurses were serving and, significantly, they were now employed in Casualty Clearing Stations in advance of the base hospitals. But still their official status in the Army was unsatisfactory; they were serving with the Army but were not an integral part of it. The 1939–45 war brought the nursing service finally into its own; the nurses obtained commissions and the principle was accepted that danger should not be a reason for barring their employment where they were needed. And soon the Army became so conscious of their great value that Corps and Divisional Commanders planning a battle began to display great interest in the siting of Advanced Operating Centres with nurses on their staff. The tale of their services in peace and war—Mons and Dunkirk, Gallipoli, Salonika, Mesopotamia, Singapore, Hong Kong, Burma, the desert, Greece, the beaches of Anzio and Normandy, Malta and on the high seas—reveals one clear outstanding pattern of devoted service regardless of self. This book shows that in each of the two great wars, 220 members of the nursing services lost their lives. In the second great war battle casualties were more numerous and deaths from disease fewer, because campaign diseases were under better control and the nursing services were more exposed to enemy action.

This book is part of the Memorial to Army Nurses who lost their lives in the wars. Those who died in 1914–18 are commemorated in St. Paul's Cathedral, in the Chapel of the Queen Alexandra Military Hospital, Millbank, London, in St. Giles' Cathedral, Edinburgh, in St. Anne's Cathedral, Belfast, and in St. Asaph's Cathedral, Flint. They are also remembered in the Five Sisters Window in York Minster and in the Scottish National War Memorial on the Castle Rock, Edinburgh. Those who died in the 1939–45 war are commemorated in the Chapel at Millbank, in the restored Cathedral in Rangoon, in the Memorial Hall being erected at St. Andrew's Cathedral, Singapore, and they share with all other nurses the Nurses' Memorial Chapel in Westminster Abbey.

Thus they are remembered and recorded in rock and stone, in glass and parchment, for all time; but the real memorial is in the appreciation, esteem and gratitude of the armies they served so well and in the hearts of so many of their fellow countrymen who owe their lives to their courage and devotion and who carry with them for ever memories of their care and skill in every theatre of war. Those of us who worked with them for a lifetime, in peace and war, in defeat and victory, at home and abroad, knew them, not as heroines which many of them were, but as highly skilled, courageous, conscientious colleagues, reliable and undefeatable, equal to all emergencies, on duty always. They had a tremendous task, they served a great cause and now they are part of the Army. The Queen Alexandra's Royal Army Nursing Corps is an autonomous corps within the framework of the medical services, with its own officers, and other ranks, a depot, a corps march, a flag, and a great tradition. The Army and the nation have every reason to be proud of their nursing service for what it has done in the past, and to look forward, confident, that Army Nursing, on a secure foundation, will progress from strength to strength, and be ready and willing to meet all demands in the future.

ALEX. HOOD.

Government House, Bermuda.
6th January, 1953.

Part One

AMATEUR TO PROFESSIONAL

CHAPTER 1

EARLY MEDICAL SERVICES

THE soldier's expectation of life in time of war is admittedly a precarious one, and is duly accepted by the soldier as such; but in time of peace, with the abundance of fresh air and physical exercise afforded by his calling, he can reasonably expect to find himself standing high in the category of general health.

This, however, has not always been the case in the history of the British Army, for the simple reason that until a century ago the bodily health of the common soldier was left to take care of itself; which means that no care was taken of it at all.

There were several contributing factors. In the first place soldiers must be regularly and adequately fed: but for two centuries our Army catering arrangements were of the most haphazard description. When serving overseas in time of war—and fortunately, so far, it has never had to serve anywhere else—the Army lived to some extent upon the country in which it was fighting, but for the most part it was almost entirely dependent for its daily bread upon the enterprise and generosity of its leaders. (That magnificent machine the Royal Army Service Corps was not fully assembled until 1888.) The general practice was to employ the services of a civilian Commissariat Officer, or Purveyor, who accompanied the regiment upon active service and was responsible for its supplies of food, liquor, and forage. From time to time, we read, a General threatened to hang a Commissary, a circumstance which gives us a fair idea of the efficiency and integrity of such gentry. In any case a soldier's rations, consisting as they did mainly of salt beef and ship's biscuit, were monotonous in the extreme and a standing menace to digestion.

15

In addition to fighting and eating, a soldier must occasionally have somewhere to lay his head.

Not that this view was supported by the military authorities of that time. In their opinion a 'marching regiment' was not a regiment at all unless it was kept continuously on the march. Soldiers therefore had no settled quarters: they were billeted, as occasion demanded, on ale-houses. Permanent barracks were regarded with disfavour, as tending to breed softness of fibre and lessen martial ardour. In the time of Queen Anne (and consequently of the great Marlborough himself) the total barrack accommodation in the United Kingdom provided for no more than five thousand men. It was not until the days of Pitt, and the period of general uneasiness caused by the French Revolution, that barrack buildings were set up throughout the country to accommodate troops which might be required (since in those days no regular police force existed) to maintain order among the civil population.

No Army cooks were provided; the men themselves took that duty in turns, with results easily imagined. In any case a man went without food from noon every day until next morning. His only solace was drinking—fiery poison supplied to him by a sutler who had paid a fee to the authorities for permission to sell the stuff.

The alternative to these not very exhilarating conditions was a period of garrison duty abroad. How desirable that alternative was can be gathered from the fact that when a regiment went overseas it was apt to be kept there indefinitely, amid surroundings usually unhealthy and frequently pestilential, where men died steadily of yellow fever and dysentery. The 38th Regiment of Foot, now the 1st Battalion, the South Staffordshire Regiment, were sent to the West Indies in 1706 and remained there for sixty years, completely forgotten. Such regiments, too, as did come back were mere relics of their former selves. The Cameron Highlanders were once so reduced by privation and disease during a period of duty in the West Indies that the survivors of the rank and file were actually transferred *en bloc* to the Black Watch. However, the officers and non-commissioned officers returned to Scotland, where they ultimately found recruits and saved a famous regiment from extinction.

II

So much for the life of the common soldier in time of peace. War-time brought with it the added risks of death or wounds. Treatment of the latter was of the most rough and ready character: field hospitals were non-existent, and ambulance work almost entirely without order or method. The wounded were tended by orderlies, usually selected for the job as being unfit for any other, working under the regimental surgeon. There were of course no women nurses, though there was no lack of female society; for until a century ago women—not merely the camp-following sisters of tradition, but respectable wives and mothers—accompanied our troops, as the merest matter of course, overseas and practically into action. In other words, a regiment on active service took its married quarters with it—only there were no quarters. But they hung on somehow, these heroic British matrons, in the wake of the men who made their world. And they took the children with them. What else could they do?

Here is an incident, probably common enough, occurring during Sir John Moore's historic retreat, in the dead of winter, to Corunna. A soldier's wife, who had been trudging for days at her husband's side, suddenly slipped apart from the slow-moving throng and lay down in the snow not far from the edge of the road. Her husband fell out and joined her, while the others stumbled on in the gathering darkness. Next morning man and wife overtook them, the woman carrying a newly born child in her arms.

That was the stuff of which those wives and mothers were made. But as already noted, they took no official part in the Army nursing services of their time. Such participation would have been regarded as improper and immodest. The very last

B

place for a respectable woman, it was held, especially a young woman, was by a man's bedside.[1] That conviction was to die hard, as we shall see.

III

Such were the conditions under which British soldiers lived and died, without any particular protest, for the best part of two centuries. Their hardships were as a rule considerably mitigated by the kindness and care of their officers—an immemorial tradition of the British Army—and the friendly attitude of the civil population, with whom they seldom failed to establish good relations, whatever the country, friendly or hostile. But the system itself remained, unchallenged and unaltered.

The men themselves never appear to have asked for more considerate treatment. They were inarticulate individuals, almost without education, and had been accustomed to discomfort and privation from birth; so they probably accepted their hard lot as one of the inevitabilities of a soldier's life.

Where appreciation of the situation should have existed, and the urgent need for reforming it realized long, long ago, was in the War Office itself. But the War Office, right up to the middle of the nineteenth century, lay fast bound in the fetters of an almost unworkable constitution. So the common soldier was nobody's child.

Then, suddenly, in 1854, we found ourselves involved in the Crimean War. This war differed from all its predecessors in one vitally important respect; it was the first war fought and followed under modern methods of reporting and publicity. In other words, the civil population at home were for the first time enabled to follow the progress of the campaign, in considerable detail and with a time-lag of not more, sometimes, than a few days.

We were living in a new era now—the era of railway and

---

[1] Still, in the interests of historical accuracy, it may be noted, according to the records, that through the influence of Elizabeth Fry some nurses were employed in military hospitals in 1799.

steamship communications, and above all of the newly invented electric telegraph. Gone were the days when the sole source of public information as to the progress of a war consisted in an occasional Commander-in-Chief's Official Dispatch, announcing operational successes to date, and conveniently ignoring, or minimizing, such uncomfortable topics as the casualty-list or the sufferings of the troops engaged. Soldiers, too, were better educated, and could write home letters containing items of firsthand and highly personal information, of a kind which no Staff Officer would dream of embodying in a Commander-in-Chief's Dispatch.

Above all, that new and portentous product of modern journalism, the War Correspondent, had appeared upon the scene, penetrating everywhere, noting everything, and flashing his impressions home by the electric cable. Neither was he content to limit himself to discussing the strategy and tactics of the higher command. He mingled with the troops, both officers and men, in camp and trench; he visited the wounded in hospital, listened to their troubles, and duly passed everything on to his editor. For the first time in our military history the public at home were presented with a picture of war, especially a mishandled war, entirely from the point of view of the men who had to wage it—a very different saga from such contemporary effusions as *The Charge of the Light Brigade*.

The effect was sensational. Hitherto the easy-going British nation had been content to accept the comfortable view of the official bulletins—after the Battle of the Alma, for instance—that 'such a victory could not be achieved without considerable losses'; but the dispatches contributed to *The Times* newspaper by its special correspondent, William Howard Russell, were much more specific. Russell contended, firstly, that our casualties were far greater than they need have been, and then proceeded to condemn, in no uncertain terms, the shameful inadequacy of the arrangements for the care of the wounded.

After the troops have been six months in the Country [he wrote from the Crimea on September 12th, 1854], there is no preparation for the commonest surgical operations! Not only are the men kept, in some cases, for a week without the hand of a medical man coming near their wounds; not only are they left to expire in agony, unheeded and shaken off, though clutching desperately at the surgeon whenever he makes his rounds through the fetid ship; but now, when they are placed in a spacious building,[1] where we were led to believe that everything was ready which could ease their pain and facilitate their recovery, it is found that the commonest appliances of a workhouse sick-ward are wanting, and that the men die through the medical staff of the British Army having forgotten that old rags are necessary for the dressing of wounds. . . .

The worn-out pensioners who were brought out as an Ambulance Corps are totally useless; and not only are surgeons not to be had, but there are no dressers and nurses to carry out the surgeons' instructions.

Then the dispatch struck a fresh and significant note.

Here the French are greatly our superiors. Their medical arrangements are extremely good, their surgeons more numerous, *and they have also the help of the Sisters of Charity*, who have accompanied the expedition in incredible numbers.

The importance of this statement lay not in the 'incredible numbers' of the Sisters of Charity—in point of fact the exact total was fifty—but in the news that there were women nurses in the Crimea at all. Here was a clear lead to the British medical authorities; surely, what a Frenchwoman could do, an Englishwoman could do.

But the appropriate response was not immediately forthcoming —on any concerted scale, that is. True, Russell's revelations had been sufficient to arouse the entire country both to anger and pity; but the anger merely took the form of a vague demand for immediate reform of the Army medical services. Pity was re-

[1] At Scutari.

sponsible for the immediate establishment of a public fund by
The Times newspaper for the provision of more abundant medical
comforts for the sick and wounded in Scutari. But that was
all. The authorities still fought shy of the suggestion implied in
Russell's mention of the fifty Sisters of Charity. The strange
belief that the nursing of sick men was somehow unbecoming to
the modesty and even chastity of English womanhood still persisted in official circles. The French Sisters of Charity, it was
asserted, belonged to a different category; they were Catholic
nuns, self-dedicated to lifelong service in such work as this;
they were beings in fact, hardly of this world at all. But ought
delicately nurtured and sensitive English ladies to be committed
to such distressing and 'unsexing' labours as these?

Still, public opinion had been coming round to the idea for
some time, and Russell's continued revelations brought the
matter to a head. All that was needed now, to blow a hoary
prejudice sky-high, was an effective detonator.

As it happened, such a detonator was already in being, and
two days after the publication of Russell's article of September
12th, it went into immediate and resounding action. The name
of the detonator was Florence Nightingale.

CHAPTER 2

THE LADY OF THE LAMP

FLORENCE NIGHTINGALE was born on May 12th, 1820, and was thus one year younger than Queen Victoria. She was the second of the two children, both daughters, of Mr. William Nightingale, a man of considerable wealth and culture, with enough spare time on his hands to supervise and even conduct the education of his daughters. (Florence read Homer with him when she was sixteen!) From her earliest days she took life with immense seriousness. Balls, parties, and social junketings in general simply bored her (though she was intensely interested in music, especially opera). For company she preferred the society of intelligent men, with whom she could discuss the social and political problems of the day. So far as her own sex was concerned, she had no lack of friends, but she took little interest in their romantic adventures or whispered confidences. Not that she was dull or unsociable: though seriously disposed she possessed a keen sense of humour, and in conversation could hold her own with the most vivacious. She is even said to have been an excellent mimic.

But though she eschewed frivolity and the pursuit of pleasure for its own sake, Florence was by no means wasting her youth. In point of fact she was preparing herself, from her earliest years, more or less unconsciously at first, for her appointed destiny. She longed for something to *do*—something continuous and constructive—and to do it for other people. For that reason her aimless and artificial existence, as she regarded it, was a constant reproach to her conscience.

Quite in her early childhood she developed a passion for sicknursing. It is even recorded that she used to nurse and bandage dolls which had suffered damage through the exuberance of her elder sister. Her first essay in the rendering of first-aid was in setting the broken leg of a shepherd's collie, which she found lying out on the downs near Embley.

But all this time she was merely feeling her way. Her own purpose was not yet made plain to her; the clear pattern of her mission in life had not yet emerged from the realm of dreams. Like Francis of Assisi and Jeanne d'Arc before her, she was waiting for her Call.

Then, quite suddenly, on February 7th, 1837, when she was seventeen, it came. On that date, as Florence herself announces in an autobiographical fragment, God called her to His Service. At the outset she was merely conscious of the Call itself; as yet she had no knowledge as to whither it was to lead her. But for the next three months, she tells us, she 'worked very hard among the poor people, under a strong feeling of religion'.

She was anxious to be a dutiful daughter, and struggled hard in the months and years which followed to persuade herself that her place was in her home; but in vain. Her sense of vocation was too strong. Her growing ambition all this time was to devote herself to nursing, and she told her parents so. But here she met with no encouragement; indeed her mother, a deeply pious and inflexibly narrow-minded lady, was frankly horrified, and her easy-going father acquiesced in his spouse's verdict.

Florence, herself, never ceased hoping and planning. She was older now, and completely sure of herself. And in due course, through the good offices of Doctor (afterwards Cardinal) Manning, whom she had met in Rome some years previously, she was permitted to undergo a course of training in a Nursing Sisterhood in Paris, and thus launch herself permanently on her true life's work. Her status here was that of a *postulante*; in this capacity she pledged herself, under the direction of the Sisters, to render service to the sick in the hospitals and assist in the education (including the games) of the small inmates of the orphanage. She was doing something useful, and constructive at last. Moreover, she now had to make her own decisions, and with her well-ordered brain and card-index memory, was learning to make them not only correctly but quickly. What was more, she was unconsciously preparing herself for the time when it would be her duty to impose those decisions, sometimes willy-nilly, upon other people.

II

It is now time to introduce into our story a character whose name will be for ever coupled with Miss Nightingale's, firstly in the matter of a joint and successful crusade for the amelioration of hospital conditions in the Crimea; and subsequently in a prolonged campaign, instigated very largely by Miss Nightingale herself, for Army reform all round.

This was Sidney Herbert, who in 1854 occupied the post of Secretary of State at War. Technically, the Secretary of State at War had nothing whatever to do with War, his official duties being confined to finance and accounting. But Sidney Herbert was not the man to be tied down by routine. He was determined that women nurses should be sent to Scutari—Russell's dispatches in *The Times* had convinced him of that—and his determination was strengthened by the circumstance that he had in mind the exact person to appoint as organizer and leader of such an expedition—Miss Florence Nightingale, no less.

He and his wife had met Miss Nightingale in Rome during a continental tour some seven years previously, and the trio had become firm friends. Indeed, it was not long before Mr. Herbert and Miss Nightingale discovered in one another kindred spirits of an identical pattern. Florence was well aware that this charming and talented man had already devoted many years of his life to the welfare of the poor in general and the soldier in particular; while her own life so far had been one long preparation for participation in exactly similar work—a fact that Herbert himself was not slow to observe and recognize. It was deep calling to deep: no wonder they became friends.

Nor was it altogether surprising either, that when in October 1854 Sidney Herbert had read Russell's flaming dispatch and decided to answer its call, the first name which occurred to him

for his female Chief of Staff should be that of the girl, that
realistic dreamer, whom he and his wife had met in Rome.

He promptly sat down and wrote her a letter, in which he
invited her to undertake the immense responsibilities of such a
task.

The letter was crossed by one from Florence Nightingale
(addressed with becoming modesty to Mrs. Herbert) offering her
services.

III

Upon Saturday, October 21st, 1854, Miss Nightingale, accompanied by a party of thirty-eight nurses (and punctiliously
chaperoned by her uncle, Samuel Smith, as far as Marseilles) left
London for the Crimea. Only ten days had elapsed since her
acceptance of Sidney Herbert's invitation—or rather appeal—days
of breathless activity and preparation, in which Miss Nightingale
impressed all about her with her clear-headedness and monumental calm.

In the formal letter confirming her appointment, Sidney
Herbert had summarized her duties and explained, in terms of
the utmost clarity, what her relations would (or should) be with
the authorities both at home and overseas.

In this thoughtful and comprehensive document, whose author
was obviously determined to make everything as smooth for
his protégée as possible, two points stand out conspicuously.
Firstly, Miss Nightingale was to have supreme and undivided
control of her own nurses. She had stipulated for that throughout, and the Secretary of State at War had seen to it that she
should have her way. Secondly, she was not to be hampered
by lack of funds. In point of fact she was even better off in
this respect than would appear. Her own services she gave
gratuitously, which meant that the allowance of £500 a year
which she received from her father was available for the comfort and welfare of her patients. *The Times* fund, already mentioned, was also at her disposal, and she received many additional
and unsolicited contributions from private individuals—some of

them friends, many total strangers—amounting to about £7,000 in all.

She had agreed with Sidney Herbert that her first nursing contingent should be limited in number to forty; but even for such a modest establishment as this it was by no means easy to obtain sufficient recruits of the right type—that is to say, women with some experience of nursing and, above all, the necessary spirit of devotion to a high calling. Many of the applicants proved to be completely irresponsible both in character and point of view.

> I wish [wrote one of Miss Nightingale's assistants] that people who may hereafter complain of the women selected, could have seen the set we had to choose from. All London was scoured for them. . . . We felt ashamed to have in the house such women as came. One alone expressed a wish to go from a good motive. Money was the only inducement.

This revelation seems effectually to dispose of the legend that Miss Nightingale's Crimean nurses were English ladies of birth and breeding, universally inspired by devotion to a noble ideal. Taking them all round, they were a rough and ready lot, and, as we shall see, it was entirely due to their Superintendent's wise direction and strict discipline that they developed their subsequent amenability and efficiency.

IV

Scutari lay on the Asiatic side of the narrow Bosphorus, immediately opposite Constantinople, and housed the four principal hospitals of the British Army. The two with which we are chiefly concerned were the General Hospital, originally designed as such by the Turkish Government, and 'so was reduced to good order early,' Miss Nightingale reports, 'by the unwearied efforts of the first-class Staff Surgeon. It was then maintained in excellent condition until the end of the War'. It housed 1,000 patients, but the Battle of the Alma made it clear that much more accommodation would be required.

A second building had therefore been taken over. This had been designed not as a hospital at all, but as a barracks, and proved unsuitable from every point of view.

As for the conditions prevailing among the sick and wounded lying there, it became immediately apparent that Russell's report in *The Times* was no exaggeration: if anything, it was an understatement.

The inefficiency of the transport service was a menace in itself. The distance across the Black Sea from Balaclava to Scutari was about three hundred miles—about as far as a coastal trip from the Thames to the Tyne. But the ships containing the sick and wounded took eight and a half days, sometimes longer, to cover the distance. After the Alma battle seventy per thousand of them died *en route*, mainly through sheer lack of attention.

But the climax of horror was reached with the description of conditions in the Barrack Hospital itself. This imposing building acclaimed by its selectors as ideal for its purpose, was a pest-house and nothing more.

> Underneath the great structures [the Roebuck Committee were informed] were sewers of the worst possible construction, loaded with filth—mere cesspools in fact—through which the wind blew sewer-air up the pipes of numerous open privies into the corridors and wards where the sick were lying. There was also frightful overcrowding. For many months the space for each patient was one-fourth of what it ought to have been.

No wonder, for at one time no less than 2,434 patients were crowded into this particular hospital. Consequently, what with wounds, frostbite, emaciation and dysentery, cholera and typhus were rife. In February 1855 the mortality in the Barrack Hospital reached the appalling total of 42 per cent of the cases treated.

But the medical authorities, especially some of the senior

officers, were far from co-operative. They were all for established tradition. They declared bluntly that what had been good enough for them, under Wellington in the Peninsula, was good enough for Raglan's men in the Crimea; adding, by implication, that it was a thousand pities that a pack of interfering women should have been sent out by Mr. Herbert to undermine the natural courage and fortitude of the British soldier by unnecessary coddling. But the main source of the trouble lay elsewhere. It arose entirely from absence of co-operation and lack of personal initiative. Miss Nightingale herself summed it all up in one brief, pungent sentence:

The root of the evils which have to be dealt with is *division of responsibility and reluctance to assume it.*

V

These two evils Miss Nightingale now set out to remedy. She was determined that divided control should be done away with, and in so far as the need for initiative was concerned, to bring the full weight of what Dean Stanley once described as her 'commanding genius'—in other words, her genius for command—to bear upon the tangled situation.

And she was, whether she knew it or not, to go far beyond that. The successful reorganization of the medical services in the Crimean War was not to be the end of her task; it was merely the beginning, as the subsequent history of the British Army, at least up to the death of Sidney Herbert, attests.

But this is to anticipate. The work immediately to her hand lay in the wards of the Scutari hospitals. She set about it in three ways. Firstly, she applied an expert's touch and a woman's insight to a hospital hitherto managed exclusively by men. Secondly, she boldly assumed responsibility—which means that if she could find no one to do a thing she did it herself. Thirdly, she relegated the role of ministering angel to a secondary position, and converted herself into a propagandist of the most persistent and ruthless description, bombarding the authorities at home with suggestions, exhortations, reproaches, and what are known in these days as 'pep talks', all upon the subject of the reform of the medical services in the Crimea.

Meanwhile, the first requisite was to make good some glaring deficiencies in hospital supplies and equipment. Her patients must at least have such elementary comforts as soap and towels, knives and forks, combs and toothbrushes. A certain supply of these she already had in hand, since she had expended a large sum of her own money, when passing through Marseilles, upon the purchase of those necessities which feminine instinct had warned her would probably be none too plentiful in a man-managed hospital.

But these, she knew, could only serve as a stop-gap until she was in a position to tap official resources, which she had good cause to know were abundant, if only she could obtain access to them. Here, she felt sure, there would be formalities to overcome, including a good deal of procrastination and possibly some deliberate obstruction. And she was right. But she possessed in a high degree the gift of knowing where to put her hand on things which she wanted, and no scruples about beating down or, if need be, circumventing official opposition to her requirements.

So, with the growth of her own experience and authority, Miss Nightingale soon developed the technique necessary to deal with such hindrances to action—'bottlenecks' is the modern term—as these. The next time a consignment of clothing arrived from home she ordered it to be 'forcibly' opened; and it was—with the Purveyor, who was nominally responsible for its custody and issue, standing by 'wringing his hands in departmental agony'.

In other words, 'the Bird', as she was sometimes irreverently called behind her back, was by this time a law unto herself.

It is interesting to note that in the ceaseless arguments in which she found herself constantly involved she never fussed or lost her temper. We are told that she was never known to raise her voice upon these occasions: she achieved her ends by quiet determination and sheer force of character. She seldom took no for an answer. When told that a thing could not be done, she simply replied 'It must be done': and as a rule it was done.

Still, in the midst of all the turmoil and distraction, Florence Nightingale could maintain her sense of balance, and above all, her sense of humour. Here, in a letter home, is a lively description of an argument between our Lady Superintendent and a member of her corps of Ministering Angels, one Mrs. Lawfield, upon the subject of hospital caps. It is headed 'Speech of Mrs. Lawfield':

> I came out, ma'am, prepared to submit to everything, to be put upon in every way. But there are some things, ma'am, one can't submit to. There is Caps, ma'am, that suits one face, and some that suits another. And if I'd known, ma'am, about the Caps, great as was my desire to come out to nurse at Scutari, I wouldn't have come, ma'am!

Miss Nightingale in due course contrived to do something even about the Caps.

VI

The incident of the redoutable Mrs. Lawfield and the caps brings us to the question, always interesting to the nursing profession, of uniform in general.

The uniform of Miss Nightingale's original thirty-eight nurses was devised, naturally, more or less on the spur of the moment. They wore grey tweed wrappers, worsted jackets, with caps and short woollen cloaks, and a 'frightful scarf' of brown holland, embroidered in red with the words 'Scutari Hospitals'. Even the Roman Catholic Sisters wore these, abandoning their own religious habit.

The short woollen cloak at least should be remembered with honour, for it was destined to serve as the model for the scarlet cape worn today by the ladies of Queen Alexandra's Royal Army Nursing Corps, and as such may be regarded as a bright memorial to the foundress of military nursing.

The 'frightful scarf', moreover, was not without its uses. Some such distinctive badge was a valuable safeguard amid the very mixed society of a base camp. The soldiers came to recognize and respect the Hospital uniform. 'A raw newcomer', we are told, was seen to accost one of the nurses in the street. 'You leave her alone,' said his mate: 'don't you know she's one of Miss Nightingale's women?'

The maintenance of discipline among the nurses themselves, as we have seen, was always a matter of difficulty, especially at the beginning. An even greater problem was that of the adequate training of a young woman with no real liking or aptitude for the calling of a nurse. Of the thirty-eight who constituted her original following Miss Nightingale considered that not more than sixteen were really efficient, though of these she classed some three or four in the very highest category. However, by judicious distribution of the stronger vessels among the weak, a general average of efficiency was successfully maintained.

Miss Nightingale's sumptuary laws, as might have been expected from their author, were both comprehensive and precise. Nurses were required at all times to appear in regulation dress, with the badge, and never to wear flowers in their bonnet-caps, or ribbons, other than such as were provided for them or sanctioned by the Superintendent. A second rule defined the exact quantity of spirituous refreshment of which a nurse might partake in a day—a reminder that the Mrs. Gamp era was not long over—while a third laid down that 'no nurse will be allowed to walk out except with the housekeeper, or with a party of at least three nurses together'.

VII

In due course Miss Nightingale found time to embark upon a tour of inspection of the hospitals in the Crimea itself. There were four General Hospitals in the Crimea, of which the General Hospital at Balaclava and the 'Castle Hospital', situated on the 'Genoese Heights' above, were the most important. Both of these by this time employed a number of female nurses under their own superintendents, and Miss Nightingale was naturally anxious to inspect these and bring them up, if need be, to the Scutari level of cleanliness and efficiency.

But she herself was already heading for a breakdown, and little wonder; for she had been labouring from morning till night, and frequently through the night, under the double strain of personal responsibility and physical effort, for many months. During her tour of the Crimea, she spent whole days either in the saddle or a rough baggage-cart, visiting hospitals, outlying batteries, and front-line trenches, where the troops' cheerful endurance of appalling conditions made a profound and lasting impression upon her. She was, as usual, fearless of contagion, and personally tended patients stricken with cholera or fever.

But the pitcher had gone to the well once too often, and Florence Nightingale was herself laid low by 'Crimean' fever. For some days, as she afterwards admitted, she lay very near death.

The news was received with consternation everywhere, not only by her friends at home but throughout England. Queen Victoria made frequent and anxious inquiry. In the hospitals of the Crimea, we are told, soldiers turned their faces to the wall and wept. But at last, after days and nights of suspense, the crisis passed, and the beloved patient was pronounced out of danger.

VIII

Let us now survey the scene as it presents itself in May, 1856.

A complete transformation has been effected. The muddle and confusion in the wards have disappeared. Order and cleanliness reign; hospital supplies are regular and abundant, and the sanitation has been completely overhauled. Most significant sign of all, the rate of mortality among the sick and wounded has fallen 42 per *cent* to 22 per *thousand*.

This miracle had been achieved in the first place by Miss Nightingale's rigid insistence on absolute cleanliness everywhere.

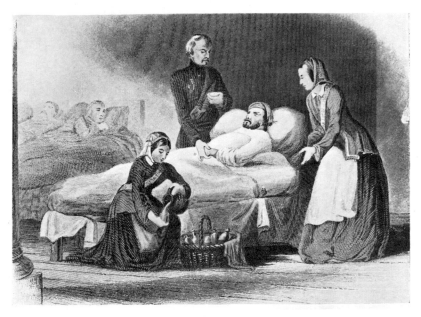

Florence Nightingale nursing during the Crimean War (*By courtesy of Picture Post*)

FLORENCE NIGHTINGALE IN THE MILITARY HOSPITAL AT SCUTARI.

The night round at Scutari

The South African War. A Sister and her mule cart

Sisters of Princess Christian's Nursing Reserve in South Africa

Antiseptics were as yet unknown, but there is a good deal of virtue in ordinary soap-and-water. *Sanitas Sanitatum—Omnia Sanitas!* was her guiding principle from the outset, and continued long after the Crimean War, when it was no longer her aim to heal the wounds of war but to maintain soldiers in health in time of peace. She had never forgotten that in the pre-war era the military mortality rate had been double that of the civil population.

Another and even more important reform was in the matter of hospital food—and not merely of the food but the manner in which it was cooked. Here she simply brought to her task the ordinary competence and care of a good housewife, though on a vastly magnified scale; for the beds in the Barrack Hospital extended over a distance of four miles, including the corridors, and it took nearly four hours to serve the men's dinner.

This meal, needless to say, was singularly unsuited to patients suffering from high fever or recent amputations. Miss Nightingale therefore set about making special provision for the more serious cases. Within ten days of her arrival she had opened two 'extra diet' kitchens in separate parts of the building, and had three supplementary boilers installed for the preparation of arrowroot and other easily digestible foods. As usual, when the Government stores failed, she met the requisitions of the hospital surgeons from her own private resources.

In 1855 she received an invaluable recruit and collaborator in the famous Frenchman, M. Soyer, formerly *chef* of the Reform Club in London. He threw himself into the work with a will, adapting and more than once improving upon Miss Nightingale's culinary arrangements. Incidentally he invented the Soyer stove, a field-cooking device of great simplicity and the utmost value. It was still being used by the British Expeditionary Force in 1939.

Soyer also accompanied Miss Nightingale to the Crimea, where he proved himself invaluable in devising improvements in the hospital catering arrangements. We shall hear of him again in a post-war capacity.

By mid-1856, then, the machine which Miss Nightingale had built up with such vision and determination was functioning

C

normally, and for the first time in the history of the British Army its Nursing Services had been stabilized.   But the strain upon the organizer of the miracle was grievous indeed, and would have been quite intolerable in the case of a lesser woman.

At the end of each day, as a matter of regular routine after the completion of her always heavy correspondence, Miss Nightingale made her final, solitary round of the wards through four miles of beds.

That scene has often been described and depicted.   A dim light burned here and there; she herself carried a hospital lantern, which she set down whenever she paused to lean over and soothe some restless patient.   To others she would nod and smile as she passed, while they in their turn kissed her shadow as it fell upon the whitewashed wall.

This was a very different Miss Nightingale from the unbending autocract whom Authority knew, capable of employing every device, legitimate or otherwise, to override resistance to her demands and get things done which she had made up her mind must be done.   But to the maimed, suffering men who lay in serried ranks, a few inches apart, along those silent, darkened passages, she was the Lady of the Lamp, and an Angel from Heaven.

CHAPTER 3

THE PROGRESS OF REFORM

THE Crimean War had been won. Peace was signed in Paris on March 30th, 1856, but Miss Nightingale remained at her post in Scutari until the beginning of July, though many of her nurses were now able to go home.

The name of Florence Nightingale was by this time a household word throughout the world, and particularly in her own country. Even before the end of the war a movement had been set on foot to recognize her achievement in some substantial way, and a 'Nightingale Fund' was inaugurated.

Needless to say the prospective *bénéficiaire*, upon hearing the news in Scutari, immediately announced that she would accept nothing whatever for herself either in cash or kind, but intimated that if such a tribute was contemplated she would devote every penny raised to the foundation of a permanent Training School for Nurses.

Her scheme was acclaimed, and money began to flow in from all quarters. Madame Jenny Lind, the famous 'Swedish Nightingale', gave a concert in its aid which realized £2,000. The soldiers in the Crimea contributed no less than £9,000. This the Other Ranks were the better enabled to do from the fact that one of Miss Nightingale's non-nursing activities had been to persuade men not to squander their pay, but to bank it or send it home. To that end a Money Order Office had actually been established in Scutari, in which, to the surprise of their officers, most of whom had not hitherto regarded the common soldier as an economist, something like £1,000 was deposited every month.

Upon the completion of her labours in Scutari and the Crimea

—she had paid two other strenuous visits to the latter since her illness—the British Government offered Miss Nightingale the use of a man-of-war to bring her home. This honour she declined.

Once back in England, official honours were showered upon her. She received the thanks of Parliament, and Queen Victoria bestowed upon her a jewelled medal specially designed by the Prince Consort. Women in those days were ineligible for Royal Orders or decorations: otherwise Miss Nightingale would probably have been awarded something in the nature of the Order of Merit. In point of fact, when that Order was created in 1907, she was the first woman, in her extreme old age, to receive it.

II

So ends the saga of the Lady of the Lamp and the miracle of Scutari. But Florence Nightingale was very far from regarding her task as ended: in her view it was only beginning, for she was determined never to rest until the living conditions of the soldier had been raised to a decent level, and his general health and happiness as solicitously assured in peace-time as his wounds had been tended in time of war.

Consequently we shall find that in the continuous record of Army Reform which marked the latter half of the nineteenth century the names of Florence Nightingale (and needless to say, of Sidney Herbert) still stand out conspicuously.

The two allies began directly after the war, by demanding a Royal Commission to investigate the conduct of the Army Medical Services in the Crimea. Miss Nightingale was not of course a member of the Commission, but its personnel was very much of her choosing. Indeed it was hinted, with some truth, that she and Sidney Herbert had 'packed' it—in the public interest. Indeed, it contained only one upholder of the old regime, one Dr. Andrew Smith.

Thanks to Sidney Herbert's vigorous and inspiring chairmanship, the Commission issued its report within three months. It was mainly the work of three hands—Sidney Herbert, Florence

Nightingale, and Dr. John Sutherland. Sutherland had been
head of a Sanitary Commission which had been sent out to the
Crimea on the urgent representations of Miss Nightingale and
her friends in 1855. Thereafter he and Miss Nightingale had
become firm and lasting associates in all matters connected
with Army health.

III

One by one, and not without many a hard struggle, the sug-
gested reforms were put into effect. Their fundamental sound-
ness was vindicated in due course by a steady improvement in
the health, happiness, and general morale of the Army through
the years that followed.

New hospitals were planned throughout the country and overseas. Hitherto the only important military hospital in England
had been Fort Pitt, at Chatham, erected for the reception of sick
and wounded from the Crimea, and where, incidentally, some
women nurses had been employed under Lady Jane Shaw Stewart.
Now, in 1856, Queen Victoria laid the foundation stone of the
great military hospital at Netley, on Southampton Water.

The design and equipment of this building had been a matter
of acute controversy. Miss Nightingale's party strongly favoured
the idea of a hospital composed of separate 'pavilions', set parallel
to one another and linked up by covered passages, thus ensuring
a maximum of light and ventilation to the wards, besides
minimizing the risks of infection. Lord Panmure, however,
Secretary of State for War, insisted upon the retention of the
orthodox 'corridor' type, and countered Miss Nightingale's
urgent representations by announcing that the foundations of the
building had already been laid, and could not be interfered with
now. Miss Nightingale appealed to the Prime Minister, Lord
Palmerston, and a few minor concessions were granted; but on
the whole the new hospital conformed to the old pattern, and
Miss Nightingale had for once to acknowledge defeat. But the
battle had not been fought altogether in vain, for practically all
great modern hospitals today are designed on the 'pavilion' plan.

St. Thomas's Hospital in London, which faces the Houses of
Parliament across the Thames, is an outstanding example.

All during these years new military hospitals were springing
up throughout the country—at Gosport, Devonport, Dover,
Shorncliffe, Dublin, the Curragh, Canterbury, Cork; and overseas at Gibraltar and Malta. The result was an ever-increasing
demand for trained Nursing Sisters. The education of these had
originally been carried out at Netley by the Lady Superintendent
there, who had herself been trained in the Nurses' Training School
founded by Florence Nightingale; but under the expanded
scheme this duty had grown beyond the control of a single
individual, and it was decided that henceforth nurses destined for
Army service must receive their initial training in civil hospitals.

An estimate of the extent of this increase may be gathered from
the fact that by 1899 (and the outbreak of the South African War)
the regular establishment at Netley alone had grown to one Lady
Superintendent, nineteen Superintendent Sisters, and sixty-eight
Sisters.

IV

Conditions in the Army continued steadily to improve. Concurrently with the new hospitals, new barracks were in course
of construction, equipped with domestic and cooking arrangements more in accordance with a woman's point of view. Such
unheard-of luxuries as reading- and recreation-rooms made a
modest appearance.

In addition to these improved amenities (most of them resulting
from the recommendations of the Royal Commission) we may
note the establishment of an Army Medical School for the education of young Army surgeons, many of whom in former times
had come to their duties with little more experience than that of
looking on at operations—some had never even dressed a wound
—and the setting up of a School of Cookery at Aldershot. In this
Miss Nightingale received valuable aid from her old ally, M.
Soyer. His sudden death in 1858 was a great grief to her.

But the outstanding triumph of the reform campaign was

represented by the fact that, while in 1857 the annual rate of Army mortality in peace-time alone was 17.5 per thousand, it had fallen by 1911 to 2.5 per thousand, or only one death in four hundred men.

Sidney Herbert himself became Secretary of State for War in 1859, and proved a tower of strength to the reformers. But like Miss Nightingale, he habitually overtaxed his strength. His death in 1860 was a shattering blow to Florence Nightingale, and for a while prostrated her. But she rallied in time, and resumed her former activities. After the Indian Mutiny she was invited, and immediately agreed, to do for the Army in India, especially with regard to sanitation and hospital management, what she had already done for the Army at home. Here she had the warm and loyal co-operation of Sir John Lawrence, afterwards Viceroy of India.

V

Miss Nightingale continued to be employed by the War Office as a general consultant on Army Welfare until 1872, when the connexion finally terminated. She was then fifty-two years old, some twenty of which years had been devoted without a break to the service of the British soldier.

Today, in Waterloo Place, London, looking out over the Duke of York's Steps to the Horse Guards' Parade beyond, she and Sidney Herbert stand side by side at the foot of the Guards' Crimea Memorial. To the right and left of them a never-ending procession of motor-traffic, much of it as scarlet-clad as the soldiers of a former day, goes surging up the long slope on its way to Piccadilly Circus. Those two eminently Victorian figures stand strangely aloof and serene in that roaring tide. Florence wears her hospital dress—crinoline and nurse's cap. In her hand she carries The Lamp, and her eyes are cast downward, as if surveying a long line of hospital beds.

CHAPTER 4

THE SOUTH AFRICAN WAR

THE South African War—the Great Boer War, as it afterwards came to be called, to distinguish it from its predecessors—is but a dim memory now to those who lived through it. To later generations, whose conception of warfare is based on the earth-shaking struggles of 1914–18 and 1939–45, it must appear as the merest affair of outposts, but it created a world-wide stir in its time, and in order to win it the British Empire had to employ the whole of its military resources—no less than 250,000 men, in fact.

Some of us can still vividly recall the breathless anxiety and suspense with which we followed the events of those first disastrous months. The British garrisons of Cape Colony and Natal had been rounded up and besieged in Kimberley in the west, Ladysmith in the east, and, far to the north, in the little township of Mafeking; and at one time it seemed doubtful whether these could hold out until Sir Redvers Buller and the British Expeditionary Force could arrive from England to relieve them.

The Boers in fact had proved far more formidable opponents than had been anticipated. They possessed no regular military organization and military discipline was practically non-existent; but each man was a crack shot, and since every one of them owned a horse, their extreme mobility imposed a sore strain upon the slow-moving British infantry. Moreover, they possessed no uniforms, which made it a simple matter for a Boer warrior in a tight corner to conceal his rifle in the thatch and resume *pro tem.* the role of peaceful farmer.

In the early battles of the campaign, during the winter of 1899 —Graspan, Modder River, Magersfontein, and Colenso—our

troops invariably assumed the offensive: advancing over open
ground and in open order against a host of sharpshooters well
dug in, usually on higher ground, and screened by a barbed-wire
fence which brought the attack to a temporary halt and furnished
a concentrated target. In any case, the attacking troops had no
shelter except an occasional donga or anthill. Practically all the
wounds incurred by our men were bullet wounds: shell-fire was
responsible for only about 5 per cent.

It should be added that in these engagements the Boers seldom
fought to a finish: having inflicted heavy loss on their opponents
they were accustomed to retire quietly, usually under the cover
of night, mount their horses, and ride away to fight another day.

This unprofitable form of warfare came to a lamentable climax
shortly before Christmas 1899—the Black Week, so called—
when the news arrived that no less than three British attacks had
been heavily repulsed within a few days of one another, at
Colenso, Stormberg, and Magersfontein.

The result (and not before it was time) was the appointment
of the veteran Lord Roberts as Commander-in-Chief, with Lord
Kitchener, the recent victor of Omdurman, as his Chief of Staff.

On arrival in South Africa Lord Roberts immediately abandoned the idea of directly relieving the beleaguered garrisons.
Instead, he advanced straight up country towards the heart of the
enemy's position—Bloemfontein, the capital of the Orange Free
State. His strategy was completely successful. To obstruct his
progress the Boers were compelled to detach troops from the
sieges of Ladysmith and Kimberley, with the result that both
were relieved in the early spring. A little later the Boer general
Cronje was rounded up at Paardeberg, with 5,000 men, and by
the middle of March Bloemfontein was entered and occupied.
Pretoria fell later, and President Kruger slipped away to Europe.
From the middle of 1900 it was plain that there could be but
one ending to the war, though the enterprise and gallantry of
the Boer Commandos, under such leaders as Botha, de Wet,
and Jan Christian Smuts, in his later days a Field-Marshal of the
British Empire, prolonged it for another two years.

II

Such, in brief outline, was the operational character of the South African War. We turn now to the human element, and in particular the task imposed upon the Army Medical Services. The outstanding problem, from first to last, was that of transport. The illimitable veldt stretched everywhere for hundreds of miles—a striking contrast to the narrow confines of the Crimea —and mechanical transport was as yet unknown. The only method of large-scale transport was by Cape cart, or even ox-wagon.

The removal of the wounded from battlefield to hospital was organized in three stages. First, the man had to be conveyed from where he lay to the nearest field hospital. It was soon found that to undertake this task under fire—extremely accurate rifle-fire—was more dangerous for the wounded than to leave them where they lay, for a man lying flat is much less likely to be hit than a man sitting up. It was discovered, too, that in that dry and bracing climate a man suffering merely from a bullet wound, or wounds, could be left out in the open for a surprisingly long time and be none the worse. (Indeed, there is a case on record of an officer of the Highland Brigade, shot through the lungs at Magersfontein, who lay out for forty-eight hours before he could be removed, when it was found that his very immobility had prevented serious hæmorrhage, and that the wound had begun to heal itself. He made a good recovery, and lived to fight again in the First World War.)

From the Field Hospital the wounded man was conveyed to a so-called Stationary Hospital, situated somewhere down the Lines of Communication. Ambulance vehicles were scarce and primitive, and if the distance was not too great the wounded were carried on stretchers. (A considerable number of Indian orderlies were specially employed for this work.)

The Stationary Hospital usually consisted of a group of corrugated iron huts. Here the patient was tended until he was strong enough to endure the journey to the railway, and thence to the Base. For this purpose a horse-drawn wagon was employed; or better still, an ox-wagon. The slow, plodding progress of the oxen was soothing to the patient, who lay upon a hay-mattress, while the considerable interval between the front and rear axles minimized jolting.

Once arrived at the railway, all discomfort ended, for the hospital trains which had been sent out from home were of the most modern type and perfectly equipped. Each had accommodation for two Medical Officers, two Nursing Sisters—the patient's earliest foretaste of the Q.A.I.M.N.S.—male orderlies, a kitchen, a dispensary, and 120 lying-down cases. The railhead, it should be noted, was the nearest point to the battle-line to which Army Nursing Sisters were at that time allowed to penetrate.

There were five such trains in the Western Section, based on Capetown, and two based on Durban. One of these took pride of place over all the others. It had been christened the Princess Christian Train, in acknowledgment of the gracious and efficient leadership of Queen Victoria's third daughter in the organization of the Army Nursing Services of that era.

This brings us to the Base Hospitals, situated, hundreds of miles from the sound of the guns, in and around such great seaports as Capetown and Durban. Perhaps the best-remembered of these is No. 1 General Hospital at Wynberg, an eight-mile tram-ride away from Capetown—a circumstance highly convenient to a Nursing Sister on her afternoon off.

The South African War was naturally responsible for a further development in the extent and efficiency of the Army Nursing Services. At the outbreak the total establishment of Nursing Sisters stood at: One Lady Superintendent, nineteen Superintendent Sisters, and sixty-eight Sisters. By the end of the war no less than twenty-two General Hospitals had sprung into existence, each of 500 beds or more, and even these were insufficient to accommodate all patients. As the British Army consolidated its occupation of Boer territory, various public buildings such as town halls and schools up and down the country, were requisitioned as auxiliary hospitals. At one of these hospitals, in

Bloemfontein, Lord Roberts' own daughter was stricken by enteric. She was nursed back to health by an Army Nursing Sister who, though long retired from active service, is still happily with us.

Queen Alexandra (the Princess of Wales, as she then was) showed early interest in this project, and herself enlisted a contingent of nurses for South Africa from the staff of London Hospital. A large number of these Nursing Sisters became permanently absorbed in the Service; others remained in the Reserve.

From this time on the proportion of Nursing Sisters grew steadily, for official opinion had at last been converted to the view that 'There is no doubt that in a base hospital the actual nursing should always be entrusted to women.' This was progress indeed.

In the whole course of the South African War some 1,800 trained nurses were sent out, eighty of whom came from Canada, Australia, and New Zealand.

III

Conditions in the South African base hospitals, not unnaturally, showed a vast improvement upon those of the Crimean War, already more than forty years distant. The reason was threefold. Firstly, anæsthetics were now available and in general use; secondly, scrupulous cleanliness everywhere was an accepted canon of hospital management and not merely regarded as a private obsession of Miss Nightingale's; and thirdly, the Nursing Sisters themselves were all women highly qualified both by training and character.

Of course, everything did not run too smoothly at first. Nothing ever does in war-time. Even an establishment as well ordered as Wynberg General Hospital found it difficult, in its beginnings, to achieve the Nightingale standard of *Sanitas Sanitatum*. The conditions under which the Nursing Sisters lived and worked were far from satisfactory. In the first place the authorities, with a mistaken regard for the proprieties, enjoined that Sisters on night duty must not remain continuously in the wards. Instead, they were relegated to a shed (known as The Bunk) close by, and were only supposed to enter a ward when summoned by an orderly. This arrangement involved much tramping to and fro in the dark between Bunk and Hut; in wet weather the mud was sometimes ankle-deep. (This last is feelingly described by a young member of the Army Nursing Reserve, in a letter to her family at home, as 'appauling'.)

In the second place many of the buildings, we are told, were infested by bugs—a not infrequent occurrence in the South Africa of those days—and for the protection of the patients it was found necessary to stand the legs of the beds in jam-tins filled with a chemical insecticide.

The hospital orderlies, too, were apt to be somewhat informal in their habits. Major-General J. F. C. Fuller, who as a subaltern spent some weeks in Wynberg Hospital during the early part of the war, tells us in his reminiscences that his bed stood next to the door of the operating theatre, from which one morning there emerged an orderly, jauntily carrying a newly amputated human leg under his arm, on its way to its place of interment.

Finally, the patients in some of the base hospitals, especially in the neighbourhood of Capetown, suffered severely during the earlier stages of the war from the attentions of a self-appointed body of Ministering Angels. The hotels swarmed with these ladies, who had arrived from England with the avowed intention of 'nursing the wounded'. Indeed, a legend survives to the effect that during what may be termed 'rush hours' more than one long-suffering warrior felt constrained to hang at the head of his bed a card bearing the notice: 'I am too ill to be nursed today.'

This campaign of benevolence, needless to say, came to an abrupt conclusion with the arrival in Capetown of Lord Kitchener, a bachelor by habit and inclination, and no mean disciplinarian to boot. He speedily disbanded the sisterhood, and dispatched most of them back whence they came. Thereafter the base hospitals were enabled to pursue a less disturbing and more efficient routine.

Every type of patient was to be found in the hospital wards, from British Staff Officers to Boer prisoners of war. Two of these latter were men of unusual and unfortunate distinction. Their names were Scheepers and Kritzinger, and both held the rank of General, for they had been leaders in a serious rebellion of a section of the Dutch-speaking population of Cape Colony. Unlike the people of the Transvaal, and the Orange Free State, they ranked as British subjects. Each accordingly was liable to be brought to trial, and perhaps shot, on a charge of high treason. It was the lot of one particular Sister, in Naauwpoort Hospital, to tend the wounds of this unhappy pair and restore to them some measure of health—a measure sufficient, in other words, to fit them for the firing-squad. Both were well-mannered, educated men, and the grim fate which probably awaited them upon achieving convalescence through her ministrations, prayed heavily upon Sister's mind. To her intense relief one of them, General Kritzinger, was ultimately reprieved.

Here is her personal reaction to another, but similar experience.

> There is a sentry on duty day and night, marching up and down, and the hut is closed round with barbed wire. When I go in in the night to dress their wounds, I have to ask the sentry to unlock the door, which he does after much fumbling. I go in, and the door clangs behind me and is locked. I am then at the mercy of twelve Boer rebels and a sentry who belongs to Marshall's Horse and is usually talking Dutch to them. (Funny, isn't it, to have a Dutch sentry to look after Dutch rebels?) I find the rebels most polite to nurse. Their wounds are all healing, which is rather sad in a way, as probably all will be hanged or transported as soon as they can crawl out of bed.

IV

Life at Naauwpoort, which was a 'Stationary Hospital'[1] differed considerably from that at a base hospital. In the first place Naauwpoort itself lay far to the north of Cape Colony,

[1] So called, apparently, because it was movable.

almost on the border of the Orange Free State, subsequently rechristened The Orange River Colony, and consequently quite near the battle zone.

We are living in exciting times here [writes another Sister]. Troops arriving daily, with field hospitals, and ambulance waggons drawn by six yoke of mules. Tents are pitched on all the hills round. We feel quite at the front, and hope de Wet won't be long in coming.

We are having quite exciting times with the Boers so near, and are constantly getting trainloads of wounded men in. We can't walk a hundred yards from the hospital after dark without being challenged by the sentries for the countersign. 'Kitchener!' 'England!' 'Cape!'—words like that.

We went to Church tonight in a marquee. The Wilts Band played the hymns, and the Tommies sang lustily. Most of the troops have just come down from Pretoria, and look so worn and tired out.

Life at Naauwpoort, generally speaking, offered more scope for adventure than in suburban Wynberg. There were voyages of discovery over the veldt, in a Cape cart which occasionally capsized and caused minor casualties. On one such occasion the mules bolted, and ended by depositing a party of Sisters in a donga, or dry ditch, fortunately without permanent injury.

There were also such fearful wildfowl as ostriches to be encountered.

Yesterday [reports one letter home] we drove out to a Dutch farm to have tea. It was funny to sit in a room with a polished floor and paper on the wall. There were also some terrible water-colours. They presented us each with an ostrich egg weighing about two pounds.

Coming home we met two enormous ostriches (the donors of the eggs) lying right across the road. Our mules were terrified: they swung round and bolted across the veldt. We had a soldier driving, so luckily he was able to pull them up. The real question was how to get the ostriches off the road. If the soldier got down the mules would certainly bolt again. Luckily we spied some Kaffir children, who were made, with some difficulty, to understand what was wanted of them. These tiny kids then ran at the ostriches, and the ostriches ran for their lives.

One feels that Florence Nightingale would have routed those ostriches single-handed.

Mention of farm-house hospitality brings us to the relationship in general existing between the Boers and the Army Nursing Services.

The service of the Royal Army Medical Corps was, by immemorial tradition, not merely at the disposal of enemy prisoners, but of the entire civil population of occupied enemy territory; and Boer mothers did not hesitate to bring ailing children to the nearest British military hospital for the necessary aid and comfort, with the full cognizance and approval of their menkind, to whom the Red Cross was as sacred a symbol as to ourselves. Such was the invariable practice in what has been called 'The Last of the Wars of Gentlemen'.

The experience of our Nursing Sisters in this respect was two-fold. There were their relations firstly with the civil population, chiefly in Cape Colony, and secondly with wounded prisoners of war, most of whom came from the Transvaal and Free State, in the great base hospitals of Capetown and Durban.

The Cape Dutch were the least happy participants in the war, for they were British by adoption and Boers by origin. Most of them were loyal enough to the British Crown, but their allegiance was sorely tried by the fact that they had many close relatives fighting on the other side. Worst of all, if they rebelled, as many did, and were taken prisoner, they had to receive the treatment not of an honourable opponent but of a traitor. The Nursing Sisters soon realized this, and many are their expressions of sympathy for these unhappy men—as in the cases of Scheepers and Kritzinger, already quoted.

But the Boer wounded from the Transvaal and Free State were

The T.F.N.S. setting out for the Coronation of King George V and Queen Mary

Q.A.I.M.N.S. assembling to attend the Coronation, 1911 (*Imperial War Museum*)

King George V with the Matron of a C.C.S. at Remy, 1916 (*Imperial War Museum*)

Queen Mary visiting a hospital at Rouen, 1917 (*Imperial War Museum*)

cheerful enough. They were out of the war, they were being treated with a kindness which most of them quite failed to understand, and knew that when their wounds were healed they would be kept safe in a great seaside camp until the war was over and they could go home again.

If you want a description of one of those camps, read Rudyard Kipling's story 'The Captive', in *Traffics and Discoveries*.

Once the disasters of 1899 and early 1900 had been retrieved, and Lord Roberts was on his way to Pretoria, our base hospitals were occupied chiefly by enteric cases and Boer wounded. The Sisters took a lively interest in these latter patients, as the following extract from a letter home testifies:

> I am having rather an amusing time just now, as I am nursing some wounded Boers. They are so funny, stalking about with their beards and talking Dutch. The absurd part of it all seems to be in dressing wounds which have been inflicted by our own soldiers.
>
> Some have been in bed for months with gunshot wounds right through their legs or lungs. They are very good to each other, and if there is anything to be done they all crowd round the beds, offering their assistance and jabbering in Dutch—most probably about *me*! They are given every luxury in the way of food, and are well treated.
>
> They are very amused because I wear a Kruger coin as a brooch. 'Fancy you wear our Oom Paul!' they say. As it is Sunday they have all been reading their Bibles, much to the amusement of some of our English Tommies.

V

The climate of South Africa is proverbially dry and healthy, and our wounded, who were mostly young men in the pink of condition, usually made a quick recovery. Moreover, hospital catering had advanced a long way since Scutari days, and the diet of the patients was both abundant and varied. Most of the

D

meat came from Australia, on ice; and the ice, having served its primary purpose, was next available for hospital refrigeration uses—a considerable boon in the days when the art of manufacturing ice artificially was as yet in the experimental stage. Fresh vegetables were more difficult to obtain, but no cases of scurvy—that ancient menace to sailing ships at sea and dwellers in arid regions ashore—were reported throughout the campaign.

As regards the catering arrangements for the troops actually in the field, the reader may here be reminded that the Army Service Corps, established in 1881, had now grown into a smooth-running and highly efficient machine: with the result that in South Africa the British Army was regularly and adequately fed for the first time in its long history. Only once during the war was a shortage of rations recorded—during Lord Roberts' great forced march from the Modder River to Bloemfontein in the spring of 1900.

Before leaving the subject of casualties, we must take note of the extremely high proportion, in the South African War, of sick to wounded.

The number of men actually killed and wounded in South Africa was surprisingly small, at any rate by comparison with the First World War and its million dead. The figures usually worked out at about 3 or 4 per cent of the number engaged. Our heaviest losses in this respect were at Magersfontein, where the attack was delivered under cover of night and was brought up short by barbed wire. The Kimberley Relief Force lost 315 killed, or 2 per cent, with 1,512, or 9.5 per cent, wounded.

We have to remember one point, however. The figures quoted of men wounded refer only to wounded men actually conveyed from the battlefield: if we include the number of those who died within forty-eight hours of reaching hospital, the proportion of dead is increased fourfold.

Officer casualties were proportionately higher than those of the rank and file, which was hardly surprising, since the British officer, by immemorial tradition, invariably goes into action in advance of his men. The advent of mechanized warfare and armoured vehicles have done something to equalize these risks.

The inordinately high proportion in South Africa of sick to wounded, already noted, was due in the main to the dust, which penetrated everywhere; to the flies; to such minor ailments as veldt-sores, and finally and outstandingly to the drinking of impure water. The last was almost entirely the fault of that incorrigibly casual individual—an Absent-Minded Beggar if ever there was one—Thomas Atkins himself.

On the march each man was provided with a full water-bottle, the contents of which on a hot day—and in South Africa the sun-temperatures were often as high as 115° F.—he has usually disposed of within an hour or so. Thereafter, too indolent or too casual to take any reasonable precautions, he was accustomed to replenish his water-bottle at the nearest available source—a stagnant pool, or even the muddied water of a stream from which transport animals were actually drinking.

The results were automatic—enteric, dysentery, and the death of hundreds of otherwise healthy young men. The total number of deaths in the South African War was about 22,000. Of these only 6,000 were due to wounds received in action: the remainder were caused by sickness, largely preventable.

Thanks to modern methods of inoculation, that danger has now passed. Today, at the cost of a few days' personal discomfort, a man—and a woman too—can be rendered practically immune to enteric, cholera, tetanus, and all other ills indigenous to overcrowding and insufficient sanitation. In other words, the increase in the modern soldier's expectation of life, thanks to the hypodermic needle, by far surpasses that provided by the stoutest of armoured vehicles.

VI

Such then, in brief outline, were the services rendered to the sick and wounded of both sides by the Army Nursing Sisters during the Great Boer War. It was only natural that with the passing of time and the steady awakening of the public conscience, the conditions under which the Army Nursing Sisters of South Africa served should have been immensely superior to those experienced (or rather, endured) by their predecessors of more than forty years ago. They were properly organized, they were as comfortably housed as active service conditions permitted, they were well fed and suitably clothed, and they were animated by an *esprit de corps* only attained by common effort and a high ideal.

Of course discipline was strict—perhaps unnecessarily so by modern standards. Sisters were forbidden to smoke, apparently because of the possible demoralizing influences of such a spectacle upon Thomas Atkins. At least, such may be gathered from a furtive postscript to one letter home:

> I am dying to smoke a cigarette, but the orderly has not been in to take away my dinner-tray yet, so I don't like to commence.

But everyone seems to have taken the rough with the smooth cheerfully enough. Discomforts arising from extreme of climate —rain, mud, bitter cold, or summer temperatures of 115° F. are merely mentioned as seasonable topics. General health was good, though not all the Sisters escaped enteric or other ills of active service; but these seem to have been accepted as part of the adventure of campaigning.

There was not a great deal of officially approved social intercourse, for female virtue, as already noted, was still rigidly safeguarded, but spare time seems to have been occupied contentedly enough. There were neighbouring towns to be visited and the spacious veldt to be explored: and there were various minor distractions and hobbies. Nearly everyone became a philatelist in a small way, sending home Transvaal and Free State stamps to be added to the collections of insistent small brothers. Several Sisters too possessed cameras, and were thus able to illustrate their letters with snapshots. Their only difficulty at times was to obtain access to the dark room. At Wynberg this apartment could only be reached by traversing the sleeping quarters of a certain medical major: and this meant that through traffic had to be suspended when that highly sensitive officer was in bed.

But in two respects the conditions under which the Army

Nursing Sisters in South Africa and Florence Nightingale's devoted followers in the Crimea performed their arduous duties remained unchanged. In the first place women still lacked official status as regular members of the Forces of the Crown, and in the second the activities of Army nurses were still restricted to regions widely removed from the battle zone and the range of the guns. The march of time, as evinced in the first case by tardy official recognition of gallant service, and in the second by the demands of total war, was destined to effect a radical change in both situations.

Let us consider to what extent the experiences of the South African War accelerated the progress of reform in these matters.

CHAPTER 5

THE BIRTH OF Q.A.I.M.N.S.

THE Crimean War (and Florence Nightingale) had been responsible, as we have seen, for the admission of women nurses to our military hospitals, and in consequence, to the establishment of the Army Nursing Service. The South African War carried these reforms a long step further, by making manifest the incalculable benefit to the soldier of a full-scale, permanent Nursing Service, both in war and peace.

Early in 1902, with peace upon the horizon, an influential committee under the chairmanship of the Secretary of State for War, Mr. St. John Brodrick (afterwards Lord Midleton) was set up to formulate a definite scheme. As the result of its labours, the existing Army Nursing Service was expanded into 'Queen Alexandra's Imperial Military Nursing Service'— Q.A.I.M.N.S. for short—and so remains to this day, except for a slight but significant change of name. Its first president was Queen Alexandra herself, who occupied that position until her death, when Queen Mary graciously consented to become the next president, and still happily remains so, though again under a significant change of title.

The establishment of Q.A.I.M.N.S. upon its inception was as follows:

Matron-in-Chief at the War Office.

Two Principal Matrons, one at the War Office and one in South Africa.

Matrons—Sisters—Staff Sisters.

Total—about 300.

The now familiar uniform of scarlet and grey had been instituted as far back as 1897. With the approval of H.M. The

King, the present Nursing Service badge was now adopted, displaying the motto, *Sub Cruce Candida*, or 'Under the White Cross'.

This motto was selected out of compliment to Queen Alexandra, who was a Danish Princess before she was married to the future King Edward the Seventh. A white cross forms part of the national flag of Denmark, and it was in graceful allusion to this fact that the motto was composed.

A word may appropriately be said here regarding the various implications of the expression 'Red Cross'. Many people in this country, most of them in fact, are inclined to apply the description 'Red Cross Nurse' rather loosely to any nurse employed in a war-time hospital, whether military or civilian. The practice has led to a sort of hazy impression that all nurses in military hospitals are under the supervision of the British Red Cross Society. This, of course, is by no means the case, for Q.A.I.M.N.S. was a strictly Army organization. The activities of the British Red Cross Society—a purely civilian body—are devoted primarily to the collection and contribution of hospital supplies and medical comforts for our troops in war-time—a contribution of incalculable value. In war-time, however, in conjunction with the Order of St. John of Jerusalem, the British Red Cross are accustomed to enlist 'Voluntary Aid Detachments' of partly trained nurses (known as the V.A.D.) to take the place in the military hospitals of as many male orderlies as possible.

In the matter of the Red Cross itself there seems to be a tendency in the public mind to confuse a corporate body with its symbol. The function of a Red Cross Society is to relieve suffering in war-time; the Cross itself is the emblem, recognized by all civilized nations, which confers immunity from attack upon all buildings and vehicles which display it, and for that matter upon all individuals who wear it—stretcher-bearers, for instance. The Cross also appears upon the V.A.D. uniform, and also, as a rule, upon the uniforms of nurses working in voluntary hospitals and those hospitals equipped and staffed by the Committee of the British Red Cross Society; but did not appear upon that of the

Q.A.I.M.N.S., the members of which, as we know, wore a distinctive uniform of their own.

The distinction of a regular Commission in the Q.A.I.M.N.S. was achieved comparatively recently. In the early stages of their existence—up to the time of the South African War, in fact—the Army Nursing Sisters enjoyed no official rank or status; they were merely trained nurses employed by the Army.

In 1919, there was a new scheme for the State Registration of all nurses. In order to qualify for Registration, nurses on completion of training were required to pass an examination set by the General Nursing Council. State Registration became a condition of acceptance for the nurse wishing to serve in the Army.

In 1926, however, came the first real step towards what may be called Regular status. In that year the members of Q.A.I.M.N.S. were granted 'relative rank' as Regular Army Officers, for the purpose of assessing allowances, as follows:

Matron-in-Chief . .	Colonel.
Principal Matron . .	Lieutenant–Colonel.
Matron	Major.
Sister or Staff Nurse .	Lieutenant.

In 1926, too, they were for the first time included for this purpose in King's Regulations.

II

But this is to anticipate. Let us revert to the early history of Q.A.I.M.N.S.

The actual date of the establishment of Q.A.I.M.N.S. (by Royal Warrant) was March 27th, 1902. At the first meeting of the Nursing Board, held some three weeks later, the following were present: The Vice-President, Countess Roberts; the Chairman, Surgeon-General W. Taylor, C.B., Director-General Army Medical Services; Members, Surgeon-General A. H. Keogh, Sir Frederick Treves, Miss S. J. Browne, Matron-in-Chief, Miss Gordon, Matron of St. Thomas's Hospital, Miss Marks, Matron of King's College Hospital, Viscountess Downe, and the Hon. Sidney Holland. Truly a notable assemblage. At the second meeting Queen Alexandra, the President, was present in person, 'who wished the Board every success, and desired that its proceedings should be carefully reported to her in full'.

Q.A.I.M.N.S. grew steadily, and like all prosperous growths, soon began to assimilate minor and ancillary organizations. In 1908 the old Princess Christian's Army Nursing Reserve was replaced by Queen Alexandra's Imperial Military Nursing Service Reserve. In the same year a Territorial Army Nursing Service came into being. These adjustments formed part of the famous Haldane Reforms, which had resulted, *inter alia*, in the creation of the Territorial Army and the Officers' Training Corps.

Looking ahead again for a moment, we may note that in 1921 a Military Families Nursing Service was founded, to be amalgamated in 1928 with Q.A.I.M.N.S. This particular Service was, and is, of enormous value for two reasons: it confers complete hospital benefit (including maternity service) upon the soldier's wife and family, and it furnishes the Nursing Sister with a valuable and welcome alternative to the exclusive nursing of men.[1]

In 1926 Queen Alexandra's Imperial Military Nursing Service, India, which had hitherto existed as a separate institution, was amalgamated with Q.A.I.M.N.S., who at the same time took over the nursing in the British Military Families Hospitals as well. From this time onward Q.A.I.M.N.S. were responsible for the men, women and children of the British Army wherever they were stationed all over the world. The jealously guarded privilege of wearing the regular Q.A.I.M.N.S. uniform, with its scarlet cape, was shared by the Q.A.I.M.N.S. Sisters both in Britain and India; and Reserves and T.A. were distinguished by a grey cape with scarlet border. We shall discover later on, however, that the exigencies of total war made it necessary at times to abandon these cherished but all too conspicuous emblems. In Normandy in 1944 the Army Nursing Sisters went about their business in ordinary battle dress and steel helmets.

[1] See Chap. 24, pp. 356–8.

III

In 1914 came the First World War (or the Kaiser's War, as it is now frequently designated), and an enormous increase in the establishment of Q.A.I.M.N.S. was immediately indicated.

The Q.A.I.M.N.S. Reserve had been in existence since 1908, so the machinery of expansion was already available, though few realized how extensive that expansion would have to be. In 1914 the Service was about three hundred strong. By the end of that year no less than 2,223 trained nurses had been enrolled in the Reserve, of whom 1,803 were sent overseas—an establishment in striking contrast to that of the band of nursing pioneers, thirty-nine strong, so laboriously acquired by Florence Nightingale in 1854. By 1919 the Service and Reserve comprised 10,404 fully trained nurses. To this total we must add the V.A.D. contributed by the Order of St. John of Jerusalem and the British Red Cross, 8,495 of whom took the place of the usual R.A.M.C. orderlies in military hospitals. The total number of trained nurses and V.A.D. actually sent overseas—all under the ægis of Q.A.I.M.N.S.—exceeded 11,000.[1]

Dame Ethel Becher served as Matron-in-Chief throughout the war. In each war area overseas was a Principal Matron, responsible to Headquarters. In this truly remarkable band the heaviest burden, naturally, was sustained by the Matron-in-Chief, British Expeditionary Force, Dame Maud McCarthy. But indeed the work done and the results achieved in every theatre of war were such as would have been deemed beyond the bounds of feminine achievement a few years before. The joint record of these devoted ladies will for ever abide as a source of legitimate pride in the annals of Q.A.I.M.N.S.

IV

Mention has already been made in these pages—and there will be more to come—of Hospital Nursing Orderlies. These men

[1] See also Chap. 11, pp. 151–2.

are all members of the Royal Army Medical Corps, and a short account of the origin and history of that famous body may not be out of place.

A complete and self-contained Army Medical Service, as we know, is a comparatively modern product, almost as modern as a regular Standing Army. Until the seventeenth century armies were only raised upon the imminent prospect of war. The war over, the armies were disbanded, and their attendant medical services, such as they were, reverted to civil life.

The birth of our Regular Army dates from the year 1660, with the Restoration of Charles II. This force included in its service a number of medical officers who, instead of joining for the period of a given campaign and then returning to civilian practice, as formerly, were prepared to devote their professional lives to the care of the soldier.

Medical services were at first, and for a long time after, mainly regimental, though a few surgeons and physicians were appointed for Staff and for work in garrison and general hospitals. Each regiment maintained not only its own regimental surgeon but its own mobile hospital, the latter being staffed by a hospital sergeant and a number of male orderlies. Medical officers possessed no distinctive uniform, but wore that of the regiment.

For a hundred years and more Army medical services were maintained upon this crude and unsatisfactory system, without any particular supervision from above or official recognition within the regiment itself. The General Medical Staff, if so it may be called, appears to have comprised a Physician-General, Surgeon-General, Apothecary-General, and later, Director-General. In 1799, however, a Medical Board, composed of one Inspector of Hospitals, one Physician-General, and one Director-General, was established to deal with the appointment of regimental surgeons and other matters of administration. Drugs and medical stores were in the hands of the 'Apothecaries'. Supplies in general were controlled by 'Purveyors', gentry with whom, it will be remembered, Florence Nightingale was to come into frequent and violent collision during the Crimean War.

Under such a haphazard regime the lot of men wounded in

war-time was unenviable in the extreme. Such field hospitals as existed were stationary in character and thus remote from the field of battle. There were no bearer companies, no field ambulances, and no casualty clearing stations. As often as not, when the regiment moved on, the wounded were left to the care of the inhabitants of the country in which they fell; which, if on 'friendly' soil, sometimes meant that they were habitually neglected, and if on 'enemy' soil, that their end was accelerated by the swiftest and most convenient means.

This state of affairs continued right up to the time of the Peninsular War, though enlightened and energetic persons were not lacking to maintain the uphill battle for proper organization and better conditions. Prominent among these was Sir James McGrigor (Director-General 1815–1851), who received continuous backing from the Duke of Wellington himself. Sir James's statue may be seen today in the grounds of the Royal Army Medical College at Millbank.

Nevertheless it was not until 1855 that, under the combined impact of the Crimean War and Florence Nightingale, an organized medical service came into being with the creation of the Medical Staff Corps, with Headquarters and Depot at Chatham. The personnel of the Corps were left in no doubt as to the lowliness of their estate in the eyes of Authority: they were given no military titles or badges of rank, their duties being designated according to the nature of their employment—Cook, Orderly, Wardmaster, and the like.

But the main handicap under which the new Medical Staff Corps laboured consisted in the fact that it was subject to the direction of purely military officers. The Medical Officers were debarred from all direct authority—a circumstance not calculated to breed pride of regiment or *esprit de corps* in an infant unit. Breaches of discipline, for instance, were dealt with by the nearest available regimental commander.

Two years later, however, came the first real break in the administrative clouds. A fresh Royal Warrant was issued under which medical Other Ranks ceased to be classed according to their occupations and were given regular Army rank, with the accompanying badges. At the same time the name of the Corps was changed to the Army Hospital Corps. It was to be recruited in the main from volunteers from the Line and Medical Staff Corps, and its members were 'to be able to read and write well' not a common accomplishment in those days—'and be of regular steady habits, and good tempered, and possessed of a kindly disposition'. All of which presaged a brighter future for the sick and wounded, besides making it clear that if these exacting conditions could be fulfilled, the Army Hospital Corps, so far as character and education were concerned, would be something of a *corps d'élite* by comparison with the Line regiments.

The new corps still lacked officers of its own, and remained to that extent nobody's child; but for all that it was generally felt that matters were genuinely on the mend, and that complete emancipation could not much longer be delayed.

A further step forward was taken in 1870, with the removal of the Purveyors from the control of A.H.C. supplies, and their transference to a new body which, by 1881, had grown into the present Royal Army Service Corps.

A further important advance was made in 1873, when the headquarters of the corps was removed from Netley to London. Regimental Hospitals were also abolished and replaced by Station (or General) Hospitals. This reform made for economy of material, uniformity of control, and saving of transport. Best of all, it greatly enlarged the scope and liberty of action of the Army Hospital Corps. Disciplinary control too was at last transferred from so-called 'Captains of Orderlies', imported from Line regiments, to the Medical Officers themselves.

Thus, step by step, the corps moved into line as an essential and important part of the military forces of the Crown. This process was greatly accelerated by the actual participation of the A.H.C. in the various 'small' wars of that period—in Ashanti, Zululand, Afghanistan, Egypt, and the Sudan. It gave both officers and men the invaluable benefit of practical experience in active service; it raised morale to a high pitch, and it advertised to the Army at large the fact that it possessed a medical service to be proud of, not merely in the matter of professional efficiency but of gallantry under fire—in recognition of which many decorations, including the Victoria Cross, had been bestowed upon its members.

The reader may be reminded at this point that the labours of the Army Hospital Corps during this period were supplemented by those of numerous Army Nursing Sisters, dispatched overseas for the first time since the Crimean War to serve in military hospitals in Gibraltar, Malta, Cairo, and even farther afield.[1]

On June 23rd, 1898, the long struggle of the Army Medical Officers for complete emancipation from outside supervision came to an end. Upon that date by a final Royal Warrant, the Army Hospital Corps and Medical Staff were united into a single body known as the Royal Army Medical Corps, with normal Army ranks and titles throughout. In addition the Corps was granted its own badge and motto, *In Arduis Fidelis*, and the now familiar dull cherry facings appeared upon the uniforms of all ranks. The new Corps made its début in the field towards the end of the year, in Lord Kitchener's triumphant campaigns (which included the victories of Atbara and Omdurman) for the recapture, after fourteen years of almost continuous effort and sacrifice, of the city of Khartoum and the avenging of the murder of General Gordon.

The Corps' high services therein were publicly acknowledged in a speech delivered by the General Officer Commanding-in-Chief in Cairo on October 8th, 1898, in which the following words were specially addressed to the R.A.M.C. :

I have lately visited the hospitals at Atbara and Abadia, and was much pleased and greatly struck with their efficiency, by the care and attention shown to the sick and wounded, and by their general appearance of comfort. I can assure you that all branches of the Service have been loud in their praise of the way that the sick and wounded were looked after, both in the hospitals and on the field, and I may tell you that I have not heard a single adverse criticism with regard to the working of the medical arrangements.

[1] See Chapter 4, Sec. III.

Such then, in brief outline, is the story of the birth, growth, and development of the great Corps with which Q.A.I.M.N.S. became so closely affiliated and with which it has now shared the labour and sacrifice of two World Wars. Indeed the two formations are now so intimately linked that in the chapters which follow it will not always be easy, at times, to speak of the one without reference, if only by implication, to the other.

Part Two

THE FIRST WORLD WAR

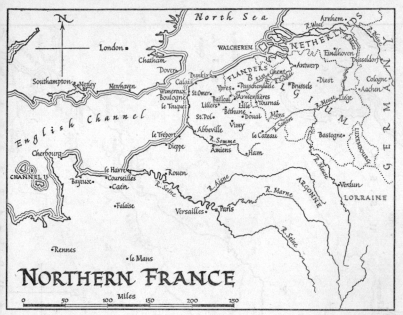

NORTHERN FRANCE

Miles
0   50   100   150   200   250

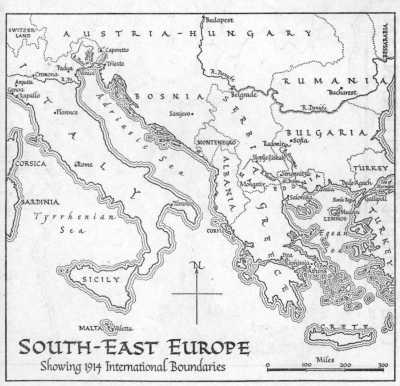

SOUTH-EAST EUROPE
Showing 1914 International Boundaries

Miles
0   100   200   300

THE EASTERN MEDITERRANEAN

Miles
0   100   200   300   400   500   600

Gallipoli
Sea of Marmara
Constantinople (Istanbul)
Dardanelles
TURKEY
Izmir
RHODES
CRETE

Ankara

T U R K E Y

R. Euphrates

Batoum

Tiflis

U. S. S. R.

Baku

Caspian Sea

Teheran
Qum
PERSIA

CYPRUS

Mediterranean Sea

Alexandria

Port Said
Ismailia
CANAL
Suez
Geneifa
Cairo
R. Nile

E G Y P T

Aleppo

S Y R I A

LEBANON
Beirut
Damascus
Haifa
Sea of Galilee
Acre
Nazareth
Jaffa
MT. OF OLIVES
Jericho
Jerusalem
ANT
Amman
Gaza
Dead Sea
ISRAEL
J O R

Mosul

R. Tigris

R. Euphrates

Baghdad
Ctesiphon

I R A Q

Kut-el-Amara
Shaik Said
Amara

Qurnah
Nasiriyeh

Basra

Abadan
Shatt-el-Arab
Persian Gulf
KUWAIT

NEUT. TERR.
NEUTRAL TERRITORY
SAUDI ARABIA

N

CHAPTER 6

WESTERN FRONT (I)

In August 1914 the British people greeted the outbreak of the Great War (as it was somewhat prematurely designated) in a very different spirit from that which they were to evince in 1939. We had not been involved in a general European conflict since the days of Wellington and Napoleon, and our attitude to another such tremendous adventure was one of almost pleasurable excitement.

Patriotic fervour rose high: all were eager to 'do their bit'. Young men flocked to the colours; young women volunteered for service among the sick and wounded; those of riper years devoted themselves to welfare work and the provision of comforts; business men diverted their energies to Government service.

The Union Jack was sported everywhere. Small boys decked themselves in monster cocked-hats of newspaper, and paraded the streets in martial gangs, brandishing wooden swords. The Beauty Chorus at The Hippodrome, with the fervent assistance of the audience, proclaimed nightly their fixed determination to 'Wind up the Watch on the Rhine'.

Optimism—blind optimism, in fact—was the order of the day. 'Der Tag', to which German Officers' Messes had been drinking for a generation, had come at last, and years of anxiety and suspense were over. All that remained now, we felt, was to square our account with the Kaiser, after which the world could settle down, at long last, to the blessings of peace and tranquillity.

Rather to the public surprise, Lord Kitchener, upon being called to the War Office, announced that enlistment would be for a term of three years. Few had anticipated so long a war: for some reason it had been assumed that a struggle so intense must of necessity be short and sharp. Not that this stayed the flood of recruits. Lord Kitchener had asked for a hundred thousand men: he got them practically overnight, and still they came. Indeed the recruiting stations had to be closed down for a time.

Hero-worship was the order of the day. Men in uniform were saluted and fêted everywhere. In Tube trains and omnibuses they were carried free, and as often as not passengers rose and offered them their seats.

II

It was in this exciting atmosphere that the Q.A.I.M.N.S., in common with the combatant Services, made ready for action. Here are some characteristic extracts from the diary of a very young Nursing Sister, begun upon August 14th, only ten days after the declaration of war. They will strike a reminiscent chord in the heart of many a 'Q.A.' of those days.

The first of these deals, naturally, with the bustle of preparation.

> Mobilized at Chatham. Twelve Q.A.'s including the Matron were put up at the Bull Hotel. . . . We all had to report ourselves at the Military Hospital, Fort Pitt, to the Colonel. Our Hospital is No. 9 General Hospital. . . . All the Staff seem very nice. There are 43 Sisters and Staff Nurses: there are seven of us from Millbank. . . .
>
> I am to instruct Territorial and Reserve Sisters in their duties in Military Hospitals, and also lecture on some of the Army forms and books used. I am to go down to the King's Head each day and lecture to them. Poor me! Poor them!

Then follows a routine tale of such matters as inoculation against enteric—there was to be no repetition of the South African visitation this time, it was hoped—and of final preparation, somewhat hampered by a sore and swollen arm and an aching head, for immediate departure to a bourne unknown.

Matron says we may start any time. Our only address
will be No. 9 General Hospital, B.E.F. . . . This evening
we were all issued out with identification discs, with our
name and religion printed on them.

As some of us may remember, not every Q.A., or for that
matter not every soldier, was able at first to realize the significance of that last item on the disc. Many of them thought it had
something to do with regular attendance at Church Parades.
Within a week of mobilization, the day of departure had
dawned, and No. 9 General Hospital was warned for an embarkation parade. In accordance with the British military passion for
what may be called premature punctuality, the Sisters were
roused from their beds at the grisly hour of 2.45 a.m., and break-
fasted at 4.0. However:

The hotel people are staying up all night, in order to see
us off and get breakfast for us. Jolly decent of them!

The train journey to Southampton, that historic starting-
point of British Expeditionary Forces from the days of Crécy
and Agincourt, occupied five hours. The distance was, and is,
seventy miles, but troop movements and traffic congestion in the
early stages of any war are synonymous terms. Upon arrival
the Sisters were given the rest of the day to themselves. They
enjoyed these last hours of personal liberty in various ways.
Some made an expedition to adjacent Netley, to look up old
friends; others were taken trips on tram-cars and generally shown
round by Boy Scouts, 'all for nothing'.
After a last dinner ashore all proceeded on board their transport
ship, bound they knew not whither. (Even the Captain, it was
rumoured, would not know until they reached Spithead. Sealed
Orders! This was the real thing!)
Needless to say, the vessel did not depart on time, as 400 horses
—'Poor things, they looked so frightened!'—had to be taken
on board at the last moment. However, the cables were let go
at last, and the following evening, conned by a French pilot and

escorted by three 'men-of-war', the ship arrived at a French port
which proved to be Havre. In 1939 the party would have been
landed much farther south, probably at Brest or even St. Nazaire,
in order to evade the attentions of the Luftwaffe. But in 1914
the menace of the bombing aeroplane was still hidden in the fog
of the future.

The sojourn at Havre was brief, but packed with interest, for
everything was new and strange. The town was full of troops,
the Frenchmen in their bright, baggy scarlet trousers—'rather unsuitable'—and blue overcoats caught in with a belt, and our own
Tommies, more soberly clad, cheerfully permitting the young
ladies of Havre to despoil them of their badges and even buttons.

There was much speculation and discussion as to how the war
was progressing. In the absence of official news rumour was
working overtime. It was naturally assumed, however, that
things were going well. The B.E.F. had joined the French in
Belgium, and were said to be putting up a highly successful performance, despite the atrocious behaviour of the Germans, who
were ignoring all the rules of civilized warfare, especially in their
behaviour towards units nominally protected by the Red Cross.

Needless to say, a Russian Army Corps was rumoured to have
arrived in France, with more on the way.

In point of fact, the French were at that moment in full retreat
from Mons, accompanied willy-nilly by the B.E.F. on their left
flank. The great rally and subsequent 'Miracle of the Marne'
were as yet some weeks away. Meanwhile hospital trains loaded
with wounded were pouring south, and it was obviously high
time that No. 9 General Hospital, among others, 'got cracking'.

Accordingly, on August 26th the Matron and forty-two Sisters
uprooted themselves from the Convent School in which they
had been billeted, and set out for Rouen. In those days mechanized road transport was a luxury unknown so far as the
infantry soldier was concerned: troops were conveyed over distances too great to be covered on foot by train, and a very slow
train at that. On the Western Front they travelled in horse-
boxes, marked in plain figures, *Hommes* 40, *Chevaux* 8. In other
words, five fully equipped soldiers were deemed by the French

military authorities to be equivalent, as occupiers of cubic space, to one horse. Those horse-boxes are now no more, but they were a familiar adjunct to every French railway siding, whether in war or peace, a generation ago.

Members of Q.A.I.M.N.S., however, were permitted to travel by passenger train, usually third class. What one of them thought of the service provided may be gathered from the following pithy comment by our diarist:

> I have come to the conclusion that the London, Chatham, and Dover Railway is quite fast compared with the French Railways.

This opinion was based not so much upon the leisurely pace of the trains while in motion as upon the inordinate length of time for which they were apt to stand still. On arrival at Rouen the party were informed that they might have to remain where they were for three days. This came as something of a shock, as the following passage attests:

> I must say here that knowing, or thinking, that we were only to be in the train for two hours, we had come away without rugs. Fortunately I had some chocolate in my bag; someone else had a tin of bully beef, another had some biscuits; so between us we shall not starve. Some tea was brought to us at 6 p.m.; but oh! the senna tea of our childhood was not in it!
>
> Altogether, we were not exactly comfortable, but at least we were cheerful. . . .
>
> Matron has left the train to see if there is any accommodation for us in the town. She has been away for five hours, and we hope she is all right.

However, this monotonous spell of waiting was not without its little excitements.

> More troop-trains of French soldiers have arrived, and we hear from them that the R.A.M.C. at the Front are being

shot down, so the newspapers are truthful for once. The
French soldiers were so delighted that we could speak French
a little, and after gazing at us open-mouthed for several
minutes came up and talked to us. They look smarter than
the men at Havre [these last were probably elderly Re-
servists, or Territorials], but they can never come up to the
English Tommy. . . .

Two dear Tommies have just come up with some coffee.
It is not exactly nice, but we are thirsty, very thirsty, and
we have been told not to drink the water here.

A wise precaution. All water issued to the troops at this time
was conveyed in mobile tanks, and was somewhat heavily chlo-
rinated. The water carried up nightly with the rations after
trench warfare set in was contained in the ordinary two-gallon
petrol tin of commerce, and the troops in the line grew quite
accustomed in time to a beverage strongly flavoured with both
petrol and chlorine.

In the end the party did not have to spend three days in a
stationary train. Matron returned safely after six hours or so,
with news of accommodation; the Sisters were packed into
British G.S. (General Service) wagons and conveyed to yet
another convent, where they set up their camp-beds in a vast
empty schoolroom, and were at last able to achieve a measure
of horizontal comfort.

Upon this particular date, August 26th, far away to the north,
the British Second Corps under Smith-Dorrien had turned about
at Le Cateau and inflicted heavy losses upon Von Kluck's advancing troops—the first German check since the beginning of
the Retreat. Elsewhere, however, the situation continued to de-
teriorate, and presently Rouen itself stood in danger of occupation. Accordingly, after a stay of only four days, No. 9 General
Hospital was bidden to be ready, at ten minutes' notice, to evacuate
southward. The war, for our Sisters, had changed overnight
from an exciting but uncomfortable picnic to a sudden and
startling reality.

The news is bad, very bad. The Sisters at Amiens are having to flee from the Germans, who are taking absolutely no notice of the Red Cross. The wounded are streaming into Rouen. They are starting to fortify the town. Cars filled with wounded Belgians are passing by on their way to the hospitals. I do wish we could get our own fixed up; but they think it better to equip one hospital at a time.

One poor man of the Royal Sussex, while helping with some of the wounded this morning, slipped on the rails and had both legs cut off by a passing train. He died two hours afterwards.

The Sisters in Amiens have had to flee with their wounded from their hospital. They are having a rough time. They passed through Rouen in cattle-trucks this morning, two Sisters in each truck and about ten wounded. All their stores and luggage they had to leave behind at Amiens, and they were most grateful for Bovril and hot milk, provided by No. 9. The Germans are said to be only fifty miles away.

This last rumour proved, if anything, to be an understatement. Rouen indeed was 'next for it', and the order to evacuate was issued forthwith. It was not found possible to remove all the wounded from No. 3 Hospital, but four devoted Sisters stayed with them.

Once more No. 9 Hospital took the road, or rather rail, and after another protracted and bumpy journey found itself at Le Mans, the pleasant country town which, twenty-five years later, was to serve as assembly point for Lord Gort and the B.E.F. prior to their advance to the appointed place in the Allied line along the Belgian frontier. Here a halt was made for further orders. Owing to the demoralized state of communications, these were now being conveyed by, and dropped from, the air.

The orders came soon enough. Off again! this time south-westward in the direction of the Bay of Biscay. On September 1st, after a forty-eight hour journey, No. 9 General Hospital found itself in the goods station at Nantes, which lies a few miles inland from St. Nazaire, the port at the mouth of the Loire, destined to be the scene in 1944 of a particularly gallant Commando raid. The heat was intense, and to add to the general discomfort, their train was hedged in by trucks full of lowing cattle on the one side and grunting pigs on the other.

But they had come to their journey's end at last, though they did not know it. Their hospital was to be set up and put into full operation as soon as a suitable site could be obtained. The choice of Authority fell upon the local race-course, and next day the tents and marquees were erected in the customary British formation—four neat parallel 'lines', with four tents in each. The Grand Stand was available for a Dispensary and Officers' Quarters; another stand accommodated extra patients. The Nursing Sisters after a night or two in the open on their campbeds under a full moon, found sleeping accommodation in a small hotel close by.

All was now in readiness, and the wounded began to arrive, in ever-increasing numbers. The less serious cases were dispatched to England by hospital ship, via St. Nazaire, conveniently adjacent, as soon as possible.

> About 150 patients [the diary reports], and several sick officers, were sent back to England by boat this evening. The poor Tommies were singing merrily, but were looking very worn out.
>
> The Hospital tents are getting into order beautifully; we shall soon have a very well-regulated Hospital under way. Some of the wounded officers have not washed for a fortnight, and the before-and-after effect of a wash and brush-up is quite miraculous. I had to do 'sentry' while the sick officers bathed next door to Matron's office!

No. 9 General Hospital soon settled down to its functions, and everybody was busy, our Sister among them.

> I am on regular duty in the Hospital now [she writes on September 7th]. The Hospital tents are arranged like this:

[Here follows a neat diagram of the entire lay-out of the hospital, grand stands and all.]

Today, first of all, I was sent to D Line and worked away attending to the patients who were admitted during the night.   At 10 a.m. Matron sent me over to Grand Stand B, where there were 84 patients waiting to be fed.   Nearly all were gunshot wounds, or else kicks from horses and rheumatism cases.   They were all very good.   I wish I could do more for them, but this Stand is barely equipped, because the men only stay for one or two nights and are then shipped off to England, where they will get better attention.

Tommy of course tells us the most harrowing of tales, but one knows Thomas Atkins too well to believe everything.

There are two sick Sisters.   I am looking after them this evening.

All of which sounds like a full day's work for somebody, rendered additionally trying as it was by the vagaries of the weather.

Oh, this heat!   Words fail to express how I feel.   I am so thirsty I can hardly speak.

Then, later in the day:

A storm has come.   It is pouring in torrents, and the thunder and lightning are terrific.   Poor night-duty people, working in the tents!

A few days later, we find, our diarist has achieved the ambition of every Nursing Sister, an independent command.

It is delightful having wards of my own, and it is most fascinating trying to improvise things. . . .   Some of the men in Tent 1 are very ill, poor things, but we have several little luxuries sent in by the Red Cross people here, in the way of grapes and the like. . . .

The orderlies on active service always do much better than at home. They are all working like bricks.

It seems that they are hearing the most awful things about us at home, and the official card issued does not convey much. I do hope we may be allowed to write soon.

What the 'awful things about us' were, and whether they called for compassion or censure on the part of the people at home, is not stated and must remain an intriguing matter for speculation; but the reference to the 'official card' can be explained.

The only communication home permitted at this time was a postcard with the following items of information printed on the back:

I am quite well.
I have been admitted to hospital.
I am sick } *and am going on well.*
I am wounded } *and hope to be discharged soon.*
I have received your { *letter, dated . . . . . .*
  { *telegram*
  { *parcel*
Letter follows at first opportunity.
I have received no letter from you { *lately.*
  { *for a long time.*

All that the sender of this eclectic missive had to do was to strike out the clauses which did not apply, and sign it. Nothing might be added to the text: many a Tommy had his postcard returned to him by the regimental Censor for infraction of this rule—the insertion, for instance, of 'I don't think!' after the word 'parcel'.

However effective the card in question might be in withholding 'information likely to be of value to the enemy', it

certainly cramped the style of any correspondent anxious to
convey a message of a confidential nature, however urgent. It
is this fact that our Sister laments in her diary: the 'awful
rumours', whatever they are, must remain unscotched until the
Censor grows a little more indulgent.

Summer ended and the weather broke, as the men fighting in
waterlogged trenches had good cause to observe. No. 9 General
Hospital suffered with the rest, and its gallant personnel tramped
perforce from tent to tent, by night and day, in gum-boots and
mackintoshes.

But they maintained their spirits, as ever.

> We must have looked like so many cats, picking our way
> about, but after a bit we ploughed merrily through the
> swamps.

The work grew continuously heavier; so did the rain. A
trench had to be dug round each of the hospital tents, to keep
the interior reasonably dry.

German prisoners were coming in in increasing numbers—
always an encouraging sign from a military point of view, but a
visitation regarded with mixed feelings by the nursing staff. It
is interesting, however, to note the progressive change of attitude
engendered between the Sisters and their enemy patients by
closer acquaintance, and especially by British inability to maintain a feud for long. Here are some extracts, each separated
from the other by an interval of days:

> They are all fine looking men. They smile at me, but
> I do not smile at them. . . .
>
> We had a large number of sick in again today, and several
> wounded Germans. Our Tommies are remarkably good to
> the latter. . . .
>
> I spoke to the German prisoners today. They don't want
> to fight against the English, they say, but the French they
> would like to blow to pieces. . . .
>
> I had a talk with a German prisoner this morning. He

gave me a button off his coat, and seemed quite pleased with my poor attempts at German.

Per contra, the Gallic approach.

> More people have been looking round the Hospital. One French General asked me why so many nice girls don't get married? I told him that if he had not been wearing French uniform I should have taken him for an Irishman! This amused him so intensely that he asked me to write my name in his book.

Work at No. 9 grew ever heavier, for a continuous stream of wounded was coming in now from the Marne battlefield. Towards the end of September we find our Sister actually apologizing to her diary for having ignored its rightful claims for five whole days.

> I have been working hard all day and far into the night. A big battle is raging, and the Germans are being repulsed. Our men seem to be fighting under very bad conditions: they arrive in hospital covered with lice. However, after two or three days in the hospital Tommy is a different man and his own cheerful self again.
>
> Several German prisoners have arrived, also badly wounded. They lack the pluck of our Tommy, though, and simply shriek when their dressings are touched.
>
> I think I have done about 400 dressings today, and am feeling dead tired; but felt I really must pull myself together and write a little in my diary.

'Dead tired' seems to be something of an understatement, if one can judge by the next day's entry:

> Feeling very seedy. Do hope I am not in for anything. Have managed to get on duty without being noticed. Temperature 103°. Patients are still arriving, so cannot

think of going off duty. A very large convoy has just arrived, and every single bed is full. The wounds are horrible, and the men so bad, but oh! so plucky.

The pluck does not appear to have been entirely confined to the men.

So the tale goes on. We are in October now, and the beneficent labours of No. 9 General Hospital are if anything intensified. There are some tetanus cases, involving wholesale injections: there is also much work to be done extracting machine-gun bullets and shrapnel. Even here Thomas Atkins's passion for souvenirs finds expression:

> The boy shot through the spine was operated on today. A large piece of shrapnel was found, and the spinal cord is injured; so the boy will always be paralysed partly. He guards his piece of shrapnel like a miser his gold. It was the first thing he asked for when coming round from the anæsthetic.

In October the Hospital was transferred to the grounds of a highly picturesque chateau four miles from Nantes, where the R.A.M.C. officers occupied the chateau and the Sisters a Girls' Summer School close by—a welcome change from canvas. In fact, conditions seem to have improved all round:

> We are all on Field Rations, and very good they are after the French dinners we have been having. We all have disgraceful appetites, being so much in the open. The air is beautiful and the surroundings lovely. I do wish the people at home could see it all.

Towards the end of October, however, signs were not lacking that the British Hospital Services in this area were beginning to outlive their usefulness. They were getting too far from their job—or rather, their job was getting too far from them—for the tide of battle was no longer flowing in their direction, but

F

receding, and the sick and wounded had to be conveyed over ever-lengthening distances. St. Nazaire, too, in the Bay of Biscay, lay a long way from England, and only the retreat of the Allies from Mons to the Marne and the Marne to the Seine had necessitated its employment as a port of evacuation at all. Now the retreat was over, and the enemy, after his heavy defeat on the Marne—the deciding battle of the war, as was sometimes said in final retrospect—had been pressed back to the Aisne, and was there held.

Indeed, the whole military situation had re-orientated itself. The enemy were now making a fierce thrust for the Belgian coast and the Channel ports, so the B.E.F. had been detached from the Aisne front and dispatched northward, with all speed, to form a new defensive line facing east, which ultimately resolved itself into the famous Salient of Ypres. The rest of the battle-front began to conform to this movement, and by Christmas the opposing armies had sunk from sight, in deep trenches, on either side of a no-man's-land running from the North Sea to the Swiss frontier, some five hundred miles in all. Here they lay sullenly facing one another, at a distance which varied from half a mile to a few feet, without material gain or loss of ground on either side, for more than three years. The Western Front had stabilized itself.

Needless to say, the British Army Nursing Services conformed to the general movement. Consequently No. 9 General Hospital soon realized from various signs and portents that its tour of duty on the Loire was coming to an end. The flow of sick and wounded dwindled—presumably they were being evacuated now from ports nearer home—R.A.M.C. officers began to depart, probably to some casualty clearing station nearer the Line, and No. 9's nearest neighbours, Nos. 2 and 6, vanished altogether. No. 9 itself had been turned out of the chateau at the behest of the French, and was under canvas again.

The only element that remained constant was the weather. Here is a final report on the subject, dated October 29th.

Pouring with rain. I wakened to find my boots floating,

and everything on the floor of the tent soaking wet. No, it is not nice getting up under these conditions. Well, well, live and learn! I know now to string up everything round the tent.

We have had a fatigue party round to enlarge the trenches so now we shall be all right. The Colonel was terribly upset that we should have been so uncomfortable. He was so afraid that we should be cold on duty that he has bought stoves for heating the hospital tents, and the patients appreciate them no end.

The very next day, our diarist and five of her colleagues were given their marching orders. They were to leave No. 9 forthwith and report to the A.D.N.S. at Boulogne, presumably for home.

It is characteristic of the spirit of *camaraderie* prevailing in this particular unit that the entry in the diary announcing its coming disruption should have begun (weather or no) with the word 'Alas!'

Next day, after numerous farewells and the gift of boxes of chocolate, the little party set off upon the usual train journey, at a strictly processional pace, interspersed with the usual maddening halts, back through Rouen, *en route* for Boulogne. Needless to say, our diarist continued to sit up and take notice.

> An R.A.M.C. Major showed us over some ambulance trains being fitted up for British wounded. The stretchers were all most beautifully swung and everything was beautifully clean. Each train has its own kitchen and is absolutely complete. . . .
>
> Passed crowds of Indian troops today, all looking very fit. . . .

These probably belonged to one of the two newly arrived Meerut and Lahore Divisions—Sikhs and Pathans.

Several H.A.C. boys (Honourable Artillery Company)

have just been up to speak to me, whom I met at Tidworth. They are fetching German prisoners down from the front. . . .

We got out at Abbeville. The Red Cross people at the station gave us a wash. . . .

We are now nearing Boulogne. . . . The train is swaying from side to side, and it is most difficult to write.

Perhaps that is why the diary comes here to an abrupt end; or more probably because the train was jolting its way into the Boulogne *Gare Maritime*, and the writer had caught a glimpse of the familiar white cliffs on the other side of the Channel, with their promise of a blessed period of rest from labour before returning to further adventure in the field of duty—who could say where?

III

Such were the experiences of one Q.A. Sister in the early days of the Kaiser's War, so vividly depicted in this brave and lively human document. Other diaries or letters, equally illuminating, will be quoted later.

The outstanding and general difficulty at first was the shortage of hospital equipment and transport—in other words, general unpreparedness for immediate action. This was not altogether to be wondered at, for it had not been expected that the B.E.F. would find itself in the actual battle-line so soon. The earliest divisions to land in France (in the third week in August) were marched straight into action upon detraining, and the casualty list sprang into being before adequate arrangements had been made to deal with it.

The opening stages of the Flanders campaign, then, were a series, in many cases, of hasty improvisation and make-do on the part of Q.A.I.M.N.S. But everyone seems to have risen to the occasion. There was a shortage of dressings, and more than one Sister tore up her own spare body-linen to supply bandages. Rationing arrangements were at first far from perfect, but shortages were made good somehow, frequently from local resources, and no one seems to have gone hungry for long.

Hospital transport presented another problem, for the field hospitals were constantly on the move and there were at first only enough ambulances to accommodate the really serious cases. Walking wounded sometimes had to walk for miles, sometimes for days.

But all these difficulties are the familiar and accepted adjuncts of the beginning of a military campaign, especially for a people whose custom it has always been first to declare war and then prepare for it; so nobody grumbled and everybody worked overtime until the situation adjusted itself.

One of the personal tribulations which the Sisters themselves had to endure arose from the prim little bonnets, tied under the chin, which they wore as part of their uniform. These afforded no protection from the blazing sun of that late summer, and it was not long before the Q.A.s, discarding peace-time formalities, provided themselves with the hats of plaited straw worn by French peasants, for use when working in the open.

Those bonnets had been responsible, incidentally, for certain misapprehensions on the part of the French civil population, who at first insisted on regarding (and greeting) the Q.A.s as Salvation Lasses—*l' Armée de Salut de l' Angleterre.*

There were the usual rumours and spy scares, one of them rather less usual than the others. In a casualty clearing station (a former Priests' College) at Baillcul, close to the Belgian frontier, the duty Sister was called one night to the bedside of a newly-arrived patient, a Signaller, who announced that someone in the upper regions of the building was operating a telegraph instrument, tapping out messages in the Morse code.

The Sister listened, and sure enough, in the stillness of night, the sound of the transmitter-key was clearly audible, stuttering out an irregular sequence of dots and dashes.

'Can you read the message?' asked Sister.

'No, Sister. It's probably in German,' added the expert, importantly.

As this seemed more than likely—the hospital had until recently been occupied by the enemy, who might quite conceivably have left someone behind to operate a buried line—Sister referred the matter to the Hospital Commandant, and a thorough search was instituted. But no trace could be found either of a telegraphic apparatus or its operator. Next night, however, when all was still, the tapping began again; and Sister, listening intently on the staircase, decided that it came from the top floor, which consisted of the usual *grenier* under the roof. With considerable courage she took a candle and proceeded upstairs.

Here the mystery revealed itself. The *grenier* was occupied in one corner by an enormous cistern, full of water—too full, in fact: for the overflow pipe was maintaining a steady, if irregular, drip-drip upon the boarded floor some ten feet below, with a resulting and most uncanny reproduction of the sound of a Morse code transmitter in action.

Sister went downstairs again and, to the profound disappointment of her patient, was able to disprove his diagnosis of a promising situation.

IV

By Christmas 1914 the long battle-line had more or less consolidated itself. We had fought First Ypres at the end of October and won it by the skin of our teeth. The British trench system was almost continuous now, and it had been found possible to organize medical and nursing services with some hope of permanency. First-aid posts were established in the trench reserve lines, casualty clearing stations were set up farther back, great base hospitals began to rise in the neighbourhood of various Channel ports.

Of course these things did not all happen at once; but the work progressed steadily, until in May 1915, when the so-called New Armies began to arrive in Flanders, the Q.A.I.M.N.S. were at their posts in the base hospitals, casualty clearing stations, and hospital trains, while the machinery of healing and comfort was in steady operation from Havre to Dunkirk.

Behind all this ordered progress stood the figure of that truly remarkable woman, Maud McCarthy, Matron-in-Chief to the British Armies in France.   Her parish extended from the Channel to the Mediterranean.

She already had a long record of service and achievement to her credit.   Australian born, she had left her ward in the London Hospital as one of a contingent of six nursing sisters selected by Queen Alexandra (then Princess of Wales) to proceed on service to South Africa and the Great Boer War.   She was thus one of the earliest forerunners of Q.A.I.M.N.S.

The London Hospital was loath to part with her, for she had proved herself a tower of strength in its service.   On the day she left a member of the medical staff inscribed with a diamond upon the window of her little ward sitting-room the single word *Ichabod*!

She served with distinction throughout the South African campaign, and in addition tó other honours was awarded a special decoration by Queen Alexandra.

Twelve years later she went to France in the first ship to cross with members of the B.E.F., and continued there in her capacity as Matron-in-Chief throughout the First World War.   She was said to have been the only head of a department in the B.E.F. to retain her original position through the whole war.   Like her great predecessor of Scutari, defeat was unknown to her.

In 1918 she was created a G.B.E., and became Dame Maud McCarthy.   She was getting on in years now, but continued to serve for another five years (1922–25) this time as Matron-in-Chief to the Territorial Army Nursing Service.   She died as recently as April 1949 at the age of ninety.

CHAPTER 7

WESTERN FRONT (II)

THE appalling casualties suffered by the British Army during the First World War—nearly four times as many men were killed as in the Second and much longer World War—created a great and ever-growing need for nursing personnel.

At the outbreak of the war Q.A.I.M.N.S. was composed of three hundred trained nurses of all ranks, ready for immediate action, with a reserve of two hundred on call at twenty-four hours' notice. Six hundred trained nurses from civil hospitals had also been earmarked for immediate service in the event of war—a total of 1,100 all told.

By the end of the war more than 10,000 reserve nurses had been enrolled, exclusive of the T.A.N.S., in which 2,783 were already serving.[1]

To give a detailed account of the service rendered on the Western Front by all the units concerned is a manifest impossibility, and would in any case involve the telling and re-telling of much the same story. The adventures of a single Nursing Sister, outlined in the previous chapter, could be duplicated in a hundred cases. Our best course will be to make a selection from the records of various representative units—in hospitals, in casualty clearing stations, and in hospital trains—and salute the effort and achievement of these as typical of the whole.

From an operational point of view the history of the Western Front falls roughly into three periods. First came the war of movement—Mons, the Marne, the Aisne, and the race for the sea—between early August and late October 1914, a campaign of swift changes, sudden emergencies, and desperate improvisations;

[1] The services of T.A.N.S. are fully noted in Chap. 23, pp. 337–9.

second, the prolonged stalemate of siege warfare, lasting for three and a half years; finally the renewed war of movement and manœuvre, this time along the whole line from the North Sea to the Swiss border, beginning with the great German attack in March 1918 and continuing without intermission until the Armistice in November.

Each of these periods made its special demand upon the energy and resource of the Army Nursing Services. Until Christmas 1914 the situation, as we have seen, was one of acute period and recurrent crisis, during which Q.A.I.M.N.S., almost overwhelmed by the unexpected number of casualties with which they had to deal, contrived nevertheless to render memorable service, however unorthodox, wherever they found themselves.

Fortunately Britannia still ruled the waves, and it was possible to ship the majority of the less seriously wounded home almost as soon as they arrived at a Channel port from their casualty clearing station up the line. By the end of 1914 there were base hospitals at Havre, Rouen, Boulogne, Wimereux (on the heights from which Napoleon's Grand Army of Invasion had once lain for two years in over-confident contemplation of the white cliffs of England), Versailles (at the Trianon Palace, the scene five years later of the Peace Conference), Dieppe, and Abbeville. To these must be added twelve ambulance trains and seven hospital ships.

One of the most important, and probably the best remembered, hospitals of those very early days was No. 13 Stationary Hospital—a group of converted sugar-sheds on the quay at Boulogne. The great doors at one end admitted the casualties as they arrived, while those at the other discharged cases fit to travel straight into the *Gare Maritime*, whence they were evacuated to England.

There were the usual delays, difficulties, and shortages at the start. Here is the scene, as described by one of the Sisters:

> What an indescribable scene! In the first huge shed there were hundreds of wounded walking cases: as long as a man could crawl he *had* to be a walking case. All were

caked with mud, in torn clothes, hardly any caps, and with
bloodstained bandages on hands, arms and legs.   Many were
lying asleep in the straw that had been left in the hastily
cleared sheds, looking weary to death; others were sitting
on empty boxes or barrels, eating the contents of a tin of
'Maconochie' with the help of a clasp-knife.[1]

Then there were the stretcher cases, for whom beds were being
brought in and partitions run up, to form some sort of a surgical
ward.   The beds as soon as they arrived were occupied by badly
wounded men who had to be put into them as they were, clothes
and all, until time could be found to cut off the clothing, wash
the patient, and dress his wounds.   Doctors, nurses and orderlies
almost submerged under the endless stream of casualties from the
Marne, Aisne, and Ypres fronts, laboured without ceasing,
almost without sleep, to meet the demands made upon them—
handling their cases as they came, with little opportunity for
ordered classification or specialized treatment.

It was not until that great woman Maud McCarthy arrived
and took personal control that order began to emerge from the
general confusion.   Reinforcements of nurses arrived, the necessary stores and equipment were made available, and presently the
gaunt sheds began to assume the appearance of a well-equipped
military hospital.   Red quilts appeared upon all the beds (thanks
entirely to the generosity of Lady Algernon Gordon Lennox, who
had forestalled official procrastination by furnishing the necessary
funds herself), and thus provided a most cheering splash of colour
amid those drab surroundings.   What is more, there were large
bowls of flowers everywhere—the gift of that famous Englishman
and sportsman, Lord Lonsdale, who had arranged for a twice-
weekly supply, direct from Bond Street.   We are told that the
sight of those English flowers moved many of those tired, over-
wrought British soldiers to tears of gratitude, and that more than
one dying man passed away with a handful of flowers in his grasp.

Upon November 11th an event occurred never to be forgotten

[1] The Maconochie was a special ration of meat and vegetables, designed as
an occasional relief from a perpetual diet of bully-beef.

by those who participated therein—a visit, no less, from Lord Roberts, V.C., former Commander-in-Chief at the War Office and the idol of the British soldier for half a century; who in his extreme old age had insisted upon travelling from London to Boulogne to greet and cheer his youthful comrades-in-arms. He spoke to every stretcher case in the hospital, bending low time and again, to murmur some word of greeting and comfort. The prolonged effort, alas, proved too much for him. Two days later he succumbed to a chill, and had himself to become a hospital patient. Next day he died, in a hospital bed, wearing a soldier's scarlet bed-jacket. (The pocket of this was found to contain a handkerchief, with a card pinned upon it, bearing the legend: 'Good luck, from Queen Mary.') Next day his body was conveyed back to England. His escort consisted of gaunt, white-faced men straight from the trenches, and his coffin was received on shipboard by a party of his special protégés, the Indian soldiers.

II

Christmas 1914 (celebrated in due form in No. 13 Stationary and indeed in all the hospitals along the line) marked the end of the war of manœuvre: the trench system was now roughly stabilized, and behind that barrier the base hospitals were able to organize their routine upon an ordered plan, with no further fear of enemy interference. The Nursing Sisters were now assigned either to permanent and regular duty in this base hospital or that, or to serve in a casualty clearing station or hospital train. Later, a small flotilla of barges was added, in which patients could be floated in peace and comfort along the numerous Flanders canals from casualty clearing station to base.

In due course the transport system at Boulogne settled down into almost clockwork precision. Cases were evacuated so expeditiously that sometimes three different contingents of wounded were known to have occupied the beds at No. 13 within twenty-four hours.

In the case of the walking wounded as many as 3,000 could

now be dressed, fed, and passed on shipboard in a single day. They were met by non-commissioned officers at the entrance doors and assigned to different benches according to their degree of wound. They were then seen by the doctors, who prescribed for them, while a Sister made a note of the necessary treatment. A band of nursing orderlies followed, and carried the treatment out. The patients were then seated at a long table, where they partook of a hot meal and a mug of tea. Finally they were passed out through the exit doors, proudly displaying their 'Blighty' tickets, to the waiting transports—and Home.

The same good order and discipline now reigned right up to the trench-line. A certain amount of intermittent shelling was all that had to be risked during the earlier months of this period: the bombing aeroplane had not yet become an active menace.

It was not until the fall of night, however, that the *hinterland* of the trench-line became really busy. Regimental transport set out from the ration and supply dumps in the billeting area— limbered wagons heavily loaded and drawn by four mules, rattling noisily along the *pavé*, or cobbled country road—and were met at the reserve line by fatigue parties from each unit, detailed to carry rations, water, ammunition, and most precious of all, mail, up through a labyrinth of communication trenches to the front line.

They were not as a rule interfered with on these occasions by hostile fire. After all, the enemy had to get his rations up too, and at normal times a sort of tacit truce prevailed from dusk till dawn. So smoothly was this service maintained, that it was not unusual for an officer, returning in the small hours from a night patrol or a wire-repairing expedition, to find his London news-paper, of even date, waiting in his dug-out.

It was under the kindly cloak of darkness, too, that we took occasion to bury our dead.

Casualties, despite the deceptive calm of many of those days, were numerous enough, for we maintained a continuous frontage of some 120 miles. There was perpetual sniping, much shelling of back areas, and a growing amount of that brand of Teutonic 'frightfulness' represented by trench-mortar activity and the visitations of the *minnenwerfer*, or aerial mine, or 'flying pig', which came sailing lazily over no-man's-land and plumped into a front-line trench with sufficient detonation to blow the parapet to pieces. During the winter, too, especially the cruel winter of 1914–15, when miles of front-line trench lay waterlogged, a man sometimes stood up to his knees in slush for days on end. The result was a case of sodden, swollen 'trench feet', which might keep him on his back for a year.

From time to time during the early years of trench warfare the monotony was varied by a series of what may be termed experi-mental offensives, designed partly to explore the possibilities of a real break-through, and partly to give the necessary experience, both to officers and men, of the conditions which would arise with the launching of the victorious 'big push' which everyone felt would be made sooner or later.

These experiments may have taught our Higher Command some valuable lessons, but they were terribly expensive. Both at Neuve Chapelle and Festubert, in the spring of 1915, our initial attack broke victoriously through the enemy's front-line trench system, only to find another, of even greater strength, lying close behind. Our exposed flanks meanwhile were subjected to a devastating enfilade fire, and in due course a well-organized enemy counter-attack was sufficient to restore the *status quo*—but not before our casualty clearing stations were filled to overflowing and our base hospitals once more working overtime.

III

Our first really serious attempt to break the German line was at the Battle of Loos, in September 1915, which was undertaken not because we were completely ready, but largely to satisfy the susceptibilities of our French Allies, who had been heavily engaged throughout the year farther south.

We attacked upon a front of no less than six divisions, with cavalry in reserve, and made a substantial advance, carrying the whole of the enemy's first line, and breaking at many places through his second. But we had not sufficient reinforcements to push the victory home, and such as we had were too far back and arrived too late. A modern battle is won only by superiority of numbers at the proper place and moment.

After three weeks of inconclusive fighting the battle petered out, and the weary round of trench warfare was resumed. Our casualties had been enormous.

From a medical point of view the Battle of Loos was historic, from the fact that here, on September 25th, the troops went into action equipped, for the first time, with an anti-gas device, a so-called 'gas-helmet'. This precaution had been rendered necessary by the fact that in the previous April the Germans had released a new horror of war in the form of chlorine gas, discharged from containers in a following breeze, in which our men suffered and died in agony and bewilderment, and which created a gap in the Ypres Salient four miles wide. A gallant rally by the Canadians saved the day, and the enemy was unable to follow up the preliminary advantage gained by this new and devilish weapon of war.

Apart from the sufferings of the troops, the whole incident was a most distressing experience for the doctors and nurses in the hospitals, compelled as they were to witness men writhing in agonies which they could do little or nothing to alleviate.

The Ypres gas attack made it instantly clear that from now on no man (or woman, for that matter) must be permitted to go within enemy range unprovided with some means of protection from the effect of poison gas; and steps were immediately taken to that effect.

Our early protective devices were not impressive. The first was a pad of cotton-wool wrapped in gauze, and a beer-bottle containing a solution of caustic soda. In the event of a gas alarm each man was to sprinkle the pad with the contents of the bottle and then tie it over his mouth and nostrils. The theory may have been sound, but in practice matters worked out differently; for the sodden pad of cotton-wool merely prevented the man from breathing at all. Presently discarded pads and bottles littered the trenches and roadsides.

A so-called gas-helmet was next issued. It was certainly an improvement on its predecessor, for it at least permitted one to breathe. In appearance it was something like a diver's helmet, made of grey flannel and furnished with mica eye-pieces. It was worn over the head and tucked into the inside of the collar. The wearer was instructed to breathe in through the flannel and out through a metal valve held in the teeth. The material of the helmet was impregnated with some malodorous compound designed to neutralize the effects of poison gas.

Whether it would ever have done so is a matter of doubt, for two reasons. In the first place Thomas Atkins, who habitually prefers comfort to security, was accustomed as soon as he was issued with this new protective device, to plunge it into a bucket of water and keep it there until it had lost not only its characteristic aroma but any prophylactic virtues which it may have possessed; in the second, no poison gas at all was employed at the Battle of Loos. By the time of the Battle of the Somme, nine months later, a really effective gas-mask had been designed (not differing greatly from the modern present-day pattern), worn over the face and supplied with oxygen from a canvas haversack carried at the 'Alert' position on the chest.

Let it be added that poison gas, so far as direct discharge from containers was concerned, was very little used during the First World War and not at all in the Second. It was too tricky a medium; its successful use depended largely on atmospheric conditions, and it was too apt to blow back upon its employers. Thus its use was generally restricted to gas-shells discharged at long range.

The net result, then, of that first gas-discharge in the Salient of Ypres was that thereafter the personal *impedimenta* of the soldier were permanently increased to the extent of an encumbering anti-gas device which he might never be called upon to use. But at least it relieved the doctors and Nursing Sisters from one particular nightmare.

IV

Of our tremendous and desperate attempts to pierce the German trench-line during 1916–17—the Somme, Arras, Passchendaele—mention has already been made. So far as the medical and nursing services were concerned, they were a repetition, upon an ever-increasing scale, of all that had happened in 1915.

But in March 1918 there was a different tale to tell. The long period of static warfare came to a sudden end; the clockwork precision of the medical services (among others) behind the trench-line ceased almost overnight, and the war of manœuvre was resumed upon a truly frightening scale.

The British Army during 1917 had assumed practically the whole burden of the Western Front, for France for the moment had shot her bolt. At the urgent request of Marshal Pétain, Sir Douglas Haig had taken over a further twenty miles of trench-line, which could only be weakly manned, for the Passchendaele operations (which had been undertaken largely to divert enemy troops from the French front) had cost us thousands of British lives. But so effective was this diversion that by the end of 1917, although we held but one-third of the Allied line, we were faced by 52 per cent of the enemy forces.

Germany, on the other hand, having beaten Russia to earth, was now in a position to transfer vast forces, which had fought no serious action for nearly a year, from the Eastern to the Western Front. Now, if ever, was the time for her to strike—and strike she did.

Our European commitments, it should be noted, had been seriously increased by the disaster of Caporetto, where our Italian Allies were suddenly attacked, on a misty morning in October 1917, by an army of six German and nine Austrian divisions, and driven in headlong rout from the Isonzo to the Piave—almost to Venice itself—with a loss of 600,000 men.

It was the gravest situation for the Allies since the crisis of First Ypres three years earlier, and had it not been for a resolute stand made by the Duke of Aosta's Third Army on the Tagliamento, would probably have ended with Italy's elimination from the war. Plainly this could not be allowed to happen. The Allied leaders, Mr. Lloyd George and M. Painlevé, with General Smuts and General Foch, hastened to Italy, and met the Italian Army leaders on November 5th at Rapallo. To these they promised substantial aid both in men and arms.

In due course the British reinforcements arrived in Italy, accompanied by a contingent of Q.A.I.M.N.S. The Sisters arrived at Genoa upon a bleak morning in December, but owing to the general disorganization of the moment it was some time before quarters could be provided for them or their duties allotted.

They were assigned at first to a Stationary Hospital in a large hotel in Genoa, a most impressive edifice of marble staircases and beautiful bathrooms; but owing to the extreme shortage of fuel—Italy possesses no coal-mines—there was an entire lack of heating or indeed of hot water.

Ultimately and by degrees the Sisters were distributed among various hospitals in Northern Italy—at Arquata (the Base), Cremona, and Bordighera. New Year's Day 1918 was celebrated at Padova. Here the fuel shortage was more apparent than ever, and the Sisters were regretfully informed upon arrival that they must choose between coffee for tomorrow's breakfast and hot water to wash in, for they could not have both.

One Sister had the happy thought of performing her morning ablutions in the water from her hot-water-bottle, which she had contrived to fill overnight. Her hopes, however, were dashed by the discovery that the water in question, when poured out, proved to have been used already—to wash the dishes from last night's supper.

With the coming of summer the situation improved. Now that it was really warm the Sisters were in a position to appreciate and enjoy the outward attraction of their surroundings, whether the surpassing beauty of the Italian scene, or the ornate character of their quarters in country villas and hill-top shooting-boxes.

There was little operational activity at this time, and life behind the line, except for periodical air raids, was pleasant enough.

G

Taranto was a particularly sociable spot, for it lay on the overland line of communication with the East, and was regularly used by troops passing backward and forward. There was a comfortable hostel, and a Nurses' Club provided by the British Red Cross Society.

Despite the strain of work and a perennial shortage of small luxuries, Q.A.s decided that the Italian adventure was to be numbered among the more agreeable of their war experiences. They were certainly better off during this period than their colleagues in Flanders.

To these we must now return.

V

Ludendorff's great 'infiltration' attack in the foggy dawn of March 21st, 1918, repeated at short intervals at other points, came near to disintegrating the undermanned and overstretched British line; and for a hectic period of months we were fighting, as Sir Douglas Haig reminded his troops in a famous and effective message, 'with our backs to the wall'. That they should find themselves in such a position was no fault of theirs. The reason was simply that too long a front had been imposed upon Haig, without a sufficiency of men to hold it.

Let us now study the immediate effect upon our medical and nursing units.

Here is an extract from a letter written in May 1918 to Lieut.-General Sir Arthur Sloggett, Director-General Army Medical Services, B.E.F., by Dame Maud McCarthy.

> DEAR SIR ARTHUR,
> I hope that the attached will be of assistance to you. They are notes which I have extracted from letters received from the Sisters in charge of a Casualty Clearing Station during the Retreat in March.
> During that time I myself visited many Clearing Stations. . . . Everywhere, without exception, I was struck by the

businesslike and orderly manner in which everything was being conducted. There was no sign of excitement or nervousness, and all seemed intent on doing the work which had been allotted to them. I particularly noticed in those Units which were expected to close at any moment the care and thought which had been expended on the patients. They were all properly dressed, and as many as possible were in readiness on stretchers, to be evacuated directly the transport arrived.

I noticed a report in the daily papers that one Sister had been killed and another severely wounded. This happened in the First Army, at the time of the Retreat in the south, during a bombing raid, while the Sisters were proceeding from the Clearing Station to their billet. Four of them were crossing the railway line, when one was killed and another badly injured. The two remaining Sisters had the presence of mind to decide that one of them should remain with the wounded Sister (and the body of the Sister who had been killed) and that the other should proceed to the C.C.S. to get help.

These two Sisters continued working in the operating theatre during the night, and I understand displayed the most wonderful courage and carried on as if nothing had happened. They have since been awarded the Military Medal.

This award, it may be noted, was a most unusual distinction. The Military Medal is a soldier's decoration, for which he is usually recommended by his own officer. The special distinction here lies in the fact that these particular Medals were 'put in' by the Army Council and approved by the King.

Next is an illuminating summary, on a more detailed scale, of the experiences, during this same period, of a Sister of the Territorial Nursing Service. The following extracts will give the reader some idea of the hardships suffered and the incredible courage displayed by all concerned in this adventure. It will also be noted that the ruthless employment by the enemy of gas-shells had by this time made a gas-mask a permanent item of a Nursing Sister's equipment.

On the morning of the 21st March a barrage started at 4.30 a.m. We were called by the Night Super about 5 a.m. and told to dress and put on our gas-masks at the alert position, as shells were coming over. We went to the mess, had breakfast, and went on duty early, as the wounded soon began to come in.

Long-range shell-fire had been responsible for these early casualties.

I had a ward full of patients for resuscitation, penetrating wounds of abdomen, chests, heads and cases requiring immediate amputation of limbs. Very few died, considering the severe nature of their wounds. A corporal and myself just worked at high pressure as long as we could. We had to work with our gas-masks at the Alert, but I confess I hung mine on to my back!

Early in the afternoon an order came from the Colonel that we were to clear out at once. The ambulances were filled with the worst cases and some Sisters went on each.

The next C.C.S. was at Ham, about 8 kilometres distant and to get there we were obliged to go along a road which was being shelled. Twice shells whipped over our heads, but we suffered no hurt, for they dropped in a field beyond. I felt so sorry for the patients, for many of them had just returned from the theatre after having major operations; but to get them away was their only chance. We passed a large ammunition dump quite close to the road; one could not help thinking what would happen to them if a shell burst there——

The only persons of whom these Sisters never seem to have thought were themselves.

——but a merciful Providence watched us that day, I am sure.

The stay at Ham was brief, for next day at noon the order was given that the entire hospital was to be cleared within twenty minutes, and the cases conveyed to the railway station, as the enemy were close at hand.

There was a prolonged and very trying wait at the station, for the promised train had not materialized.

Shells were falling on either side of the station. One shell fell quite close, and a lot of Tommies, who were laying temporary lines, shouted to us to duck and get under cover. But we did not need telling. I discovered next day that a piece of shrapnel had cut a hole in the back of my coat. . . .

At long last, with the enemy only twenty minutes away, the wounded were absorbed by a Red Cross train, and the Sisters, who had started to walk along the railway lines, were picked up by the Colonel in a couple of lorries and conveyed to No. 50 Casualty Clearing Station at Roye; where, exhausted though they must have been, they immediately set to work wherever they were most needed.

The first day I fed the theatres and kept the tables going with dressings and gloves. Next day I worked in the dressing tents. Men seemed just to pour in. Surgeons and the Matron were simply splendid: they worked with the rest of the staff day and night. There was no time for regular meals or sleep.

On the 25th, the fifth day of the Retreat, came another complete and hasty evacuation.

As many officers and men as could possibly walk were advised to walk on until picked up, for there were only sufficient trains for the stretcher cases. I shall never forget the look on the poor lads' faces when told they had to go farther; but they preferred to do so rather than be taken prisoner. They showed such pluck, and all helped one another. Men with arm-wounds were crutches for men with leg-wounds. It was a pitiable sight, but showed the amount of grit a British Tommy has.

So the tragic, heroic Odyssey continued. They were clear of the battle zone now, and moving through country as yet undevastated.

We went through village after village, in beautiful country. We passed many refugees, with their household effects piled in a cart, the cows following tied to the back; children with blankets twisted round their shoulders in the manner our men carry their greatcoats. There were troops of all sorts—Indian, Portuguese, Chinese. . . .

But port was almost in sight. Next day, at Hardecourt, word was received from the Matron-in-Chief that the remnants of this particular C.C.S. were to proceed that night to Amiens. They arrived about midnight. Needless to say the city was being heavily bombed.

We were just dead tired and covered with dust. There were no beds available, so we lay on the floor of the mess-room and tried to sleep; but for most of us it was impossible. The noise was terrific and the hospital shook every time a bomb fell.

We left Amiens on March 27th and went by ambulance train to Abbeville, where we reported at the Sisters' Home. Here they were crowded with refugee Sisters: the bedrooms were full again. However, the staff provided us with mattresses and blankets, and a comfortable bed was quickly made up on the floor. There, for the first time for a week, we undressed and slept. It was just splendid.

Next morning the Matron-in-Chief addressed us, thanked us for all our work, and asked if we felt able to go on again. (How like the Matron-in-Chief!) Of course we all said yes.

How like the Sisters!

After that our gallant band dispersed to other duties elsewhere, whither we need not follow them. They were still under intermittent shelling, but they were no longer refugees. Our particular Sister served for the rest of the war at No. 20 General Hospital at Camiers, the headquarters of the B.E.F. Machine-Gun School, between Boulogne and Le Touquet. Here is her final summation of her war experiences.

I feel honoured and glad to have had the opportunity of nursing the boys at home and in France and Belgium.

The honour was not entirely unilateral.

VI

In the end Ludendorf's great attack failed, and Germany had shot her bolt.

Foch had been appointed to the supreme command of the Allied Forces, and this enabled him to distribute his reserves where they were most needed, with the result that by the end of the struggle French, British, and occasionally American troops found themselves fighting side by side. The spirit of unity was in the air. French morale had risen again to the standards of Verdun. In Britain the military age-limit had been raised to fifty, and fathers and sons were sometimes serving in the same unit. In the ordnance factories the workers gave up their Easter holiday in order to make good our losses in guns and stores. Two British divisions arrived in France from Palestine. The dispatch of American divisions to Europe was expedited.

By the beginning of August the tide had turned for good, and the Allies advanced to the attack along their whole line, from the Belgian coast to the Argonne Forest—an advance which never ceased until the first week in November, when Ludendorff resigned his command and the Germans asked for an armistice.

CHAPTER 8

GALLIPOLI AND SALONIKA

The Gallipoli Expedition in April 1915 was the most imaginative and promising enterprise of the First World War.

Its purpose was to force the passage of the Dardanelles, capture Constantinople, put the Turks out of the war, and gain direct access to the Black Sea ports. This would have enabled us to supply our Russian allies with the munitions of war of which they were being starved. If the break-through could be achieved, Britain and France would be in a position to unite with Russia in an all-out attack upon the enemy's Eastern (and weakest) flank, by way of Bulgaria and Rumania.

Had that vast strategic conception been fulfilled, we might have shortened the war by two years and completely altered the history of the world, particularly that of Russia. But it was not to be. The scheme failed, chiefly for want of ordered planning at the outset and resolute direction at the critical moment.

But it only just failed. So near were we to complete occupation of the Peninsula that once, after the Suvla Bay landing upon its northern edge in August 1915, New Zealanders and Ghurkas contrived to scale the intervening heights and stood gazing triumphantly down from the summit of Chunuk Bair upon the sparkling waters of the Dardanelles, which led to the Sea of Marmara and Constantinople. The way was clear; all that was needed was an immediate advance in full force. But the necessary support was not forthcoming: there was an inexplicable delay of twenty-four hours upon the beaches in the rear, during which Kemal Attaturk was able to rally his forces. The men on Chunuk Bair lay helpless under a heavy bombardment, and were finally compelled to seek shelter farther back. Direct observation and control of the Dardanelles was lost, never to be regained, and the old stalemate was renewed.

For the remainder of the campaign the Allies could only hang on round the fringes of the Peninsula; until, with the approach of winter, the project was abandoned altogether and Gallipoli evacuated, fortunately without loss.

It was a tragic business, but an epic story for all that. The tactical advantage had lain everywhere with the enemy. We were operating sixty miles from our base, and all transportation was by water. Our only artillery support was furnished by the guns of the *Queen Elizabeth* and such other warships as could be spared from the Atlantic operations.

As for the long, flat, tongue-like peninsula itself, a visitor to Gallipoli today, standing on the summit of Achi Baba at the root of the tongue, the principal observation point of the Turkish and German gunners, and gazing down the narrowing vista towards Cape Helles and its beaches, with every yard of the sandy, scrubby, barren expanse exposed to view, could not fail to realize how utterly and entirely the defence dominated the situation. He would be divided between two emotions—amazement at the sheer audacity of the actual landing, and dumb pride in the dour and dogged spirit with which our men maintained their footing on that deadly strip of shell-swept coast during nine heart-breaking months.

As an instance of the exceptional difficulties of the Gallipoli campaign, it may be mentioned that eighty tons of drinking water had to be conveyed to the beaches per day, over a distance of 500 miles.[1]

II

Such, in brief, was the Gallipoli picture. A campaign so unusual was bound to involve the Medical Services in many a diversion from normal routine.

Let us first visit the base, at Lemnos. The Isles of Greece are lovely, but Lemnos during the Gallipoli campaign was anything

[1] Noted in *Gallipoli*, by John Masefield.

but a paradise. In normal times it is an island of green hills, with bare stony summits crowned by unexpected windmills. It is particularly attractive in the spring, and was in happier times a favourite resort for visitors from the mainland.

But war-time conditions have a way of disfiguring the face of nature almost overnight—a fact which the British nation were destined to realize to the full a generation later, when in 1944 the whole of Great Britain had been converted into one vast training camp.

In 1915 the great harbour of Mudros contained over a hundred ships of every type, from battleships to Greek fishing craft. Ashore, the island was overcrowded beyond belief. Clouds of dust hung over the camps and hospital tents; flies swarmed everywhere, contaminating food and infecting wounds.

No Sisters at that time set foot upon Gallipoli itself. There was little enough room for the troops, crowded as they were along the narrow strips of beach below the towering bluffs, and the erection of hospital tents was out of the question. Indeed, with the scanty cover available, first aid could only be administered under conditions of appalling difficulty. Fragments of bursting shell, we are told, frequently fell round the stretchers in the dressing-stations.

Q.A.I.M.N.S. were based on Lemnos, where they reported for orders on board the *R.M.S. Aragon*, the headquarters of the Medical Staff. But though they were not permitted to land on the Peninsula, some of their most urgent and dangerous duties were performed within a stone's-throw of its shores, on board the hospital ships lying off to collect the sick and wounded from the lighters—usually under machine-gun fire from hidden emplacements in the cliffs. German U-boats had now arrived to add to the danger and suspense, and there were mines everywhere.

On occasions of exceptional activity—the Suvla Bay landing, for instance—the hospital ships sometimes carried twice as many patients as they had been designed to accommodate. On board the *Gloucester Castle* room had frequently to be found for an additional 400 cases, by laying mattresses along the open deck so closely as to touch one another.

As soon as the ship was full—and she filled quickly at that period—she pulled out for Lemnos, pausing, when out of range of the Gallipoli coast, for the reverent committal to the deep of those who had not survived their injuries.

On arrival at Lemnos the wounded were conveyed ashore and comfortably bestowed; and as soon as they were fit to travel were dispatched to England, or to other and healthier Mediterranean stations. Mudros was no place for a sick man to linger in, especially those suffering from gangrene or dysentery.

It was a hard time, as ever, for the Nursing Sisters; but their letters home, as usual, dwelt far more upon the courage and endurance of their patients than their own dangers and discomforts.

Here is a characteristic extract. It deals with the period which witnessed the climax of the Suvla Bay landing.

> Upon the arrival of the *Gloucester Castle* surgical operations commenced, and were continued for thirty-six hours without a pause, and it is fortunate that the weather kept fine. . . .
>
> The poor maimed suffering boys—for the majority of the wounded are nothing more than boys in years—lie in rows on the deck outside the operating theatre, just as they are taken from the lighter, awaiting their turn. After being operated on they are carried to the wards. How wonderfully brave and uncomplaining they are! . . .
>
> The mental strain on the officers runs through their delirious mutterings. One captain must have been hit just after he had sent an important dispatch, for he is continually muttering: 'He got through all right; I watched him all the way down. It's time he was back; I can't think why he doesn't come!' Only death released him from his anxiety.
>
> The less seriously wounded were full of fun. One staff officer, from whose leg a bullet had been extracted at his own request without chloroform, insists on hopping round on his good leg to talk to the others. He does them so much good that the nurses pretend not to see him disobeying orders right under their eyes.

Oh, wise nurses! They know that in war-time the moral is to the physical as three to one.

Some years after the end of the First World War a party of British ex-Servicemen and their ladies (more than one of whom had seen active service with Q.A.I.M.N.S.) arrived in Lemnos to visit certain island graves. They were greeted by the Lemnian Boy Scouts, who had mobilized and marched twenty-five miles across the island to do them honour.

> Of course [wrote one of the party afterwards], the honour was not ours, as we gladly recognized: it was addressed to certain former guests of the island—thousands of them—the recollection of whose conduct and bearing during the period of their sojourn their hosts were eager, even after ten years, to acknowledge with a fitting gesture. . . .
> Mudros itself is a solitary enough spot now. During the war its great harbour sheltered battleships, destroyers, transports, submarines, colliers, hospital ships, even Grimsby trawlers, every one of them flying the White Ensign. Now there is nothing—only a great waste of tumbling waters and a little white village in one corner.
> Still, the Boy Scouts had not forgotten.

More than one Nursing Sister will recognize that picture.

III

After the withdrawal from Gallipoli the Allies, frustrated in their hope of attacking the enemy from the East, concentrated their effort upon Serbia, with General Headquarters at Salonika, in Macedonia—after Athens and Constantinople the most historic city in South-Eastern Europe.

It was upon Serbian territory that the Serajevo 'incident'—the murder by an irresponsible fanatic of the heir to the throne of Austria, the Archduke Franz Ferdinand and his consort on June 28th, 1914—had brought the seething cauldron of European politics to boiling-point and precipitated the First World War. The world has been at war somewhere, practically without intermission, ever since.

The Serbian Army, although they had but recently emerged from an exhausting war of their own (first against the Turkish Empire and subsequently against their recent ally Bulgaria, with whom they were now at war) put up a stout resistance: indeed, they defeated, with almost presumptuous thoroughness, the Austrian troops which had been sent to chastise them. Later, however, Germany herself took over the administration of chastisement, and this time the odds were too great. Belgrade fell, and German divisions swarmed across the Danube to the assistance of the Bulgarians.

The Serbians, fighting desperately but in sore straits, appealed to Britain for aid—aid to which our country had long been pledged.

Here a most serious and critical decision had to be made. To intervene in Serbia with any hope of success we should have to send a force at least 300,000 strong, and this, in 1915, we simply could not do without dangerously weakening our hold on the Western Front. In other words, it would probably have been wiser, from a strategic point of view, to deny to Serbia troops which could be employed far more profitably elsewhere. But we had pledged our word, and in warfare the moral issue must sometimes take precedence over the physical. Upon this occasion, it was realized, to abandon Serbia to her fate would create a serious, perhaps fatal, rift in Allied unity.

So the great gesture was made, and in October 1915 an Anglo-French Army under a French general, Sarrail—the British forces were subsequently commanded by Major-General G. F. Milne— were landed at Salonika, and took over the defence of what was left of Serbia. The remnants of the gallant Serbian Army were transferred to the island of Corfu for rest and refitment, whence ultimately they emerged, 100,000 strong, with equipment and morale fully restored, to take their place in the theatre of war— to the left of the French, who with two Italian divisions occupied the centre. On the right the British faced the Bulgarians, on a line extending roughly from the Vardar valley to Struma, about ninety miles in all.

How overlong that line was, and how severe the strain upon the gallant but inadequate force which manned it throughout those years, was never quite realized by the people of England. Compared with the memorable and highly dramatic struggle for Gallipoli, it offered few thrills to the seeker after military sensation, especially since by this time the eyes of the world were fixed on the Western Front, where the heroic and successful defence of Verdun by the French, and the British advance on the Somme, expensive though these ventures were, had gone far to deflate the German boast of German invincibility.

But the Salonika campaign, though comparatively unspectacular (chiefly owing to its desultory character) was by no means a secondary affair. A convenient index to the strength of the British force there engaged is supplied by the figures of its medical services. By August 1917 those services comprised:

General Hospitals	17
Stationary Hospitals	4
Casualty Clearing Stations	5
Convalescent Camps (1 for officers, 1 for nurses) .	2
Ambulance Trains	2
Field Ambulance	1

To these must be added the Royal Serbian Hospitals:

General Hospitals	4
Stationary Hospital	1

The members of the nursing staff (including members of the Canadian and Australian Army nursing staff) comprised no less than 1,066 trained nurses and 224 V.A.D.s.

Four of the base hospitals, it should be noted, were in huts, some of which, with their nursing staff, had already done good service at Mudros. The tented hospitals were equipped, in addition, with huts for operations, patients' baths, and a Nurses'

Mess. These amenities were doubly welcome, for life in the Macedonian theatre was a grisly business. There were few roads, building material was hard to come by, and the climate most trying. Indeed, in the summer, additional hospitals had to be created to cope with the increase in sickness from malaria, enteric, and dysentery. The Nursing Service suffered severely in this respect, and special accommodation had to be provided for them in a permanent Sick Nurses' Hospital, where up to one hundred cases could be treated at once. This was in No. 43 General Hospital, situated, with others, on the Hortiach Plain, a comparatively healthy area some seven miles from Salonika.

By 1917 communication by sea had grown extremely difficult, for the U-Boat campaign was now in deadly operation in the Eastern Mediterranean, as elsewhere. It was therefore decided to evacuate as many 'sitting' cases as possible by the overland route to Taranto, in the heel of Italy, via Bralo and Itea. A hospital was opened at Bralo, with a much needed rest-camp for the Nursing Sisters attached.

One of the most spectacular and disastrous events of the Macedonian campaign owed nothing to enemy action, though it threw an additional burden upon the medical services. This was the great fire which broke out in the Turkish quarter of the city, spread with devastating effect, and at one time, fanned by a strong wind from the valley of the River Vardar, threatened to destroy Salonika, with its picturesque minarets and famous White Tower, the centre of the town's social life, altogether. However, the combined and strenuous efforts of the Allied troops were successful in arresting its course, but not before 100,000 people had been rendered homeless.

Military transport thereafter was kept busy conveying women, children, and such of their humble possessions as could be retrieved, to a place of safety. In particular, the kindly help rendered by the British soldiers was a revelation to the civil population, who had fully expected that their rescuers would be unable to resist the opportunities for looting which everywhere presented themselves. That expectation was entirely unfulfilled, and the praises of Thomas Atkins were loudly sung.

In a very short time three refugee camps had been set up, each with its hospital tent, and two Nursing Sisters in charge. Business was brisk, and one Sister had occasion to comment shrewdly upon the number of elderly citizens who availed themselves of a heaven-sent opportunity 'to have their old ulcers and other chronic ailments attended to!'

Meanwhile the campaign continued, and towards the end of 1918 the dogged persistence of the Allied effort began to reap its reward. It became possible at long last to embark upon a combined and successful offensive. North-west of Salonika, Monastir, the most ancient city of the Balkans, fell to the Serbians; Uskub, in the Vardar Valley, to the French and Italians; while on the right the British swept the Bulgarians from their path and advanced on either side of Lake Doiran.

Close behind the battle-line, as usual, came the medical services. By October our casualty clearing stations were in operation as far ahead as Lake Doiran, Strumnitza, Radomir, and Ralrova: later, sections were opened at Kavalla, Dede Agach, and Sofia, in Bulgaria itself.

Our base hospitals were kept busy right up to the end of the campaign, for the enemy were resisting desperately and casualties were grievous. The terrible influenza epidemic, destined within the next twelve months to spread over the whole of Europe, was already at work. The labours of our overworked Nursing Service were increased by the necessity of admitting to our hospitals hundreds of Greek sick and wounded, for whom no adequate provision could be made by their own Government. The Greeks, it should be noted, were now definitely in the fight. Venezelos had displaced the pro-German Zaimis, and Greece's long period of uneasy neutrality was at an end.[1]

By the end of November, however, the casualties slackened, and it was found possible to close some of the hospitals. The rest remained open, perforce, until well into 1919. True, the final victory had long been won; but the proclamation of an armistice does not automatically heal the victor's wounds.

Bulgaria surrendered unconditionally on September 30th, 1918

[1] Salonika, our base, was actually situated in Macedonia and not in Serbia.

the first enemy country to get out of the war as she had been
the last to come in. Her rulers had hastened to join what they
clearly regarded as the winning side on the strength of our failure
at Gallipoli: they were the first of the Central Powers to realize
that mistake.

IV

Relieved of the greater part of their duties in Serbia and
Macedonia, our hospitals and ambulance services were now free
to proceed elsewhere. The war was practically at an end everywhere, but there was much human wreckage to salve, and this
duty took Q.A.I.M.N.S. far afield.

No. 28 General Hospital was transferred to Constantinople.
No. 21 Stationary Hospital travelled as far east as Batoum, at
the extreme end of the Black Sea. No. 18 Stationary Hospital
penetrated to the 'frosty Caucasus', and set up house in Tiflis.
A much-needed Convalescent Home for war-weary Nursing
Sisters was opened at Bebek on the Bosphorus in July 1919.

Weary indeed some of them must have been, for the conditions
under which they laboured called for the highest degree of
fortitude and staying power. To prevent infection during the
so-called malaria period of the summer months, the Sisters were
constrained to perform their duties wearing mosquito veils over
their hats, mosquito gloves, and thick puttees. The difficulties of
a 'ministering angel' so arrayed stagger the imagination.

However, though many had to be invalided home each month,
the mortality among the Nursing Sisters in the Salonika campaign was only thirteen, including two killed in an air raid.

Of one of those raids something more must be said here, for
it brought forth one of the first and finest displays of courage
and devotion, under the new horror of aerial bombing, in the
annals of Army nursing.

The raid took place on February 27th, 1918, and was delivered
by German bombers, from a height of less than fifty feet,
upon No. 37 General Hospital, attached to the Royal Serbian
Army.

H

The whole of the Nursing Staff, reports the Commanding Officer, behaved magnificently. He proceeds to quote in detail three outstanding instances.

The names of the Sisters mentioned are those of Staff Nurses Margaret Smith Dewar, Annie Rebecca Calhoun, and Ethel Garrett, all of the Q.A.I.M.N.S. Reserve.

Seventeen bombs were dropped that morning in half an hour. Sister Dewar was fatally wounded in the act of placing a pillow over the head of a patient, in order to shield him. A portion of a bomb passed through her chest as she was kneeling over the patient, who himself escaped.

> Had she not risen to perform this act it is probable that she herself would have escaped. The act showed complete disregard for herself: her chief thought seems to have been for the safety of the patient.

Sister Calhoun was in the same tent, and had been assisting Sister Dewar in the case of a patient who was helpless and unable to move. She was herself struck by a fragment in the back, but not injured, so was able to turn her attention to Sister Dewar, by whose side she remained until death came. She then returned to her helpless patient, and tended him until relieved. Later in the day, though almost completely exhausted, she insisted upon carrying out heavy duties in the hospital operating theatre.

As regards Sister Garrett, the report states that after the bombardment she was found still tending her patients. One, a private of the R.A.M.C., was suffering from compound fracture of the skull, caused by one of fourteen bombs which had fallen close to the tent.

> During this period she attended to her patients, in spite of the fact that bombs were dropping so close to her that the tent itself was wrecked and full of dust and smoke. In addition to Private Cozens she attended to one Serbian patient. She seems to me to have shown extreme coolness, courage, and devotion to duty in the treatment of these cases.

A few weeks later the Crown Prince of Serbia, through the Director of Medical Services of the Royal Serbian Army, bestowed upon Sister Calhoun and Sister Garrett the Serbian Military Medal, 'For Valour', in gold—the first ladies upon whom that high honour had ever been conferred.

But courage and devotion was not limited to any particular hospital or occasion. More than one Nursing Sister died, not by direct enemy action, but from sheer overwork and exhaustion. One instance will stand for many, as in the case of Staff Nurse Jessie Ritchie, of Q.A.I.M.N.S. Reserve, who died of dysentery in August 1916.

> Her death can be attributed to her devotion to duty. Most of her time was spent in nursing enteric or dysentery. She would never spare herself. The well-being and comfort of her patients was always her first consideration, and she was untiring in her care of them. There was no doubt that the heat during June and July last year tried her very much; but she would never give in, and had even signed on for another year. . . . She had no reserve of strength left to fall back upon.

The report concludes with these words:

> It seems invidious to single out instances when the whole of the Nursing Sisters of the various hospitals displayed such endurance and devotion to duty during the great heat and sickness of last summer; yet the conduct of the Sisters mentioned stands out so prominently that their names have been selected for this report.

v

Such is the Salonika story. Today ten thousand British soldiers lie buried in the soil of Macedonia and Serbia, together with their French and Italian comrades. In one cemetery, Lembet Road, just outside Salonika, the soldiers of all three nations sleep side by side. The French have white wooden crosses—though these may by this time have been replaced by material more substantial —the Italians, crosses of marble; and the British, the familiar upright headstones, standing in long level ranks like soldiers on parade.

But elsewhere the British rest apart. Their cemeteries are usually set on hillsides, with the Stone of Remembrance at the foot and the Cross of Sacrifice gleaming overhead. Outside each cemetery, written in English and Greek, is an inscription which proclaims that the ground is a free gift from the Greek people— British territory for all time.

Here and there a visitor to one of those cemeteries may behold the grave of a military Nursing Sister, in no way differing from those of the hundreds of men around her. A lonely grave, in one way; yet what woman that ever died could have asked for a more gallant escort across the River?

CHAPTER 9

EGYPT AND PALESTINE

DURING the First World War Egypt, that land of immemorial antiquity, became automatically a strategic centre of the highest importance to the Allies in general and the British Empire in particular; for whoever controlled Egypt, controlled the approaches to the Canal, and with them the road to India and the Persian Gulf.

Turkey had joined the Central Powers, so the need for that control had become self-evident and urgent.

Our forces in Egypt at the beginning of 1915 consisted of certain Indian troops, some Lancashire Territorials, and the newly arrived Australasian Corps.

The Turks, deciding to strike while our defences were still weak, took the offensive forthwith, and launched a direct attack against the Canal. It was a hasty and ill-organized affair, and was so heavily repulsed that the experiment was not repeated.

Except for intermittent shelling on either side, a stalemate of nearly two years now ensued. This gave Sir Archibald Murray, the British Commander-in-Chief, opportunity to bring his forces up to adequate strength. A successful offensive against the Turks in Palestine would call for careful planning, and above all for time. The outstanding difficulty would be that of transport, for it would be conducted for the most part over a trackless, waterless desert. Lines of communication would be long, and would grow longer if the campaign was successful; so a railway must be constructed to keep pace with the advance of the Army. There must also be elaborate arrangements for a continuous water supply. Upon this tremendous task General Murray and his staff toiled unceasingly, and by the spring of 1917 all was in readiness.

In invading Palestine our troops were traversing historic ground, the scene of battles, in succeeding centuries, between Jew and Philistine, Crusader and Saracen, Sidney Smith and Napoleon.

General Murray's first serious obstacle was the ancient city of Gaza, from which Samson is reputed once to have emerged carrying the city gates on his back. The place was situated in a mountainous district ideal for defence, and was strongly manned and fortified. After fierce fighting, lasting a whole fortnight, with heavy losses on either side, General Murray was constrained to break off the battle and resume, *pro tem.*, a defensive attitude.

This was a severe blow to British prestige, as severe almost as the Gallipoli failure; and it was universally realized that immediate and vigorous steps must be taken to retrieve the disaster—for disaster it was judged to be.

Further reinforcements were at once sent out from England, headed by Sir Edmund Allenby, a great cavalry leader and perhaps the most brilliant and consistently successful soldier produced by our country in the First World War.

In October 1915, with a force increased to seven infantry and three cavalry divisions, Allenby launched his offensive, once more against Gaza. The attack, largely owing to his skilful handling of his cavalry, was completely successful, and by the beginning of December British troops, some of whom had covered seventy miles in nine days, were in Jerusalem itself.

Allenby's own entry into the Holy City was characteristic, and has become historic. He entered on foot, accompanied only by his personal staff, the commanders of the French and Italian detachments, and a representative of the United States. Having issued a tactful and reassuring proclamation to the inhabitants, he then withdrew from the City with all his forces.

The story went round the world, and created a profound impression. As a strategic centre Jerusalem itself was of trifling importance, but the moral effect of its liberation was immense, and restored British prestige everywhere.

Incidentally, the British occupation of Jerusalem fulfilled an ancient prophecy, to the effect that one day the Holy City would be entered by a deliverer from the West, who would bear the

name of the Prophet of God, but who would not appear until
the Nile flowed into Palestine. Both conditions were now fulfilled, for Allenby's name in Arabic signified 'The Prophet', and
his men had been sustained throughout the campaign by water
conveyed from the Nile itself.

Allenby did not rest upon his laurels, but, advancing like a
second Joshua, captured Jericho and pressed on northward. He
was delayed however for some time during the summer of 1918,
owing to the grave situation, already mentioned, on the Western
Front. All his white troops that could be spared were dispatched
to France, and their place taken by units from India and
Mesopotamia.

But by September he was ready again. On he stormed,
making as usual skilful use of his cavalry—it was the last time in
history that the horse was to be employed in shock tactics: here-
after its place would be taken by the 'armoured fighting vehicle'
—and by October 1st was in Damascus. During the previous
twelve days three Turkish Armies had melted away. All that
was left now was a mixed mob of Turks and Germans, flying
northward. The Turks were practically out of the war, and
the Ottoman Empire was crumbling.

II

Egypt, throughout the war, served as a base and supply
centre for at least four different campaigns—Palestine, Gallipoli,
Salonika, and East Africa.

More important, however, for the purposes of our present
narrative, is the fact that it was to Egyptian hospitals that
thousands of sick and wounded men were conveyed from the
various theatres of war, to be tended by the Army Nursing Sisters.

Of course, as is inevitable in war-time, when so much is a
matter of improvisation, regular routine was not established
immediately. The Gallipoli landing took place on April 25th,
1915, and during the ten days immediately following no less
than 16,000 casualties were landed in Egypt. It was a difficult

moment, for only a small number of nurses were immediately available. The difficulty was heightened by the fact that two General Hospitals, Nos. 15 and 17, had arrived from England without their Nursing Sisters—an omission due, apparently, to the assumption that these hospitals would be set up on Gallipoli itself, in surroundings to which women in those days must not be exposed.

The mistake was rectified as soon as it was realized, and in due course a contingent of Nursing Sisters arrived from England. Every one of them was needed, and more. Not only had staff to be found for the hastily improvised hospitals of Lower Egypt and the ships bringing casualties from the theatre of war, but for the hospital trains conveying sick and wounded to Cairo. For this latter duty the services of local voluntary helpers were requisitioned.

At the end of July another 200 Nursing Sisters arrived. To ease the heavy strain upon Egyptian hospital accommodation these were diverted to Mudros, where Stationary Hospitals Nos. 3 (Australian), 15, 16, 18, and General Hospital No. 27 were being set up. The nurses were conveyed thither in the P. and O. liner *Simla*, and were distributed among the hospitals just mentioned—or as many of them as by that time existed—or else posted to the ships engaged in conveying the wounded from the Gallipoli beaches, as described in Chapter 10.

These vessels were technically described as 'Carriers', presumably to distinguish them from regular hospital ships. Many of them were quite unsuited to their purpose, being devoid of proper accommodation or equipment; and until better arrangements could be made many of the wounded suffered considerable hardship. However, the officers and crews, as usual, devoted to them all the care and attention in their power, and Thomas Atkins accepted the situation with his usual cheerful resignation. From September onwards properly equipped hospital ships took the place of the Carriers, and the sick and wounded were restored to their rightful comforts.

Egypt, lying remote from the turmoil and confusion of the battle zones of Gallipoli, Salonika, and Palestine, and preserving practically intact the atmosphere and amenities of peace-time, might well have been regarded as an exceptionally 'cooshy' and desirable base for our Hospital Services. Cairo, with its fascinating blend of unchanging East and up-to-date West, was a never-failing source of interest to Sisters on leave or off duty.

The Egyptian had (and has) the Parisian's fondness for street-life. In Cairo, between Shepheard's and the Continental Hotel, a distance perhaps of a quarter of a mile, the pavement was thronged with insistent persons prepared at any hour of the day or night to sell the visitor a Turkey carpet, a walking stick, an amber necklace, a glass of lemonade, or a lottery ticket. Outside the innumerable *cafés* sat white-robed gentlemen, making one small cup of coffee last as long as possible, and arguing shrilly with one another amid the roar of motor traffic and electric trams.

It was rarely that the visitor saw the face of a woman, for those faces were all closely veiled, as strict *purdah* demanded. The woman herself was swathed from head to heel in nun-like black. Through her black veil could be observed the outline of a curious little gilded cylinder, worn down the bridge of the nose. (This cylinder is a model of the Nilometer, the ancient device for recording the level of the Nile.) When a dozen of these ladies came to town on a marketing expedition, packed into one small cart drawn by one small donkey, they presented a truly startling appearance. They looked like a plague of widows, and would have alarmed the elder Weller considerably.

Thus, compared with the mud, mosquitoes, and other discomforts of Macedonia and Mudros, not to mention perpetual danger from the air, the clean, safe Cairene hospitals and the pleasant distractions of the Cairo streets seemed to promise an almost idyllic existence for those fortunate enough to be employed there. But no field of human activity is ever quite free from the mischances of total and amphibious warfare. During the First World War twenty-two Nursing Sisters and V.A.D.s died in Egypt from sickness or accident, and nine met their death by drowning.

This last tragedy occurred on October 19th, 1915, when the

steamer *Marguette*, conveying the nursing staff of No. 1 (New Zealand) General Hospital *en route* from Port Said to Salonika, was sunk by enemy action. Nine of the Sisters lost their lives: the survivors, twenty-six in number, were taken back to Egypt, bereft of all their possessions and suffering from shock and exposure.

III

By February 1916 the Gallipoli campaign was a memory of the past, and the hospitals at Mudros were being evacuated. This made it possible to dispatch certain nursing units to face fresh experiences and adventures in other theatres of war. Some went to Salonika, others to Mesopotamia; Nos. 15 and 16 Stationary Hospitals were dispatched bodily to German East Africa, and No. 27 was established in Cairo.

Meanwhile in Egypt arrangements were in hand for the mental and moral refreshment of the war-weary divisions from Gallipoli. Convalescent camps and homes were established in Ismailia, Kantara, Port Said, and Suez, all in convenient proximity to the Canal and its supply ships. But that was not all. A great rest centre was established at Luxor, far up the Nile, a place of intense historic interest and a popular tourist centre. Here large and luxurious hotels were commandeered, and 2,000 convalescent soldiers and their entourage were enabled to combine the pursuit of fresh health and vigour with agreeable researches in amateur Egyptology, either in the great Temple of Karnak, or among tombs of immemorial antiquity in the Valley of the Kings across the river.

By this time, however, our troops based on Egypt had become involved, as already noted, in an increasingly bitter campaign against the Turks in Palestine. Once again the hospitals in Cairo and elsewhere were filled to overflowing.

More than that. As the Turks retreated, the British Hospital Services moved up. Nos. 43 and 45 Stationary Hospitals were established at El Arish, an admirable site close to the sea, and Nos. 36, 44, and 18 in Gaza itself. Nos. 69 and 78 General

Hospitals were set up at Belah, about an hour's journey from Gaza. Q.A.I.M.N.S. were on the move once more.

After Allenby's occupation of Jerusalem a body of Nursing Sisters was attached to the great casualty clearing station which had been installed in the Italian Hospital there. The hospital itself was only partially completed and entirely unequipped. A casualty clearing station, being only a casualty clearing station, possesses few of the amenities of a Stationary Hospital.

Fresh wounded came pouring in almost daily, and so great was the congestion, and so inadequate the accommodation, that many of the cases had to be nursed on stretchers or mattresses, for lack of bedsteads. However, with their usual determination and resource, the Sisters, aided by invaluable contributions of equipment from the Red Cross Services, British and Australian, finally succeeded in making good the worst deficiencies. Similar difficulties were successfully overcome, a little later, at Jaffa.

IV

The final surrender in Palestine and Syria was followed almost immediately by the outbreak of an epidemic of influenza, of the most virulent type, destined to ravage the world for the next two or three years. By 1920 it had even spread to the United States and Canada.

In our Egyptian Hospitals, as elsewhere, the strain upon the Nursing Services increased almost to breaking-point, for the Sisters were now called upon to tend thousands of enemy sick as well as our own. No. 70 General Hospital at Cairo had actually to be cleared for the sole reception of Turkish and German cases.

Administrative difficulties had been increased almost beyond measure by the fact that in 1917, owing to increasing man-power shortage on the Western Front, all the Class A orderlies of the R.A.M.C. in Egypt had been recalled for duty in Flanders, and their place taken by Arab boys.

Boys will be boys whatever their nationality, and this particular breed proved a sore trial to the long-suffering Sisters. They could not speak a word of English, they were extremely dirty and quite unreliable, and could not be entrusted with the smallest nursing duty. They were employed for the most part in fetching and carrying; but even here they required so much supervision that the Sisters would for the most part have preferred their room to their company.

However, with the dawn of peace—and with the surrender of Bulgaria and Turkey it dawned sooner in the Middle East than the West—the strain grew less and matters settled down to a more ordered routine. Sisters were available again for work in more distant fields, some of them as far away as Beirout and Aleppo.

Needless to say, the Sisters themselves had been by no means immune from sickness. The wonder was that so few succumbed. Special hospital accommodation was provided for them in Cairo and Alexandria, to which in due course was added the unspeakable boon of a convalescent home and rest-centre at El Arish, on the coast.

And now at long last, with the cessation of hostilities the flow of wounded ceased, and convalescents were duly shipped home. The work of the Army Sisters, in this theatre at any rate, was done, and their warfare accomplished.

v

Apart from Egypt and the Sudan, Q.A.I.M.N.S. (and T.A.N.S.) served in another African theatre of war—in German East Africa.

This was a fantastic, uncanny campaign, in a country where outposts were driven in by lions, and engagements with the enemy were complicated by the frequent intervention on a strictly impartial basis, of a hippopotamus or two; all in a world whose standard of civilization was of a refreshingly uninhibited character. It was not unusual, in an up-country village, to encounter a local 'lovely' wearing a pair of ear-rings devised from a couple of discarded Bovril bottles.

The climate was equatorial and pestilential, and death lurked in every pool and swamp. Only a truly great leader like General Smuts could, and did, triumph over such obstacles, backed as he was by troops of the highest training and discipline.

The principal base hospital was at Dar-es-Salaam, some ten days' voyage up the coast from Durban. This was the 2nd South African Hospital, consisting of five good German-built buildings, with an isolation section under canvas and a section for British West Indians. Early in 1918 this hospital was taken over to become the 84th British General. The staff here included forty South African V.A.D.s popularly known as 'the Bluebirds', from their uniform.

There was another hospital, twelve hours by rail up country at Morogoro, No. 15 Stationary.

The danger to life in the East African campaign, except in the earlier and more critical stages, arose less from the hazards of bush warfare than from sickness—chiefly dysentery, malaria, and blackwater fever. There were men in hospital who had been through fifteen or twenty bouts of malarial fever, and the nursing staff themselves suffered severely. At one time twenty-one members thereof were in hospital, leaving only forty-two on duty. They were equipped with mosquito boots and veils, but even these did not render them immune. Moreover, to breathe through a veil in that climate was an effort in itself.

The native 'boys' had been thoroughly and ruthlessly trained by their German masters, and were much more amenable and industrious than some, already described, in other theatres. Their principal weakness was for finery of any kind, regardless of its congruity to the occasion. In their native dances articles of feminine attire, usually pilfered from the Sisters' quarters, were much in evidence. One mess-boy attended one of these functions clad in a camisole and a pair of attenuated shorts.

By the beginning of 1918 East Africa had been practically cleared of Germans, and as a German Colony had ceased to exist. Its Teutonic administrators were no more, and their place was now being taken by British Civil Servants and other administrative officers. With the arrival of these, and the near approach of peace, the Colony sprang to new life, especially in social matters. There were even two Q.A. weddings.

By the end of March 1918 nearly all resistance had ceased, and troops were actually leaving the country. Few wounded were arriving from Morogoro, and No. 84 General Hospital might well have been closed down but for the persistence of malaria. This was of a most malignant type, and could only be held in check by liberal and indeed extravagant doses of quinine.

However, the battle was won at last, and a long, dreary, and most exacting campaign brought to a comparatively happy ending.

CHAPTER 10

MESOPOTAMIA[1]

THE Mesopotamian Expedition was originally intended to forestall a German invasion of India. This was successfully accomplished by our occupation of Basra in the Persian Gulf and the establishment of a footing in the Tigris Delta. We would have been well advised to leave it at that.

Unfortunately it was decided to continue the campaign northwards, in the hope of expelling the Turks from the Tigris basin and Baghdad. The result was a long, expensive, and highly unsatisfactory campaign, which included the surrender of a British garrison and the relegation of thousands of British soldiers to a Turkish prison.

Matters were complicated by the fact that these operations were directed from India, where a recent economy campaign, especially in the matter of the medical services, had left the Indian Army short both of men and equipment. A further handicap to efficiency arose from the constant clash of authority between the War Office in London and the Commander-in-Chief in India.

In pursuance of the new strategic plan, Sir John Nixon arrived at Basra in April 1915 to take command. A water-borne advance followed, in very moderate force, to Amara, ninety miles up the Tigris. This was followed by a further advance of 150 miles, to Kut. Enemy opposition was almost negligible: the real difficulties of the undertaking were furnished by immensely long lines of communication, and the climate. The summer temperature was seldom less than 120°, and there was little or no shade from the blinding glare. In winter the country was usually flooded and always marshy. It should be added that

[1] Today Iraq.

there was barely enough medical equipment for more than one division.

About the same time General Gorringe led an expedition westward, up the Euphrates valley, with Nasiriyeh as its objective, and after experiencing difficulties which involved much wading and frequent recourse to portages, occupied the town in July 1915.

Meanwhile General Townshend, who had succeeded General Nixon, had reached Kut, which he occupied without much difficulty. There was no reason to go farther, but the lure of Baghdad persisted, and the advance was continued.

The results were almost inevitable, and the blame lay at the door of the British Cabinet. Both Lord Kitchener, the Secretary of State for War, and Lord Curzon, the Viceroy of India, had dissented strongly from the pursuance of the scheme, but political pressure had won the day.

At first matters went not too badly, and the Indian Expeditionary Force, as it was called, actually penetrated as far as Ktesiphon, some thirty miles from Baghdad. Here the Turks made a resolute stand, and an 'inconclusive' battle was fought. Inconclusive it may have been from a tactical point of view, but it involved General Townshend in the loss of 4,500 men (of whom 800 were killed) and left him with no option but to retreat to Kut.

By the end of September 1915 Kut was closely invested by the enemy, and our invading force found itself almost entirely cut off from its base of supplies at Basra, some 240 miles away, its sole line of communication being furnished by the almost unnavigable Tigris. There could be no hope of reinforcement for months to come. Kut surrendered, almost inevitably, in April 1916, and the entire force, with its leader, went into captivity—a disaster which, following so closely upon the Gallipoli failure, discouraged the Allies and once more lowered British prestige throughout the world.

Thereafter the Mesopotamian campaign followed a pattern not unfamiliar in the annals of the British Army. A campaign, launched almost on the spur of the moment, without any particular preparation and with inadequate forces, had proved an

A Ward in the hospital at Wimereux, formerly a Casino

Sisters in a B.E.F. hospital packing up to leave

"Q.A.s" auctioning a German steel helmet on the hospital barge *Peronne,*
June, 1917 (*Imperial War Museum*)

General Plumer presenting Military Medals to Army Sisters for bravery when
their hospital was bombed, Blendecques, June 1, 1918 (*Imperial War Museum*)

ignominious failure. A period of uneasy stalemate next ensued, during which the whole operation was re-planned, proper transport provided—this included the construction of a strategic railway—and an adequate force equipped. General Sir Stanley Maude took command, and in due course the campaign was renewed upon lines which gave the British soldier a reasonable chance of success.

And it was so. Under Maude's brilliant leadership all that had been lost was regained, and more. Kut was recaptured on February 24th, 1917, after an interval of ten months, and Baghdad itself was occupied less than a month later. Triumph, not for the first time, had followed on disaster, and British prestige was restored.

II

We now turn to the experiences of the Mesopotamia Medical Services, and in particular those of Q.A.I.M.N.S.

With the evacuation of Gallipoli various hospital units had become available for service in the new theatre of war. It was obvious, especially in view of the climatic conditions to be expected, that a particularly large and efficient medical service would be required in Mesopotamia. So far the burden had been borne by the Indian Medical Service (assisted by No. 3 British General Hospital) and controlled by the Indian Government, directing through Army Headquarters at Simla.

In March 1916 No. 23 Stationary Hospital, accompanied by No. 32 General Hospital (minus its Sisters) sailed from Egypt and arrived at Kuwait, at the head of the Persian Gulf, on April 1st.

It was a new and strange world in which Army nurses now found themselves, and a complete contrast to the crowded, bustling streets of Cairo, or the ups and downs of shipboard life in Mudros harbour or off the Gallipoli beaches. They were approaching a land almost of Old Testament antiquity—of Ur of the Chaldees, the birthplace of Abraham, of the Garden of Eden, of the site of the Tree of Knowledge itself.

At Kuwait the Sisters and some of the officers took a trip

I

ashore, but their reception by the native population was anything but cordial, and they were glad to return safely to the ship and resume their voyage up the Shat-el-Arab, threading their way through an endless flotilla of Arab dhows and other unfamiliar craft; past Abadan and Mohammerah, at each of which places they found a small British colony, composed for the most part of the employees of the Anglo-Persian Oil Company, who so far had not been molested by the Turks. Apart from these modernistic excrescences, the landscape was one of pastoral serenity, with sheep and goats grazing, and date-palms lining the banks on either side.

They reached Basra, the chief port of the Tigris Delta and the reputed birthplace of Sinbad the Sailor, but for all that lacking so much as a pier or jetty, on April 9th. Here the Arcadian atmosphere ended, and grim reality raised its head.

No. 3 British General Hospital, already mentioned, had been in operation in Basra, in a 'palace' belonging to the Sheikh of Mohammerah, since November 1915, and was now fully occupied with the care of the sick and wounded from Ktesiphon and Kut, who were being evacuated to India. Most of these unfortunate men were in a pitiable condition, for they had been conveyed some 200 miles or more in open barges, destitute for the most part of hospital comforts or sanitary equipment, and almost completely exposed to the weather. In addition to the war-wounded there were a very large number of cases of dysentery and malaria—an ominous sign of things to come when the great new campaign should be launched.

Eleven of the Sisters of the newly arrived No. 23 were immediately detached for hospital-ship duty, and sailed for Bombay at half an hour's notice. Eight were left to assist the over-driven nursing staff of No. 3. The remaining seven, with their Matron, continued upstream to Amara.

The voyage lasted four days, and the scene lost nothing of its novelty or interest. Their ship was an ancient Irrawaddy paddle-steamer from Burma, which travelled with a barge lashed to either side, an arrangement which rendered it so broad in the beam that collisions with one bank or the other were frequent.

But there was nothing serious to complain of. Rations, mostly tinned, were ample and satisfactory, so little cooking was needed. True, the infant population of the district were in perpetual attendance along the bank, proffering eggs, lambs, and even goats at what can only be described as bargain-basement prices; but only the eggs proved acceptable, for the lambs and goats were as 'lean as greyhounds'.

This peaceful voyage was lightened by various interesting experiences. At Qurnah, at the junction of the Tigris and Euphrates and the legendary site of the Garden of Eden, the Sisters beheld the Tree of Knowledge itself, standing conspicuous upon a ridge and performing the somewhat mundane function of a telegraph post. Twenty-four hours later they were indulged with a short trip ashore, to visit the tomb of the prophet Ezra.

Arrived at Amara, work began in earnest. The Sisters were received by the Lady Superintendent of the Indian Nursing Service at her headquarters in Rawalpindi Hospital, so called from the Indian North-West Frontier Station where it had been mobilized. The hospital was in two separate sections, about a mile apart, and our seven Sisters divided themselves as evenly as was arithmetically possible between the two.

No. 23 Stationary Hospital lay farther up the river, upon the opposite bank to the Indian hospitals. It was all under canvas and was growing rapidly. Presently it mustered 1,000 beds.

The rainy season now set in, and life resolved itself into the perpetual wearing of gum-boots and topees, with a prolonged struggle against mud and fleas. Nursing staff was still woefully short: indeed at one time the Matron found herself running the hospital single-handed, returning to sleep at night in 'Rawalpindi'. It was not until the end of June that her scattered flock had reassembled. Of her original faithful seven two did not return. They had succumbed to the climate within a month, and had been evacuated to India.

Then came the summer, and with its advent the temperature rose to an average of 115° in the shade—where there was any shade. It was damp heat of the most trying kind. Sleep was almost an impossibility, and even to breathe required conscious effort. Cases of heat apoplexy were frequent, aggravated by shortage of ice or fans. Sand-flies and mosquitoes took the place of the fleas. Most of the hospital wards had punkahs, 'but the Arab boy,' we are told, 'does not make a good *punkah-wallah*'.

The Arab 'boy', incidentally, proved deficient in various other virtues. (It should be remembered that the majority of the British medical orderlies in Cairo and elsewhere had by this time been dispatched homeward for duty on the Western Front.) He was a practised pilferer, his principal liking being for soiled linen from the enteric and dysentery wards; but his special passion was for a scarlet Army blanket. One night every bed on each side of a ward of fifty patients was deprived of its blanket, and that too without attracting the attention either of the staff or the patients, most of whom were not asleep.

Altogether it was a testing time. The Sisters stood the climate wonderfully well, better than the men, in fact. This was probably due to the fact that they were better accommodated and their food was properly cooked—above all, owing to a wise moderation in the matter of alcoholic refreshment.

Seven senior officers died during this summer, including Sir Victor Horsley and a much-loved Catholic padre.

Mention may also be made here of one of the most tragic occurrences of the campaign—and at the same time the most unnecessary, because it owed nothing to enemy action—which took place as late as January 15th, 1918, when active hostilities had practically ceased.

On January 8th No. 65 General Hospital, with sixty-one nurses (half of them trained and half V.A.D.) arrived at Basra from Salonika, bound for the Advanced Base near Baghdad. Until arrangements for their transport up the river could be concluded, they were entertained as the guests of the various Basra units.

One afternoon shortly after their arrival, the Colonel, Matron, and twelve Nursing Sisters were sent downstream in a launch to visit and take tea at Beit Naama Officers' Hospital. On their return in the gathering darkness the launch was run into and sunk by a steam-tug. Three of the Sisters (Sisters Tindall, D'Oyly Campion, and Welford) with Nurse Faithfull, of the British Red Cross, lost their lives, and several others suffered severely from injuries or shock.

III

With the beginning of 1917 the situation began to brighten. The British Red Cross had arrived and set up a depot in Amara, and hospital patients found themselves supplied, for the first time in many months, with such small but inestimable comforts as tobacco and cigarettes. Roving bands of those stout-hearted harbingers of better times, Concert Parties, arrived from India and cheered everyone mightily.

Our nursing establishment was increasing. In July No. 32 General Hospital—or rather, its female personnel—arrived at last from Egypt; and with the hospital buildings fully staffed and equipped—such luxuries as ice and soda-water were now available —there came a general lifting of hearts all round.

Hospital facilities were being expanded in other directions. Farther down the river, at the liquorice factory at Makina, near Basra, No. 33 General Hospital had been set up, with 500 beds. Nasiriyeh, on the Euphrates, the occupation of which by General Gorringe we have previously noted, had now a combined British and Indian hospital, connected, moreover, by rail with Basra. The new strategic railway line, too, from Basra to Amara and beyond was in operation by November 1916, when the final and successful advance upon Baghdad began, closely attended as usual by ambulance units and casualty clearing stations. Shaik Said was now the advanced base, but was considered too near the firing-line for the Sisters.

There was a regular service, also, up and down the Tigris from a new and improved type of river steamer, each carrying two nurses; so the long voyage down to the base had ceased to be a wounded soldier's nightmare.

Needless to say the occupation of Baghdad brought small relief to Q.A.I.M.N.S., for hundreds of sick and wounded men had still to be nursed back to convalescence. The only difference was that these had now to be transferred from field hospitals along the lines of communication to permanent buildings within the city itself.

No. 23 Stationary Hospital was set up there in May 1917, in the Turkish Military Hospital, which is described as 'filthy and verminous'. Summer arrived before the necessary Augean process could be completed—an earlier summer than usual—and the strain both upon Sisters and orderlies became almost intolerable.

The state of affairs at Basra, the distant base, was even more difficult, owing to its unhealthy situation in the Tigris Delta. No. 3 General Hospital lost no less than forty cases in one day.

However, victory is a great stimulus to further effort, and in the end order was restored out of chaos. Baghdad was ultimately equipped with no less than five hospitals—Nos. 23 and 21 Stationary, an Isolation Hospital, an Officers' Hospital, and an Officers' Convalescent Depot.

No one greeted the victor of Baghdad more thankfully than the nuns in the French Convent. Throughout the hostilities they had nursed both in civil and military hospitals, bestowing upon the British wounded all the special care and attention that they dared. Sir Stanley Maude at once took them into his special care, issued them with regular rations, and notified the news of their safety to their Community in Paris, who had heard nothing of them for months.

To the grief of all, General Maude himself died suddenly in Baghdad in November 1917. But his task had been accomplished, and his work endured.

The labours of our Sisters continued throughout the winter of 1917–18. The weather was particularly cold and bitter, and brought with it an outbreak of the pneumonic influenza which was then beginning to sweep the world.

Nevertheless, the general verdict among the Sisters who had laboured so long and faithfully in this particularly difficult vineyard was by no means entirely unfavourable. After all, it had been a great adventure, in inspiring surroundings. Mesopotamia, they felt, despite the heat, desert sandstorms, mud, fleas, flies, sand-flies, mosquitoes and all other plagues, had a fascination all its own.

We cannot sum up the story of the service rendered by the Nursing Sisters during the Mesopotamian campaign better than by reproducing the following letter to Miss (afterwards Dame) Sidney Browne, Matron-in-Chief.

Gen. Headquarters,
Mes. Exp. Force.
dated 1st Nov. 1918.

To :-
Matron-in-Chief,
Mes. Exp. Force.

Memorandum.

An armistice has been signed between the British and Turkish Governments as from twelve noon on 31st October. The exact terms of this armistice will be issued as soon as possible.

In making this announcement to the Army in Mesopotamia, the Gen. Officer Commanding-in-Chief wishes to convey his most hearty and sincere thanks to the Matron-in-Chief, Matrons, and Nursing Sisters serving with this Force, and to congratulate them on the final and happy results so largely contributed to by their untiring hard work and devotion to duty.

Sgd.   L. G. WILLIAMS, Lieut.-Colonel,
Military Secretary.

Miss (later Dame) Sidney Browne, it should be noted, was at this time Matron-in-Chief of the Territorial Nursing Service, having retired from Q.A.I.M.N.S. in 1906.

CHAPTER 11

TRANSPORT BY LAND AND SEA

FREQUENT mention has been made in these pages of Hospital Trains. In Macedonia, as already noted, there were two of these, and by 1916 a regular service had been established in Egypt, conveying sick and wounded from the ports to the hospitals and rest-centres of Cairo and Luxor.

In France these trains were at first made up of a number of ordinary passenger sleeping-coaches, or *couchettes*, together with a rear-section composed of ordinary third-class coaches, intended for 'sitting' cases. French third class is not by any means the same thing as British third class, for the wooden seats are both narrow and devoid of cushions. But they were better than nothing.

Hospital train accommodation improved steadily with the course of the war. The corridor system was introduced, and this made it possible for a nurse or an orderly to walk from end to end of the train without having to wait for a station stop, or attempting the hazardous feat (officially forbidden) of clambering from coach to coach while in motion by way of the footboard —a spectacle which never failed to excite the mingled alarm and admiration of French country station-masters.

By 1916 these makeshift ambulance trains had been replaced by an entirely modern type. They were clean, comfortable, and perfectly equipped. Each of them carried three Sisters, whose personal quarters comprised separate sleeping cabins and a cheerful little mess devised from an ordinary first-class compartment.

Service in ambulance trains appears to have been highly popular, for life there was never dull. In fact, it was a series of new adventures.

Seldom were two days alike; no one knew where we might be sent next, or what awaited us on the road. Our train might be 'in garage' somewhere up the line, awaiting orders: all day nothing might happen, and we would retire to bed at the usual time. Suddenly there would be a bump —the usual intimation that our engine had come on—and away we would go into the night, wondering as to our destination.

Procedure in the matter of taking on board a fresh consignment of wounded had by this time become a matter of smooth and almost mechanical routine.

When loading was finished, our immediate duties were to inspect the medical cards, diet the patients, and take a note of all treatment to be given during the journey. After this had been carried out, cigarettes, sweets, and books were handed round, and the Sisters usually had time for a chat with the patients.

On reaching the base the train was quickly unloaded, beds changed and made up again, wards scrubbed out and everything made ready for the next journey. The train usually remained for a few hours to take on stores, which gave us the opportunity to go shopping for our mess. Then up the line again, or best of all, load up with patients for England. The latter was always a joyous thing. We would take them to Calais or Le Havre, and see them safely on board 'the ship that was bound for Blighty'.

Such was the procedure during the three years of so-called static warfare. But these journeys were not by any means free from excitement, for the German airmen usually regarded a British hospital train, red cross and all, as a legitimate and even desirable target. Time and again the windows of a train were shattered and the woodwork splintered.

During night-raids all lights were put out, and the train brought to a standstill. For badly wounded men, to lie quiet in the darkness listening to the explosion of the bombs was no mean feat of endurance. Probably that endurance was fortified by the spectacle of the calm unruffled way in which the Sisters went about their duties. The Sisters on their part were admittedly inspired in the performance thereof by the fortitude and cheerfulness of their patients.

Almost the first of the hospital trains to distinguish itself in action was one of the earliest type, No. 7. This was by reason of the conduct and courage of its staff during the night of November 1st–2nd, 1914, at the very height of the First Battle of Ypres.

The train was standing in Ypres station, entraining 'seriously wounded' cases, when it came under heavy shell-fire. The time was about midnight, and the bombardment, consisting of high explosive and shrapnel, continued for more than an hour. British soldiers were killed in the Square outside, and others wounded. The train itself was but slightly protected by the station buildings, and suffered severe damage in the form of wrecked coachwork and broken glass. It was unable to move, for its engine had gone down the line to Hazebrouck, in search of water. Still, never for a moment was the bombardment permitted to interfere with the course of duty.

> Although the four Nursing Sisters in charge [says the Report] perfectly well realized that the next shell might mean the complete wreck of the train and station, they remained calm and collected, asked for orders, and continued dressing and attending to the wounded already received in the train.

The Report selects for special mention a certain Sister who, 'by her smiling cheerfulness, carried off a difficult situation and set an example of great value to others'.

The labours of the Sisters in charge of these trains were greatly lightened after the establishment, by the R.A.M.C., of regular casualty clearing stations. Previous to this patients were entrained practically straight from the firing-line, often completely encrusted in the mud and blood of the battlefield. Many had not had their boots off for weeks.

Only those who have the experience [reports one Sister] know what it means to undress a heavy man, badly wounded and lying on the narrow seat of a railway-carriage. . . . But when the deed was done and the man undressed and in soft, dry pyjamas, even maybe though there had only been time to sponge his face, hands and feet, then indeed labour had its reward. The gratitude, the patience, the unfailing endurance of the men was a constant miracle to behold.

II

With the steady increase of our forces in Flanders, and the consequent growth of the intensity of the fighting, casualties increased at a proportionate rate.

Mention has already been made of the transport difficulties of the casualty clearing station staffs during the retreat after the German penetration in March 1918. Prior to this, namely in 1916 and 1917, things had been the other way round. We had been the attackers then, and our field ambulances and casualty clearing stations had moved steadily forward in the wake of the advances on the Somme, at Arras, and during the Third Battle of Ypres.

Work in these clearing stations was of the most trying description, for the enemy were fighting back hard, and powerful counter-attacks, supported by long-range artillery barrages, were frequent. In consequence the Nursing Sisters had not only to attend to the needs of the wounded, but were compelled to remain in constant readiness to evacuate the station at a moment's notice—or be shelled out as an alternative.

Neither were the hospitals themselves immune, as is evinced in a letter written to Dame Maud McCarthy by a Nursing Sister from No. 4 General Hospital at Brandhoek, in Belgium, in October 1917, at the height of the Passchendaele struggle. It is an interesting and significant document.

The hospital was placed in front of the railway-line, just in front of our heavy batteries.

We had a fortnight of most acute work, as we received day and night. The Sisters worked splendidly. There was not much sleep for any one: there was the noise of the artillery at night, and the shells falling on the railway most of the day. A bridge near us was nearly always under high explosive fire.

It ended in a sort of climax on Sunday, June 3rd. It was a lovely clear day, and we had 14 observation balloons up all along the line, with two of them just over the hospital. The Germans shelled them all Sunday, and about 6 p.m. the shells began to burst a bit low.

In other words, the enemy were now firing, not at the balloons but at the hospital.

Things were getting really serious, so the Colonel decided to evacuate the patients to the Sunken Road, where most of the Sisters were already taking shelter.

It was just at this time that the Colonel was hit. We had taken him to the theatre to be dressed, and afterwards he came down to the Sunken Road beside the patients. By 9 p.m. they were all safely evacuated.

The next day the Germans dropped a note to say that the hospital would always be shelled if we hung balloons over it.

This last passage throws an interesting sidelight on German mentality. It amounts of course to a suggestion—a suggestion made again and again—that the British were in the habit of shielding their artillery sites and other military dispositions from hostile fire by an illegal and cowardly abuse of the Red Cross.

Let it first be explained what the balloons were doing there. They were so-called observation balloons, each of them manned by an officer-observer, 'spotting' for the artillery—a duty performed in the Second World War by the aeroplane. These nodding monsters, hanging high in the sky at intervals on either side of no-man's-land, were a permanent feature of the battle-line, and defined its entire trend from the North Sea to the Alps.

The lot of the spotter himself was not a happy one. At any moment his balloon might be set on fire by an incendiary shell, and he himself compelled to make a precarious descent by parachute.

In the case of the Brandhoek incident these balloons were being put to a perfectly legitimate use, for without them the guns below would have been firing 'blind'. Still, the question may be asked, not unreasonably, why had the hospital been sited in such an exposed position?

In all probability it was because there was nowhere else to put it. In that cramped and restricted terrain it was sometimes impossible to keep hospital and heavy artillery sufficiently far apart to comply with the accepted rule on the subject; and the hospital simply accepted the risk.

But the real answer to the question—and no one knew it better than the self-righteous Boche—was that we had long since ceased to expect any kind of regard for the rules of civilized warfare from our opponents, and had decided, reasonably enough, that to persist in punctilious observation of the strict letter of a law which the enemy habitually ignored would be the merest pedantry on our part.

So No. 4 stayed where it was, balloons or no balloons, and stuck things out.

Such were some of the hazards incurred and the risks taken by the Q.A.I.M.N.S. in the course of duty, in hospital trains, casualty clearing stations, and even in the hospitals themselves, sometimes as far back as Boulogne or Etaples.

A single instance will suffice. It is contained in a brief and strangely moving letter from a hospital Matron to the Matron-in-Chief, in August 1917, regarding the death of a very young Nursing Sister.

Of course by this time you know all about the death of Miss Spindler, but I thought you might like a few details.

The child was asleep in bed when she was hit. I got to

her about three minutes afterwards. She only knew me for a moment, and then mercifully became unconscious, and remained so until she passed away about fifteen minutes later. I have written to her mother.

III

We come now to the story of the hospital ships in the First World War. As a people we were particularly dependent upon the employment of these vessels, for living as we did upon an island, every sick or wounded man of our forces evacuated home, from any theatre of war in the world, had to travel by sea, whether from the Persian Gulf or merely across the Straits of Dover.

In the earlier stages of the war, in conformity with the dictates of the Geneva Convention and of common humanity, our hospital ships were rendered as conspicuous as possible. They were painted white, and displayed a large red cross on either side of the hull. At night-time the cross was brilliantly illuminated. But this merciful device had soon to be abandoned, for all it achieved was to render a hospital ship an exceptionally easy mark for the U-boat commander, to whom everything afloat, whether Allied or Neutral, was a legitimate target. (After all, he could always assert, and usually did, that our hospital ships were habitually employed to carry troops or munitions.) So during the latter stages of the war these noble vessels were compelled perforce to assume the dull grey camouflage of the transport or merchant ship, and take their chance as members of a convoy, strongly escorted.

The work of the hospital ships employed to evacuate our sick and wounded from France and Belgium, and the duties of their nursing staffs, varied in intensity with what was going on 'up the line'. During our heavy offensive operations in 1916 and 1917 a hospital ship often made the cross-Channel trip twice a day. But whatever the pressure of work, the general routine was the same.

As soon as we were warned, each Sister went to her own ward, where cots were made ready, feeds prepared, hot bottles filled, and everything put in readiness for the reception and comfort of the wounded and helpless patients. The patients were usually kept on board for the day only, but occasionally they remained overnight. In this way it was found easier for each Sister to take three hours on night duty; and thus we were all in readiness for the unloading, which usually took place first thing in the morning. As a general rule the patients made very bad sailors.

Which is not altogether surprising.

Upon arrival at Dover the patients were conveyed by train to London, where they were transferred to motor ambulances holding four stretchers apiece and dispatched to various convalescent hospitals all over the country, as near as possible to their own home district.

Each afternoon during 1917 and 1918 the trains from the coast began to arrive in London, at Charing Cross Station, and the endless string of motor ambulances, stretching down Villiers Street from the Strand to the Embankment, never failed to attract a number of interested spectators. Many a word of cheer was spoken, or packet of cigarettes (or even flowers) tossed in by kindly Londoners to the occupants of the stretchers, lying duly ticketed and usually clasping a German helmet or other trophy to their bosoms, while philosophically awaiting departure for a destination unknown, with all their troubles behind them.

Considering the enormous amount of shipping which crossed the Channel daily during those years, casualties through enemy action were comparatively slight. (So far as the conveyance of fighting troops were concerned, not a man was lost throughout the war.) But for the occupants of a hospital ship the consequences of such an experience could be both serious and tragic.

Here is a single instance. About 12 noon on November 17th, 1915, the Hospital Ship *Anglia*, a former mail-steamer of the London and North-Western Railway, while carrying a full complement of wounded from Calais, struck a mine about six miles out from Dover. Here is a description of the scene, as related by one of the Nursing Sisters on board.

> There was a tremendous crash, and iron girders and other wreckage came splintering down, like matchwood. My first action was to fix a lifebelt on myself, feeling that I was then in a better position to help others. All Sisters and orderlies did likewise, and the patients who were able to do so were ordered to put on theirs.

(Each man had a lifebelt under his pillow.)

> The walking cases were ordered on deck. We immediately set about removing splints, for the obvious reason that if a patient with his legs in splints got into the sea, his legs would rise to the surface and his body go under. As many stretcher-cases as possible were carried on deck, and those that could threw themselves into the sea.
>
> Others were let down in a lifeboat: unfortunately, as the ship was sinking so rapidly, it was only possible to lower one of these.
>
> The patients kept their heads wonderfully. There was no panic whatever, and when one realizes that in the majority of cases they were suffering from severe wounds and fractured limbs, it speaks volumes for their spirit, grit, and real bravery, for they must have suffered agonies of pain.

Presently the ship's bows were under water and her stern high in the air, with both propellers spinning furiously. Not till then did the Sisters and orderlies abandon further efforts at rescue.

> We got down on to the rudder, and jumped. Hundreds of patients were struggling in the water. It was some time before the destroyers could get out (from Dover) to render help. When they did, boats were quickly lowered and survivors taken into them. Unfortunately in some cases the struggling patients hung on to the sides of a boat and capsized it, and once again all were thrown into the sea.

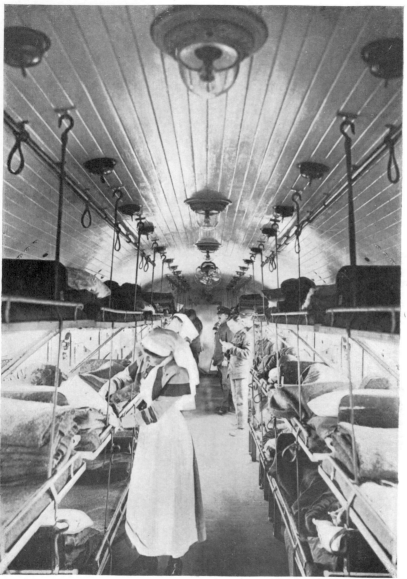

Ward interior in a British Ambulance Train near Doullens, April, 1918
(*Imperial War Museum*)

Gas mask drill in No. 8 General Hospital, Nantes Sub-Area, April, 1940
(*Imperial War Museum*)

1939–1945. "Q.A.s" in a warm climate

I personally was in the water about forty minutes before being taken on a destroyer. The kindness of the men in the destroyer we shall never forget. Their helpfulness was beyond words.

Eventually the survivors, clad in a miscellany of incongruous garments furnished by the officers and ratings of the destroyers, came safe to Dover, whence, after a good meal on board the train, they arrived in London for the most part none the worse. Our Sister's narrative ends upon an interesting note.

The King, who had personal experience of the *Anglia*, on hearing of the loss of the ship, made special inquiries as to the welfare of all who had been on board at the time.

This refers to the fact that King George V, while upon a visit to the troops on the Western Front in the autumn of 1915, met with an accident which nearly cost him his life. His horse, startled by a sudden burst of artillery fire, rose straight on its hind legs and fell right back upon him. He lay insensible for some days, and though the full facts were not revealed at the time, his life was almost despaired of.

His Majesty was conveyed back to England on board the *Anglia*, upon which our Sister was serving. Hence her reference to his 'personal experience' of that gallant vessel.

IV

Mention has already been made of the hospital ships of the Mediterranean, based for the most part on Egypt and serving such hospital bases as Mudros and Salonika. Life on board these, owing to increasing U-boat activity, was no safer than in the transports or supply ships which ploughed the Eastern Mediterranean on their way to the Middle or Far East.

One of the most serious losses in this theatre, from a material point of view, was the sinking of the great White Star liner

K

Britannic, of 50,000 tons, on the morning of November 21st, 1916, in the Aegean, off the coast of Greece. (She was a new ship, and had been built to take the place of the ill-fated *Titanic*, which had gone down on her maiden voyage, through collision with an iceberg, in April 1912.) On completion the *Britannic* was fitted out as a hospital ship and dispatched to Mediterranean waters. But her career was almost as short-lived as that of the *Titanic*. Fortunately there were no hospital cases on board at the time: she was on her way to Mudros to collect a shipload of Gallipoli wounded. Had it been the return journey there would have been a very different tale to tell. There were some casualties among the ship's company, owing to the capsizing of two boats, but the medical and nursing staff were all saved. None the less, it was a sad sight, as one Sister recalls, 'to see this wonderful ship gradually disappearing from our sight, and none will ever forget the way her siren-calls became more and more muffled as she sank'.

The German U-boat campaign came to a head in the spring of 1917, not only in the Mediterranean but in the Atlantic Ocean and English Channel. Its avowed intention was to sink one million tons of British shipping a month. That figure was never achieved, but the situation grew desperate enough.

Amid the many narratives of survivors from sunken hospital ships, one stands out by the fact that, instead of the almost invariable description of the gallantry of the rescue-parties and the cheerful fortitude of the helpless wounded, as in the case of the *Anglia* already described, this particular narrative for once deals with the individual experiences of a single Sister.

The occasion was the sinking, in the small hours of the morning of August 3rd, 1917, of the Australian Hospital Ship *Warilda, en route* from Havre to Southampton.

There were seven women on board, travelling home on leave as passengers, after two years on the Macedonian Front—two Sisters of the Territorial Force Nursing Service, an officer of the Women's Auxiliary Army Corps and her orderly, two members of the V.A.D., and a Nursing Sister of Q.A.I.M.N.S., who tells the story. They had travelled overland and had joined the *Warilda* at Havre.

At 1.30 a.m. all were roused from sleep by a resounding crash, and the cry: 'To your boats at once, Sisters! We have been torpedoed!'

So imbued with the holiday spirit were the leave party that they had gone to bed in the flimsiest of night attire; with the result that in the hurry and confusion of the moment they arrived at their boat clad in little more than their nightdresses and life-belts.

Our Sister found herself being handed, in gross darkness, into a boat already full of wounded men. The boat was then lowered from the davits into the water. In the ordinary course of procedure the falls should next have been cut away with a hatchet. Unfortunately no hatchet was available, and there was considerable delay in getting the boat clear of the sinking *Warilda*. To make matters infinitely worse it was discovered that the plugs were out, with the result that the boat filled with water and began to settle down rapidly.

> Being at the bottom of the boat, and not able to move, I had a very unpleasant experience.

The 'unpleasant experience' consisted in coming as near death by drowning, yet living to tell the tale, as is humanly possible.

> I must have lost consciousness for a time, for the next thing I remember was feeling myself choking with the salt water, and struggling. I felt there was no chance of my being saved, for all the boats would be filled with wounded and other survivors; so I resigned myself—hoping it would not be long.
>
> Presently I felt myself coming to the surface again. I found myself being drawn into something which turned out to be a small boat, upside down. The waves were very strong, and dashed me against the sides unmercifully. This, with the terrible cries of the men and women in the water, was horrifying. I sank again. . . .
>
> Once more I came to the top. How I longed to die and

escape those awful cries! . . . As I went down for a third
time I felt that this would be my last, as my strength was
nearly gone, and I felt so hazy.

But this time she was seen, and hauled on board a boat crowded
with people as scantily clothed as herself, engaged in picking up
survivors. It was hazardous work, for there was a high sea
running, and the depth-charges being dropped by the escorting
destroyers added to the noise and confusion.

One boy in the boat tried to cheer us up by singing. He
did not fail entirely: soon we were all joining in. Suddenly
we stopped, for we had sighted a destroyer coming out of
the darkness.

Ultimately the little band were all taken on board the
destroyer, clothed, and revived with cocoa and brandy. They
had been in or on the water for more than two hours. The
Warilda sank shortly afterwards.

The survivors were landed at Southampton at 8.30 and taken
to Netley Hospital, where after a medical inspection they were
given permission to travel, and were so enabled to depart upon
their period of leave, 'though much bruised and stiff'.

And now [concludes our Sister with characteristic *sang
froid*], the past is being forgotten, and we are ready to start
again.

V

Yet another hospital ship remains to be mentioned, not because
of any particular hazards which it encountered, but because of the
unique surroundings in which it completed its service.

One of the most fantastic campaigns of the whole of the First
World War began when the war was, for all practical purposes,
at an end. It arose from an eleventh-hour effort on the part of
the Allied Governments to help what was left of the Russian

Imperial Army to maintain some sort of resistance against Germany and the Bolsheviks.

The only port from which such aid could be rendered was Archangel, on the White Sea. The Ukraine and the control of the Black Sea were in the hands of the Germans.

Wherever British troops are dispatched upon active service, a hospital unit accompanies them. In October 1918, therefore, a contingent of Q.A. Sisters, fourteen strong, sailed from Cardiff for North Russia in the Hospital Ship *Kalyan*, a former P. & O. intermediate.

So far the *Kalyan* had plied only between England, Egypt, and Salonika, which meant that in order to equip her to face the rigours of an Arctic winter much internal adjustment would be necessary. Accordingly, inner wooden walls were set up about three inches from the ship's side, and the intervening space was packed with sawdust, thus converting the *Kalyan* into a species of floating thermos flask. Glass skylights were covered over with asbestos matting, and steam radiators were installed everywhere. Finally, the Lascar crew were replaced by Europeans more acclimatized to Arctic temperatures.

The Sisters themselves were issued with a special kit of truly formidable warmth, consisting of leather jerkins, windproof linen coats lined with sheepskin, cloth caps with fur peaks and ear-pieces, and serge gloves. The boots ultimately supplied were high felt boots reaching to the knee, such as were worn by Russian peasants. They were not ornamental, but were proof against frostbite.

Arrived at Archangel after a voyage of twelve days, the *Kalyan* was made fast to a wharf in the Dwina estuary, and there remained for eight months, under the protecting guns of a French cruiser.

It now transpired that the ship herself was to be employed as an actual (and stationary) hospital. There were some hospitals ashore, staffed by Russian Red Cross nurses, but in view of the tensity of the political atmosphere at that time it was decided that British Nursing Sisters would be more safely and profitably employed afloat. Sick and wounded therefore were conveyed to the *Kalyan* by barge, and taken on board to be nursed there. After long and grim experience of dark and dank billets and blockhouses up the line, without anything to read or smoke—the battle zone was some 200 miles from Archangel—the cleanliness, comfort, and cheerfulness of the *Kalyan*'s wards was a revelation to these patients.

They were not all British soldiers and sailors: there were Americans, French, Italians, Chinese, and even a few Russians. During the summer they were conveyed down the line to Archangel by water, along the winding Dwina, but with the first breath of winter the whole system of transport had to be revolutionized, almost overnight.

That particular winter arrived suddenly: the Dwina was frozen solid. Snow lay deep everywhere. However, within a week a railway line had been laid down upon the frozen surface of the river. Large numbers of patients too began to arrive in sleighs, wrapped in fur-lined sleeping-bags and ensconced in what they themselves described as 'coffins'. But these were comfortable enough.

One of the outstanding problems on board the *Kalyan* was that of adequate ventilation. With the thermometer registering 35° F. below zero—67 degrees of frost—or even lower, the wards within the double-skinned hull were overpoweringly hot, and to open a porthole even for a few minutes invariably involved a burst radiator and 'heap big trouble' with the chief engineer.

Local food supplies were scanty, and could only be procured by barter, for the rouble by this time was valueless. No fresh fruit or vegetables were obtainable, and it was necessary to make-do with germinated peas and beans, together with a regular ration of lime juice—a precaution, and quite a successful one, against scurvy. Frostbite was more common, largely owing to Thomas Atkins's happy-go-lucky incaution in the matter of ear-muffs, and the like.

Exercise for the Sisters was a difficult matter, but there were opportunities for skating and ice-hockey. On the whole, however, most recreation had to be enjoyed indoors, or rather below decks, in the form of knitting, reading, and bridge. A sewing machine, the thoughtful gift of the Matron-in-Chief, was much in demand.

Letters from home were rare and intermittent—sometimes none arrived for six weeks—and news of the outer world was meagre and tardy. The war was over now, and people at home were presumably celebrating the Allied victory, but there was no peace as yet in Russia, nor, to all appearance, ever would be—always a disheartening state of affairs for men still in the field, especially an ice-field.

However, by April 1919 the snow and ice had begun to melt; ice-breakers conveying reinforcements and reliefs came grinding their way through the melting Dwina, and deliverance from a hard and monotonous winter was at hand.

In May the *Kalyan* was at last enabled to cast loose from her eight-months' mooring, and the whole party landed safely at Leith early in June.

VI

Such was the record of Q.A.I.M.N.S. during the Kaiser's War. It only remains to sum up, and fill in a few gaps.

Between 1914 and 1918 the following are the figures of enrolment:

Year					Numbers
1914	.	.	.	.	. 2,223
1915	.	.	.	.	. 3,903
1916	.	.	.	.	. 2,226
1917	.	.	.	.	. 1,608
1918	.	.	.	.	. 444

Total 10,404

In addition to these, 8,495 nursing members of the Voluntary Aid Detachments, a few of whom were trained nurses, served under Q.A.I.M.N.S. in military hospitals at home and abroad.

These figures do not include the members of the Territorial

Army Nursing Service employed in the numerous territorial hospitals, nurses employed in the many civil hospitals and institutions where military patients were received and treated, nurses working in the numerous voluntary hospitals or those hospitals equipped and staffed by the Committee of the Order of St. John of Jerusalem and the British Red Cross Society.

The total number of deaths in the Q.A.I.M.N.S., its Reserve, and in the Voluntary Aid Detachments working in military hospitals was as follows:

Killed or drowned through enemy action . . 36
Killed or drowned accidentally . . . 9
Died abroad while serving 71
Died at home while serving 79

Total 195

Dame Ethel Hope Becher, G.B.E., R.R.C., Chevalier of the Legion of Honour, was the Matron-in-Chief at the War Office throughout the war. She served in Q.A.I.M.N.S. from 1902 to 1919.

Part Three

THE SECOND WORLD WAR

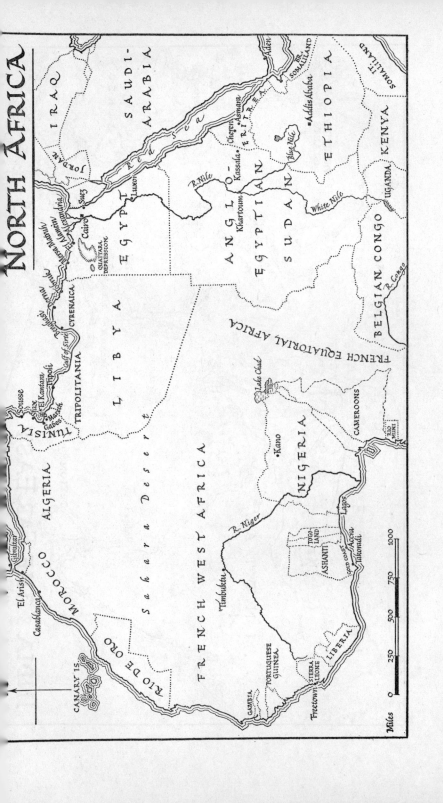

INDIA & THE FAR EAST

CHAPTER 12

FLANDERS, 1940

THE years of peace which followed the First World War were by no means uneventful years for Q.A.I.M.N.S., which throughout the period between 1918 and 1939 grew steadily in prestige and efficiency. There was continuous progress, especially on the administrative side. Again after the Second World War ended, Q.A.I.M.N.S. (and with it T.A.N.S.) were to undergo a complete transformation into a self-contained and self-administered Corps of the British Army Medical Services, of equal standing with the R.A.M.C. and the R.A.D.C.

How that transformation was brought about is described in full detail in Chapter XXIII of this volume.

In the meantime we will continue with the operational history of Q.A.I.M.N.S.—this time during the Second World War.

Few of us will ever forget Sunday, September 3rd, 1939. The recollections of the present writer are vivid enough.

At 11.15 on that morning I switched the desk-telephone in my room at the War Office through to the Press Room, in which a loudspeaker had been installed, and heard Mr. Chamberlain announce to a listening world that the British Empire was now at war with Germany. Almost directly afterwards the sirens sounded, and we descended dutifully to our emergency offices in the sub-basement, there to await our first raid. It proved to be a false alarm, but the incident emphasized the grim reality of the whole situation. The balloon had gone up at last, and Armageddon was on the way.

In September 1939, as the reader will remember, our country had had a full year in which to make up some of the time lost during the previous era of indecision and inertia, and we were now at least as well equipped, so far as the Army was concerned, as we had been in 1914. Mobilization, including that of Q.A.I.M.N.S., Reserves and T.A.N.S., was effected with efficiency and dispatch. The story of the Q.A.I.M.N.S. is that of Reserves and T.A.N.S. also, and 'Q.A.I.M.N.S.' (Q.A.s) should be taken for all.

As in 1914, the first task of the War Office was to dispatch the British Expeditionary Force to its battle stations in France, in conformity with a solemn agreement long concluded between our French Allies and ourselves.

But here we were confronted with a difficulty never previously experienced in our history—the possibility, the certainty almost, of overwhelming attack upon our transports from the air. Britannia still ruled the waves, but no one could tell for certain as yet who was going to rule the skies. At any rate, it was known that some 950 enemy bombers were assembled in the aerodromes of Western Germany, ready to pounce when the word came that our 'troopers were on the tide'.

Obviously, to dispatch great convoys to France by the shortest route (as had been done in 1914) was out of the question, for Calais and Boulogne lay nearer to the German frontier than any other ports on the French coast. Landing ports as remote as possible from enemy air bases must be the objective of our crowded troopships.

Finally Cherbourg was selected for the troops, and Brest, Nantes, and St. Nazaire (this last on the Bay of Biscay) for the landing of their vast stores and innumerable vehicles. By this precaution, and the employment of a minimum of advertisement —here our Press co-operated most loyally—the entire Force was conveyed safely across.

The risk was shared, and as cheerfully accepted, by the Nursing Services. A standing tradition of the British Army had ceased to be: henceforth there was to be no male monopoly of any of the hazards of active service. Equipped with steel helmets and gas-masks, Q.A.s went overseas like the rest. The first contingent were landed at Cherbourg on September 10th and 11th, within one week of the Declaration of War.

Here are the experiences, in brief, of a later contingent—bound for Havre in this case.

The routine followed was much the same as that of twenty-five years previously. The party arrived at Southampton by train and were sent straight on board ship. Here they were issued with life-jackets and iron rations and were allotted cabins. The furniture of these was not luxurious, consisting as it did of a single mattress, without blankets or pillow. But no one cared: 'fair stood the wind for France', and the spirit of adventure soared high.

There was the usual delay in the Solent, as the ship swung at anchor waiting for the fall of night. Relief from monotony, however, was obtained by listening in to a characteristic disquisition from a neighbouring N.C.O. to his followers upon the regulations governing the proper handling of the iron ration.

After impressing upon the men, a Sister tells us, that the iron ration could only be consumed on the order of an officer, the N.C.O. continued:

> When you are torpedoed, though, and have remained in the water for not less than twenty-four hours, you are at liberty to open your iron rations without waiting for any officer's order at all.

Truly, the spectacle of a contingent of R.A.M.C. privates placidly swimming the Channel with an iron ration in one hand and a penny in the other, with which to open the tin when the appointed twenty-four hours should have elapsed, would have reassured anyone foolish enough to question the high morale and perfect discipline of the British soldier.

At last the anchor was weighed, and the silent, stealthy crossing was made under the escort of a British destroyer, which was relieved by a French destroyer in the early dawn.

After a brief pause at Le Havre came a series of aimless excursions from pillar to post, common to that period of the war —Mr. Churchill has recently described it as 'The Twilight War' [1]

[1] In the second volume of his War reminiscences, *Their Finest Hour.*

—in search of legitimate employment. *Faute de mieux*, this particular unit settled in a French village, opened an out-patient department, and visited the sick of the local population in their homes. Their outstanding obstacle in this self-imposed task was to overcome the passionate objection of their patients to having a window opened.

II

The early dispositions of the B.E.F. were based, not unnaturally, upon the experience of the previous war.

But not entirely. The French frontier, where it actually marched with that of Germany, was now covered by the much advertised Maginot Line, which was deemed by all patriotic Frenchmen to be impregnable. To the left lay the little neutral State of Luxembourg, and beyond that the Franco-Belgian frontier, which the British Expeditionary Force was busily fortifying in considerable depth. It was therefore generally assumed that there could be no lightning invasion by the enemy of Northern France, *via* neutral Belgium, this time.

This being so, our Medical and Nursing Services could approach their task with some degree of method. Permanent General Hospitals could be erected in the principal base-ports, railheads established at suitable points behind the line, to and from which the hospital trains could ply; and a provisional chain of casualty clearing stations organized at appropriate points.

In other words, the general expectation at this time seems to have been that we were in for another prolonged campaign of static siege warfare, waged upon either side of a trench-line running from the North Sea to Switzerland.

But the campaign, whatever form it was to take, hung fire strangely. It had been generally expected that the German Army which had been training intensively for this war for at least four years, and for the moment had no Eastern Front to consider, would take the initiative and advance to the attack at once. However, Hitler seemed in no hurry to begin; for nine months deceptive calm reigned in the West—a respite which the Allies

gratefully employed to strengthen their defences and complete
the training of their troops.

The Medical Services likewise made the most of their opportunity. General Hospitals sprang up in the neighbourhood of Le
Havre, Dieppe, Le Tréport, Étaples, Camiers, and Boulogne—all
completely furnished and equipped, and all destined, alas, to be
utilized within a few months' time not by the British but the
German Medical Services.

More Q.A.I.M.N.S. arrived from home with their various
units, hospitals, casualty clearing stations or hospital trains. The
Principal Matron[1] arrived in France and took complete control.
Lord Gort had established his General Headquarters at Arras (a
centre familiar enough to the old soldiers of the 1914 war),
situated at a convenient distance from the Belgian frontier, along
the whole length of which the B.E.F. now aligned itself. Its
front covered some fifty-five miles, extending from Maulde, in
a north-westerly direction, to Hallvin immediately south of
Menin—another familiar name—then south-westerly, along the
little river Lys, to Armentières and Grisons. Within the salient
formed lay Lille, the second city of France.

III

The winter of 1939-40—and a cruelly hard winter it was—
passed by, and still the Phoney War hung fire. Only in Lorraine,
on the banks of the Rhine, was there any actual contact with
the enemy, and our sole casualties were those incurred by British
troops attached to the French Army in this particular theatre for
actual experience of fighting. Q.A.I.M.N.S. for the time being
had little to do beyond the nursing of the sick and ministering to
the needs of the local population—an attention highly appreciated and conducive to good feeling all round.

Still, no one was altogether happy. The troops had come to
fight, and the Medical Services had come to tend the troops.
But the troops had no one to fight and the Medical Services had

[1] Miss K. H. (later Dame Katharine) Jones.

L

few casualties to occupy them.   There was a growing feeling of
boredom and frustration, which peripatetic concert parties from
London did little to allay.   Moreover, reports regarding our Ally
were not reassuring.   The French soldier in the heat of action is
incomparable; keep him in idleness and suspense and he begins
to brood.   He has not the cheerful endurance and *sang froid* of
the Anglo-Saxon.   There were disturbing rumours of *cafard* in
the Maginot Line, where the Fifth Column had been busy.

Then suddenly, and practically without warning, the storm
burst.   On May 10th, 1940, with complete and characteristic dis-
regard for the sanctity of treaties or the rules of civilized warfare,
Hitler invaded Northern France, via neutral Luxembourg, simul-
taneously with neutral Belgium and Holland.

The B.E.F. immediately crossed the Belgian frontier, on to soil
hitherto denied to them by the obligations of neutrality, and took
up their battle positions along the little River Dyle, with the
French First Army on their right and the Seventh Army on their
left; and the battle was joined.

Then, and not till then, was it fully realized how utterly
obsolete the tactics of the 1914 war had been rendered by the
march of time and the phenomenal development of the internal
combustion engine.   Gone for ever were the days of pitched
battles and limited objectives.   The total mechanization of
ground warfare, supported from the air, had bestowed a new
and terrifying mobility upon the attack.   Concentrating upon
the weakest point in their opponent's line, the German Panzer
(or Armoured) Divisions were enabled to crash through the
resistance of the French Ninth Army, already demoralized by
propaganda, and cleave their way, without once pausing to con-
solidate positions or secure flanks, straight for the Channel ports.
Within a week they were in Abbeville, and a few days later in
Boulogne.   Thus, within an incredibly short space of time, the
Allied Armies had been cut in two by a corridor many miles
wide, and several British coastal bases overrun.

The combined effect of this unbelievable catastrophe upon the
organization of the Medical and Nursing Services of the British
Army can only be imagined.   It certainly cannot be described in

full detail here, but the story can be pieced together, in some measure, from a study of the very large number of individual reports and personal narratives available to us.

These fall into three categories—the Hospitals, the Casualty Clearing Stations, and the Hospital Trains. Let us consider them in turn.

The story in most cases is much the same. It begins with a record of intensive bombing raids upon most of the base hospitals during the night of May 9th, and of the brief period of shock and bewilderment which resulted, occupied chiefly in the hasty improvisation of shelter for the patients. Then came the turmoil and confusion engendered by a panic-stricken civil population, intensified by the arrival of a horde of Belgian refugees, streaming southward with such of their worldly possessions as they had been able to salve, and thus hopelessly impeding the movements of the troops.

In these circumstances each Q.A.I.M.N.S. unit became a law unto itself, coping to the best of its ability with its own particular emergency. One and all displayed the same resolute indifference to their own welfare and the same cheerful devotion to their patients.

Then, in due course, came the resumption of official control, the gathering together of scattered units, and finally, from this port or that, by any means of conveyance available, evacuation to England.

IV

Let some of the participants in this nightmare period speak for themselves.

Here is an average example. The Sisters concerned in the matter—or one might with truth describe them as the heroines of this particular story—were the members of a casualty clearing station warned for immediate duty upon the announcement of the German attack. There were eight of them in all, that being the number normally allotted to a C.C.S.

The unit was somewhat scattered at the moment, upon tem-

porary duty at Le Tréport and in its vicinity. The group with
whom we are concerned were bidden to repair forthwith to
Béthune, where the rest of the unit were 'reputed' to be.
(Nothing was certain in those days.) They accordingly left Le
Tréport by train early next morning, only to be held up at St.
Pol, the line ahead having been heavily bombed. St. Pol itself
was a highly important road junction and traffic centre, some
twenty miles west of Arras.

> The streets [reports the Sister who tells the story] were
> full of transport of all descriptions, while more and more of
> it, approaching the town, added to the general confusion.
> It was quite impossible to obtain anything to eat, though it
> was not yet 11 a.m. This was the first time any of us had
> seen a mass evacuation, and one so completely uncontrolled.
> We were appalled to see it, and amazed at the number of
> young Frenchmen not in the Army. We saw none of our
> own troops till much later.

Our own troops of course were farther north, in Belgium by
this time.

By three o'clock in the afternoon, however, contact had been
established with Béthune, and a lorry had arrived. Béthune
itself was already being evacuated, and the orders of the party
were to proceed northward with all speed. The lorry made its
way, not without difficulty, through Arras and Lille to a small
village, Avelin, not far from the Belgian frontier, where a neighbouring chateau was being converted into a hospital, or rather,
first-aid post.

The earliest patients to arrive were French and Belgian civilians,
suffering from wounds arising from the inveterate German habit
of machine-gunning all refugees within range.

The following day came the order for all civilians to evacuate.

> Being a small village, the evacuation had some semblance
> of order. Before leaving, the shopkeepers sold us all their
> remaining stocks of chocolate and biscuits—not a great deal,
> but very welcome to us.

Our Sisters, it will be observed, being cut off from their unit, were cut off from their rations as well.

That evening the Sisters were the only people left in the village itself. The men were accommodated in the chateau and grounds. My billet-companion and myself felt so lonely that we went to bed early.

But not to sleep; for they were aroused almost immediately by a medical officer with orders that, for greater safety, they were to transfer themselves to the chateau, some two miles away, through the pitch darkness of the black-out. Even so—

We had little sleep that night. An anti-aircraft battery was stationed in the grounds, and what with enemy bombing and A.A. firing, the noise was guaranteed to prevent anything of that kind.

Next morning came yet another move. The eight Sisters were packed into an ambulance and dispatched in the direction of Lille, only to be diverted from their course by the proximity of the advancing enemy. Ultimately they found themselves in Lincelles, near Armentières, where they were billeted in the local civilian hospital, staffed by French Sisters of Charity. They were still cut off from all supplies, and were grateful for the contribution, meagre though it was, made to their scanty stock by these kindly women.

But this was destined to be the briefest of respites. Early next morning came an order for four of the party to report for immediate duty at a field ambulance outside Tournai. This was unusual, for as a rule no Sisters are employed in a field ambulance; but in this hectic Odyssey everything was unusual.

On arrival two of us went to the improvised operating theatre and two to the wards.

(Let us bear in mind that they had now been on the move for

four days and nights, practically without sleep and on the scantiest of rations.)

We worked in the theatre continuously for over twelve hours, having one short break of about a quarter of an hour, when we ran out of anæsthetics. During this break we managed to make and drink a cup of tea. Our sterile dressings were soon used up, so we improvised by soaking the uncut rolls of gauze in a Lysol solution and cutting off a length as needed.

It was impossible to keep track of the patients operated on. We had no pause for clearing up during cases: as one man was removed from the operating-table another was placed on it. Instruments were hurriedly washed and then flung into a bowl containing pure Lysol. We kept on the same rubber gloves until they split. The whole day the hamlet was being machine-gunned from the air.

Late that night we were told we must evacuate, as the position by then was unsafe. The patients had been evacuated throughout the day, as soon as their condition warranted. It was our first experience of really extensive wounds. I well remember one man of, I think, the Green Howards, who had a large gaping chest wound, with part of his lung shot away. It was impossible to give him an anæsthetic: we could do nothing for him but apply a dressing. His only remark was: 'You *will* patch me up, so that I can get back to my pals, won't you?' He died later during the day, and so was saved from becoming an 'un-evacuable wounded'. We could never reconcile our feelings or our training to leaving such cases.

The four Sisters returned to Lincelles that night. The other four were still absent, and during the day transient refugees had looted the hospital of every scrap of food, except some very dry prunes. Next morning was devoted to a search for further provender, without success. But there was plenty of hot water.

We were now feeling distinctly dirty. We tossed for

who should have the first bath. Just as the lucky Sister started to undress, a rather perturbed Staff Officer came to the front door. 'You must be out of here within five minutes,' were his words to us.

Thereafter their experiences were merely a repetition, or rather an intensification, of those already described. After two more strenuous days with the same field ambulance, with little rest and less food, they encountered their own Quartermaster, who informed them that they were urgently needed by their own unit, who were now somewhere in Belgium.

Needless to say they discovered upon joining their unit that, owing to the overwhelming number of cases to be dealt with, they must get to work without waiting for the full meal and brief rest for which they had been longing.

I worked until 4 a.m. and then rested until 8 a.m. I say 'rested', but the only spot to rest was on a deck-chair by the side of a lift. . . . During our working hours we did occasionally swallow a cup of coffee, which our batman seemed able to produce on demand. Our sterilizing orderlies were grand. The surgeon and the anæsthetist never seemed to take any rest. The anæsthetist did one spell of thirty-six hours on duty.

There were stretchers everywhere: we even had wounded men on stretchers in the bathroom. Air activity was persistent. Ypres was in flames, and waves of bombers were continuously passing overhead: at times it seemed as if they mistook our hospital for some kind of headquarters.

The invincibility of the human spirit is a wonderful thing, as the reader may judge from the final passage in this narrative:

On May 28th, *to our great sorrow*, the Sisters were ordered to leave. With very sad hearts, and feeling like deserters, we said good-bye to the unit.

They were driven to the outskirts of Dunkirk, which was under heavy fire, and after a most trying wait of several hours were embarked upon a waiting transport, which then set out for Newhaven, pursued by artillery fire from the French coast.

They landed next morning, safe, 'but very dirty, very untidy, and very tired. It was twelve days since we had taken off any of our clothing'.

The rest of the unit followed them two days later, leaving an R.A.M.C. corporal, according to traditional practice, to take care of the unevacuable wounded. He was of course taken prisoner, but was later heard from in a camp in Poland.

Another such experience, perhaps even more testing, was that of two C.C.S. units which, after the usual period of intensive ambulance and hospital work, followed by the usual sudden evacuation order in the small hours, eventually joined forces at Lillers. (Arras, Béthune, Lillers, Aire, and Hazebrouck all lay more or less in line on the road to Calais in the north-west. Twenty-five years previously, and for nearly four years more, that line had covered part of the trench system of the old Western Front, and each of those little townships had furnished a well-remembered and well-loved billeting area for the B.E.F. of those days.)

From Lillers on May 19th the Nursing Sisters were dispatched by train to Hazebrouck, the lorries and ambulances proceeding by road. The railway line was frequently blocked by enemy bombing, and stoppages were numerous and protracted; but it was now evident that the party were *en route* for one of the Channel ports, and hearts were uplifted accordingly.

But danger and discomfort were by no means ended. There was the usual difficulty about obtaining water for washing, while drinking water was unobtainable; so 'dry rations' were the order of the day.

After Hazebrouck the situation became distracting in the extreme.

> About 1 p.m. [one Sister tells us] while the train was running parallel with the road twenty yards away, enemy aeroplanes appeared. The road was crowded with lorries

full of soldiers and of refugees. All were bombed or
machine-gunned. The sight was appalling. One lorry of
French soldiers directly opposite our carriages suffered badly.
Our Medical Officers rendered first aid.

Matters however became so serious that at 4 p.m. it was
decided to leave the train and continue by road to St. Omer.

An ambulance came out for us, and we were immediately
taken into a wood and given shelter and some tea. From
there we proceeded to an empty chateau, where we spent
the night in a cellar. We did not move till next morning.
Enemy aeroplanes were constantly overhead.

By 8 a.m. an ambulance was ready to take us nine Sisters
and the padre. At Bergues our orders were changed, and
we were told to proceed to Calais. We passed through
Dunkirk about 12 noon. It had just been bombed, and
at one part a huge fire was blazing.

Between Dunkirk and Calais we were delayed three hours,
as we were refused permission to cross a fortified bridge.

(This was probably because the bridge had been mined for
demolition. Ultimately the party made a detour and crossed by
a smaller bridge.)

We reached Calais at 4 p.m. The Alert sounded as soon
as we got into the town, and we had all to take to the
shelters. The place was deserted except for refugees. The
shops were shut, buildings burning and smoking. We said
good-bye to the padre, who handed us over to the Area
Commandant.

Next morning, after another thoroughly disturbing night, the
nine Sisters were embarked on board the cargo steamer *City of
Christchurch*, crowded with some 2,000 soldiers. They were
accommodated in the cabins of the captain and his officers.
Their last memory of Calais was that of two enemy aircraft shot
down as they left the harbour.

The gallant padre, previously mentioned, did not accompany them. He stayed on the quayside at Calais, tending the wounded and dying until he was himself killed.

'I shall always remember his goodness to all of us,' another Sister tells us. 'He was indeed a very brave man.'

v

We turn now to the experiences of Sisters serving in hospitals. Here, as usual, our choice must perforce be selective.

In contrast to the casualty clearing stations, the General Hospitals, especially those lying near the Channel ports, enjoyed a brief period of immunity before being subjected, apart from some inevitable bombing raids, to the full fury of the Nazi invasion on May 10th. Indeed the tribulations of a fortunate few were comparatively short-lived, for at the end of the first fortnight it had become clear to the British military authorities, with the severance of General Georges' command (including the B.E.F.) in the north, from the main body of the French Army south of the thirty-mile 'corridor', and the surrender of the Belgians on Lord Gort's left, that a complete evacuation of Northern France (if that were still possible) was the only course left open to our forces.

Consequently various base hospitals were ordered to evacuate forthwith. Some of them so far had received no patients to speak of, which meant that the evacuation in their case would be limited to members of the nursing staff, who could no longer be usefully employed in France. Other hospitals were to carry on, tending and evacuating the wounded for as long as possible. If the present situation worsened, a further, perhaps complete, exodus might become necessary.

Such an evacuation was not going to be easy, hampered as it would be by transport difficulties consequent upon the almost complete dislocation of road and rail services; for the enemy had penetrated as far as Abbeville and the Channel coast less than ten days after the initial attack. The bombing menace had also to be considered.

There were, as we know, General Hospitals at Dieppe, Boulogne, Camiers, Le Tréport, Étaples, Cherbourg, and La Baule, all situated on the coast, and some of these were evacuated with comparative dispatch. No. 16 General Hospital, at Boulogne, was shipped to England within ten days of the invasion.

Others fell into a different category. The British Army at this time occupied something like one-third of the soil of France, and several General Hospitals were situated some way inland, remote both from the Channel ports and the battle-line. Indeed, it was some little time before the full gravity of the situation was brought home to these.

> The only indication of the state of affairs in Northern France [reports a Sister of No. 9 General situated near Le Mans] was the increase of traffic, caused, first of all, by a stream of private cars loaded with family possessions, then lorry loads of refugees from Belgium, and later still the usual pathetic procession of weary pedestrians.
>
> Finally the war casualties began to arrive; at first the slightly wounded, then patients evacuated from other hospitals nearer the Line, and then men evacuated straight from the Line itself.

It should be noted that this particular hospital was able to carry on at full pressure as late as June 9th, almost a week after the final evacuation of the B.E.F. from Dunkirk, and without interference from the enemy. This was because it lay south of the 'corridor' and was presumably in no immediate danger.

But on the evening of that day came the ominous order, 'Pack!'

The first reaction of the Sisters to this abrupt command was acute annoyance.

> We had felt [remarks one Sister] that we were at last doing the work we had been waiting to do all these months; and now that we were really needed, we were told to leave it

all, without so much as hearing a gun fired or a bomb dropped!

However, orders are orders, and by four o'clock next morning the evacuation had taken place to Le Mans, where the Sisters were entrained for Cherbourg. (Presumably such hospital patients as remained at this time had gone forward by road.) The Sisters had accommodation reserved for them in the train: the rest of it was packed with refugees. Food was, as usual, unobtainable, and recourse was had to private stores of chocolate and biscuits. The journey was slow and tedious, but Cherbourg was reached at last. (Cherbourg, La Baule, and St. Malo were by this time the only ports in this particular theatre unoccupied by the enemy. Q.A.I.M.N.S. units were evacuated from St. Malo as late as June 15th, 1940.)

The Sisters were embarked next day, and after travelling through a thick mist, which slowed the ship's progress to a crawl but screened her from enemy bombers, reached Southampton the same evening.

No. 9 General, incidentally, was not the last of the hospitals in Northern France to be evacuated during this period. No. 1 General, based on Dieppe, did not reach home until June 18th, by which time France had asked for an armistice, and the entire B.E.F. was booked for evacuation.

One other evacuation should be mentioned here—that of No. 10 General Hospital, as described in the words of a Nursing Sister of the Q.A.I.M.N.S. Reserve. Her story brings out, poignantly enough, the special difficulties attending the evacuation of a hospital containing a number of particularly helpless patients.

The first fortnight was a busy one for us at No. 10 General Hospital. Convoys of wounded arrived four-hourly, and patients were evacuated once or twice a day.

We saw no newspapers, and had no time to listen to the wireless news, and therefore knew nothing of the German break-through, so it was a great surprise on May 21st to go on duty and find others coming off with orders to pack and leave.

The Matron chose sixteen of us to stay and evacuate the patients. One Medical Officer, one Anæsthetist, the R.C Padre, and sixteen orderlies also remained. The rest of the unit left in ambulances to form a new hospital where we should soon join them—so we thought.

About 2 p.m. several officers arrived from another hospital and told us that the Germans were getting close. Eventually ambulances arrived, and patients were transferred to them. I was in charge of an orthopædic ward, and the majority of the patients were on Pierson beds, or had limbs suspended from Balkan beams. Many of them had to have a short anæsthetic before they could be transferred to a stretcher.

When we arrived in Dieppe we found the two hospital ships on fire! We returned to No. 10 for the night.

At 5 a.m. next morning we set off again to Dieppe. There we sat in the rain for two hours, and eventually climbed into cattle-trucks marked 'Forty men or Eight Horses'. They had recently been used for horses, and now held 75 of us, mostly women and children refugees.

Dieppe being for the present out of action as an evacuation port, the party set out in their horse-van for Cherbourg. Fortunately their numbers were reduced in time to twenty-six, and there was room to lie down.

The first stage of the journey took them as far as Rouen. It is superfluous to mention that the trip is described as slow and uncomfortable, with frequent stops to mend the line. Meals, too, appear to have been even more unorthodox than usual, even for that time.

At 5 a.m. we had breakfast of French bully beef and champagne. It was horrid. Later, an officer-patient produced two dixie-cans, and the ten of us drank red wine out of one and washed in weak red wine in the other!

We reached Le Mans about 5 p.m. and sat on the road-side waiting for some conveyance. A lorry arrived after about two hours and took us to a hotel. We slept two or three in a bed, which had been vacated for us by the officers living there.

The party reached Cherbourg next day, and crossed in a hospital ship. Our Sister, whose morale nothing seems to shake, ends her narrative on this most characteristic note:

While on board, we managed to make ourselves look fairly presentable.

VI

The experiences of the Sisters in charge of the ambulance trains was in some respects more continuously trying than those in the hospitals and casualty clearing stations, for trains are continuously on the move, and moreover furnish a conspicuous and inviting target for the German bombers.

These trains fell roughly into two categories—those actually operating in the Low Countries at the time of the invasion, and thus liable to encounter the enemy at close quarters and at un-expected moments, and those based farther south. These latter continued to operate right up to the final evacuation. Many, in the forward areas, were immobilized or put out of action com-paratively early in the campaign, and their nursing staffs had to be evacuated home after a fortnight of shattering experience. Others, operating farther afield, were at work right up to the time of the French surrender in the middle of June and the final evacuation of the B.E.F. and of Q.A.I.M.N.S.

The function of all the ambulance trains was normally the same: they plied between railhead and base, conveying wounded for evacuation. But after the invasion, and the consequent dis-integration of all transport services, these ceased to run to any regular schedule or to carry purely military cases. They travelled wherever they could find an unblocked line, picking up their passengers as often as not at some wayside station or remote siding, under constant threat of attack from the air.

Coming to actual instances, let us begin with a brief description of what may be called an average routine evacuation of that period—that of Ambulance Train No. 13.

The story begins on Wednesday, May 15th, when the train lay awaiting orders just outside Lille—in other words, well within the battle zone. The invasion had been in progress for five days, and all available reinforcements were being sent up into the Line. One of the Nursing Sisters on board the train gives us a vivid description of the scene, most of it familiar enough to the reader by this time:

> We saw more British and French troops moving up. The windows in a great many of the carriages of the train carrying refugees were broken, and many of the carriages themselves riddled with holes made by machine-gun bullets. The station was crowded with lost and terrified-looking refugees, who continued to stream into it, in train after train of cattle trucks.
>
> As was becoming now quite normal, sirens wailed almost ceaselessly, and aerial battles between our own aircraft and those of the enemy were taking place over our heads at very frequent intervals. The Belgian engine-drivers who had driven the refugee trains through were a frantic and hungry collection of men, and told tales of bombardment *en route*; of the rapid advance of the Germans, and of the plight of Belgium. With British troops preparing to evacuate,[1] we all wondered quite what *we* were waiting for.

The question was soon answered by an order to be prepared to take on a trainload of patients, who were due to arrive from various casualty clearing stations that afternoon. The loading was uneventful but laborious, for each stretcher had to be carried over two railway tracks and down a long platform—170 cases in all. They were a motley collection. Some had just been

[1] These were probably Administrative units. The time for evacuating the fighting forces was not yet.

released from hospital and were practically convalescent, others, mostly Belgians, had come down the line from Ghent, and were seriously ill.   Later on the train moved right into Lille, where a fresh batch of wounded were taken on board, by bright moon-light now.   Most of these were serious cases—men straight from the casualty clearing stations, many of them with nothing but a first field-dressing.   It was one o'clock in the morning before the work was done, and there were now 350 patients on board —French wounded, a Spahi, and a severely hurt Belgian civilian. There were five German officers, of the most arrogant type, quite certain that they had won the war and demanding preferen-tial treatment—which they did not get.   Indeed, they were un-ceremoniously dumped at the first opportunity and left for their friends to take care of.

Obviously the next and most pressing need was to get the train to some port of evacuation; but for reasons already stated this was not too easy.

At six o'clock next morning we reached St. Omer, where the station was entirely blocked with traffic. While our water-tanks were being refilled we saw poor helpless refugees begging to be taken on board trains, and noticed English nuns among the mass of humanity being loaded into the cattle trucks.   At seven o'clock our train moved on, this time with Calais as our objective, and spirits rose high.

But hope was disappointed.   Calais proved to be under heavy bombardment: the harbour was practically out of action and the railway tracks broken up.   After a wait of several hours the train moved slowly on again, by-passing Boulogne, to Étaples, near Le Touquet.

The congestion on the line was terrific; continuous dog-fights were going on overhead, and bombs were bursting close by.   We gave a second shot of morphia to all our seriously wounded and bad fracture cases.

But Étaples had no comfort to offer.   An agitated French

station-master announced that the Germans were only eight miles away, and that the station was to be blown up forthwith! So the weary pilgrimage was resumed—this time back to Boulogne, which, it was found, was being very heavily attacked from the air. The spectacle, however, appears not to have been without its attractions.

> We waited outside the town and had a magnificent view of the town and harbour. The roar of planes overhead was terrific, and we saw British Blenheims fly over the town. Then bombs began to fall. The train shook and rocked violently, but we came through quite undamaged, without even a broken window, though the patients, in that confined space, were badly frightened.

There was nothing for it then but to beat a retreat from Boulogne, down the line as far as Dannes-Camiers, some twenty miles south. Here the German wounded were unloaded, and some welcome comforts, in the form of N.A.A.F.I. cigarettes and chocolates, taken on board in their place.

At one o'clock next morning a second visit was paid to Boulogne, now quiescent. It was Wednesday, May 22nd, and Ambulance Train No. 13 had been on the move for the best part of a week.

But the journey was nearing its end at last, for some of its personnel at least—probably selected as being especially deserving of a rest.

> The train was moving slowly, though we had no idea where we were or where we were going. At 7 a.m. we were told to pack. Then, much to our surprise, the O.C. gave us orders to be ready to get off the train, which had by this time come to a standstill in a station. It started to move again, so, acting on orders, we jumped out in what we stood up in, and sadly watched the train move off.
>
> There were nine of us all told—three Sisters, one Officer patient in charge of the party, another Officer acting as guide, and five British Other Ranks.

M

We crossed from one Boulogne station to another [Boulogne Ville to Boulogne Maritime, presumably] in a downpour of rain which did not look as though it had the least intention of stopping for days. We were met by an officer who told us that we were going home, but as yet there was no boat to take us. Our guide having left us, we waited on the station platform amidst hundreds of battle-worn troops. A cheerful Padre brought us cups of tea. Finally we moved off in single file, between lines of troops with fixed bayonets, who were stopping the refugees from rushing the ships at the quayside. We climbed up a gang-plank on board a destroyer, where we were taken down to the Petty Officers' Mess and given breakfast.

The destroyer in question put forth about noon. It was a noisy journey. Depth charges were dropped, a mine exploded by machine-gun fire, and there was a low-flying attack by an enemy aircraft. But our little party were safely in Dover by the afternoon and the adventure was over.

So much, then, for a comparatively normal evacuation. But those concerned in our next story had a sterner time of it. The story deals with the adventure of No. 3 Ambulance Train, during the final week of the Battle of Flanders.

On Sunday, a most beautiful day [the tale begins], we stopped at a small railway station. There was an air of excitement and tension among the French there: the advancing Germans were only four miles away. The convoy of wounded that we had come to meet had not got through to us.

We picked up about 50 of the refugees and took them along to a safer place, the poor creatures being most grateful for the rest and food.

Early next morning we stopped at Verneuil, having heard that the convoy would meet us there. We were just finishing a meal when one of the batmen came racing down the train, shouting, 'Sisters, get your tin hats! Jerry's here!'

We rushed to our bunks to get them. I glanced up and saw three planes, flying low and coming like the wind towards us. There were seven altogether, I believe. I reached No. 1 Coach, where our patients were, as the first bomb exploded. Two Sisters were seized by an Orderly, who made them lie on the floor and not move.

This orderly, a very young man, seems to have behaved like a veteran. He exhibited the greatest courage and devotion, we are told, and helped our Sisters to soothe the patients, some of whom were already badly shocked and kept screaming at the explosions. Fortunately there were only ten of them, for the main body of the convoy had never arrived.

Bombs, aerial torpedoes, and machine-guns were all employed. A French troop-train lying alongside was in equal danger. An ammunition train, a most undesirable neighbour on such occasions, had left just before the raid began. The station itself was crowded with civilian refugees.

At last the raid was over. Our beautiful ambulance was cut in two. No. 5 Coach was like a crumpled matchbox; some of the carriages were tilted over; broken glass and earth covered the train. The French troop-train was in ruins; the poor dead horses looked most pathetic; the station was devastated. Sadder still, one Orderly had been killed and nine or ten others more or less injured. Some of them had wonderful escapes, one being blown clear of the train as the middle coach collapsed.

The dead were taken to a convent near, poor little girls and women among them, also dead soldiers (French). In the evening we got away in the first three coaches of the train, feeling it dreadfully that we had to leave the body of our brave Orderly under the wreckage.

All this, as already indicated, happened a few days before the final French surrender. Our Sisters' task was done. They were conveyed to La Baule, a pleasant little watering-place on the Brittany coast, and two days later arrived at St. Nazaire.

Crowds of our troops kept pouring in, on their way home. Some of them came up and asked us for food as we sat on what was left of our luggage: they had been for hours with nothing to eat. We gave them chocolate and biscuits, whatever we had. They were wonderfully cheerful; many had pink roses stuck in their caps.

Next morning the Sisters of No. 3 Ambulance Train, with others, embarked on board the C.P.R. liner, *Duchess of York*, and after two days at sea came safe to Liverpool.

We come lastly to Ambulance Train No. 4, stationed on the fateful May 10th at a village just outside Dieppe. The staff consisted of five medical officers, three Sisters, and forty orderlies.

For the first few days their work was of a routine character and comparatively free from serious alarms. Then real trouble started. The train at this time was standing at the village of Nivose, in Belgium, loading up with wounded from a casualty clearing station.

> Very soon our convoy was coming on board [says the narrative], and we eventually filled up. Two cases had to be operated on at once in our little train theatre.
>
> By this time enemy activity was intense. The C.C.S. had to be disbanded. We took the Sisters and some Medical Officers on board our train about midnight, with enemy aeroplanes over us dropping bombs near; but anti-aircraft guns kept them at bay.

The departure of No. 4 from Nivose was rendered no easier by the fact that by this time the Belgian railway system had lapsed into chaos. Indeed the British medical officers on the train had themselves to assume the role of traffic directors—a duty in which they displayed considerable resource and *expertise*.

> When we were ready for departure, the Belgian engine-driver refused to take the train out of Belgium: the O.C. had to put a British armed guard on him before he would move.

Our next difficulty was that all the signals were against us. The O.C. had to get off the train and right the signals at every station until we got out of Belgium.

Dieppe was reached next day, May 18th. Here the arrival of No. 4 was greeted with joy, for the train had been absent for a week and almost given up for lost.

The sick and wounded were immediately distributed among various General Hospitals, pending the time when they should be fit for the strain of evacuation home. This was just as well, for next day Dieppe was heavily bombed.

'We all sheltered under the train,' remarks our Sister casually, 'until the raiders had passed.'

Upon May 21st No. 4 set to work again, evacuating the occupants of Nos. 1 and 10 General Hospitals, together with the Indian Hospital, from Dieppe, which was getting altogether too hot for a hospital centre.

There were between six and eight hundred people on board. Many of the patients were seriously ill, and the hurried journey in the ambulances from the hospital to the train did not improve their condition. However, we made them as comfortable as we could in the circumstances, while waiting patiently for an engine for the train.

The reader will not be altogether surprised to learn that the engine was not immediately forthcoming, and that while it tarried a heavy raid took place. The train endured several near-misses—almost as demoralizing as direct hits—and two hospital ships, *Maid of Kent* and *Brighton*, lying at the dockside close by, with a tanker, were set on fire, to the imminent peril of No. 4 itself, which soon began to burn too.

Our walking cases ran off the train to shelters, and were machine-gunned on the way; many of them were killed and many wounded.

The train was now a blazing inferno. I went along to see

how the patients in the other wards were. It was a very pathetic sight to see men in Thomas splints hobbling along by the bedsides; also, patients with heads swathed in bandages. These advised me not to enter, as the ward was 'gassed'. This gas was really the fumes from the tanker, which had been bombed near to the ward. All the windows being broken, the fumes quickly entered, and the ward was a mass of thick black smoke. It cleared off fairly quickly, and the patients were put back to bed and reassured that they would be all right.

Many huge pieces of iron from the oil-tanker shot through the woodwork of the train from one side to another. Fortunately nobody was hurt.

Meanwhile the O.C. train, with much willing help, had contrived to uncouple the burning coaches from those still intact. This done, and the wounded men having been transferred from the train to the care of the medical officers in a neighbouring shed, he ordered a motor ambulance, and insisted that our three Sisters should proceed by it to Le Havre forthwith.

One of the three could not be found, and it was at first feared that she had become a casualty. Finally, after an anxious search, the other two were compelled to set off without her.

The pair arrived at Le Havre the same evening, having characteristically broken their journey long enough to pick up a boy of eleven years old, suffering from a compound fracture of the femur, bandage him up with the field-dressing attached to their gas-mask equipment, and deposit him at the first French hospital.

Upon arrival at Le Havre, they found to their dismay that the hospital to which they had been ordered to report had evacuated. It was a bitter blow, for they were reaching the end of their strength, and no wonder. However, a cup of tea and a few helpful words from the R.T.O. had their usual effect, and they took the road again, this time for Rouen, which they reached in the small hours of the morning.

Needless to say they found an air raid in progress, so pressed on to a large military camp beyond the city. This too, they found, had evacuated, but by a dispensation of Providence the canteen workers were still there. The immediate result was a proper meal and a couple of stretchers to lie on for an hour or two.

But not to sleep. Another air raid started, answered by A.A. artillery, and our Sisters, deciding that a military objective was no kind of dormitory for Q.A.s, summoned their ambulance and its driver and set off, in heavy rain, for Le Mans. Our recording Sister does not forget to note, with gratitude, that when the need for more petrol became pressing, the Red Cross allowed them precedence over a long string of other applicants.

They reached Le Mans next afternoon, and made immediate inquiry of the R.T.O. as to whether No. 4 Ambulance Train had passed that way.

He said that it had passed through, bound for La Baule, and he 'could see nothing but heads, there were so many people on board'. We were delighted to hear that they had got safely away. We took a new lease of life, and joyfully proceeded to Rennes, where we arrived at 10.30 p.m.

At Rennes the R.T.O. rang up the Matron of No. 8 General Hospital on their behalf, and the Matron sent the Assistant Matron to meet them at the station and convey them to comfortable quarters. They had fallen on their feet at last. Indeed—

We were treated more like heroes than refugees by the Matron and Staff [reports our Sister, to her evident surprise].

The missing Sister also rejoined them about this time.

It was now May 29th, and evacuation of hospital units had become general. Upon that day our Sisters received orders to rejoin No. 4 Ambulance Train at Rouen, which they did 'joyfully'.

Their next summons was to Le Mans, where they found all the patients from No. 9 General Hospital laid out on stretchers on the platform, having lain there all night. For once they did not have to wait for an engine; with the result that they were able to reach La Baule next morning, where they deposited their patients at the now unoccupied No. 4 General Hospital. On the way to Le Mans they had been heavily bombed while standing in a wayside station. But this time the visitation presented one element of novelty. The train had come to a standstill alongside a huge gasometer. The Sisters took shelter under the usual hedges, with the gasometer towering above them—a most uncomfortable neighbour in the circumstances. Fortunately it did not explode.

Upon their return to La Baule the party were informed that 'the Sisters of No. 4 Train were released from duty, and were to remain at La Baule pending further orders'.

This news was greeted much as the reader would have been justified in expecting.

> Needless to say, we were very upset at leaving our train and the people we had worked with for over eight months.

But the 'upset' was sensibly mitigated when it was revealed to our Sisters that their supersession was a prelude to evacuation. They were going home at last, after more than six weeks of nightmare journeyings, continuous duty, and perpetual danger.

Next morning they proceeded to St. Nazaire, to find themselves, after climbing 'very steep ladders from the tender to the first deck', on board the *Duchess of York*, in company with some 5,000 troops and many other Sisters.

Two days later they found themselves in Liverpool, whence they proceeded to London.

> On the afternoon of June 19th [concludes our matter-of-fact young historian] we reported at Millbank Hospital, received orders for leave, and so ended our B.E.F. experiences in France.

VII

As a postscript to the foregoing record, and a reminder that the adventures of Q.A.I.M.N.S. during this period were not confined to Northern France, here is a description, by a Nursing Sister stationed in the British Military Hospital in Marseilles, of the events leading up to our final evacuation of Southern France.

Marseilles, it seems, was left in comparative tranquillity until the beginning of June, when German bombing set in in earnest. On June 1st there was a heavy raid on the docks, and the Orient liner *Orford*, now a transport conveying coloured troops, received a direct hit, with casualties which filled the British Hospital to overflowing.

Bombing soon became a daily occurrence, and the hospital had several narrow escapes. With Italy's entry into the war the situation intensified, for there were hundreds of Italian residents in Marseilles, and the police were soon busy rounding up suspects. The French population, too, were getting out of hand. They were increasingly hostile towards the British, having been persuaded by skilful Fifth Columnists that our country was somehow responsible for their misfortunes.

Finally, with the surrender of France on June 17th, it became obvious that the sooner the British element, which included hundreds of refugees, was transported home, the better.

The British Hospital was evacuated on June 19th, and patients and Nursing Sisters conveyed on board an old tramp steamer, the only vessel available. She was packed to suffocation, but room was found for thirty patients, eight Sisters, and some orderlies. The British Consul and his entourage were also on board.

Ten days were occupied in a slow and cautious crawl along the Spanish coast.

We had been warned [says our Sister] to render our uniform as inconspicuous as possible, and not let our red capes be seen. The ship following us was attacked by a German submarine, but we proceeded safely.

Gibraltar was reached on June 29th, and here it was found possible to transfer the entire party to a properly equipped transport, the *Dunera*. It was a difficult operation, for the race was running high, and some of the stretcher cases had a rough time of it. But all bore up bravely.

The ship, of course, was crowded. Besides British military and hospital units, there were some 1,800 refugees, mostly semi-invalids from the Riviera towns.

There were many pathetic cases—elderly and infirm people who had lost literally all they possessed, quite bewildered and unable to understand their plight. Many were suffering from physical and mental shock; they had endured great privation in the colliers and other small craft in which they had escaped.

The worst cases were taken, with the military casualties, into the ship's hospital, where they were tended by the Nursing Sisters and so enabled to recover their morale.

The spirit of all on board was marvellous [concludes our Sister], in spite of anxiety over lost possessions and the future.

All arrived safely at Liverpool on July 4th. More than three years were to elapse before a Nursing Sister would again set foot upon the soil of France.

CHAPTER 13

MIDDLE EAST: THE DESERT CAMPAIGNS

W<small>ITHIN</small> a month of their evacuation from France, certain Army nursing units were on their way out to Egypt and the Middle East.

Before proceeding to detailed narrative, let us endeavour to grasp the exact scope and significance of the expression 'Middle East'. It was an elastic term in those days, and covered every theatre of war, small or great, in North, West, and East Africa; in Iraq, Persia, Syria, and Palestine. (For good measure we may throw in the small island of Mauritius, far out in the Indian Ocean.) Q.A.I.M.N.S. served in every one of these areas.

Medical and nursing service under such varied conditions was to be very different from that hitherto experienced in the highly modernized terrain of Western Europe, with its hedge-lined, metalled country roads and built-up urban areas. Nursing Sisters might find themselves quartered now in an occasional marble palace, in wooden huts, in tents with no floors, in native mud-huts specially built for them, in houseboats moored to a river-bank, at a casualty clearing station in the Western Desert, or in a sunken tent, concreted and furnished with 'rabbit-hole' dug-outs to sleep in.

They would meet warriors of almost every race, colour, and creed, and would nurse countless patients of whose language they were as ignorant as their patients were of theirs. Their duties would be carried out in every variety of climate, from fierce heat to bitter cold, and, in North Africa, in inches of mud, amid which the only rational nursing uniform would consist of service slacks and gum-boots. They would be plagued by mosquitoes, ants, scorpions, and other even less respectable insects, and would be-

187

come acquainted with diseases, such as typhus, hitherto unknown to them. But the Q.A.s accepted the prospect with complete equanimity, even eagerness. It was all part of the great adventure.

II

The Middle Eastern theatre was of vital importance to the Allies. It was certain that as soon as Mussolini decided that he was betting on a certainty, Italy would declare war on Britain and France, thus imperilling Allied control of the Mediterranean, the Suez Canal, and all direct communication with India and the East.

The situation was rendered more difficult—desperate, in fact—by the collapse of France and the setting up of the Vichy Government. The defence of the Eastern Mediterranean had been left very largely to French troops, with the result that in June 1940 General Wavell, Commander-in-Chief Middle East, found himself bereft at a single stroke of the greater part of his command and opposed by a force of some 415,000 Italian troops, distributed over Libya and Italian East Africa. His own remaining forces comprised about 118,000 men, British, Dominion and Indian, most of them half trained and only partially equipped, spread thinly over Egypt, Sudan, and Palestine.

There was only one thing to be done in the circumstances, and the British Government did not hesitate to do it: they immediately dispatched further troops to the Middle East, ill though these could be spared from the protection of Britain, now lying wide open to invasion by sea and air.

Three months of acute anxiety and suspense followed, for these reinforcements had to travel the long and perilous road round the Cape of Good Hope, and might arrive too late. Fortunately the Italians showed no immediate desire to take the initiative. Meanwhile General Wavell was able to make full use of the opportunity to train his available forces in the unfamiliar art of desert warfare.

The reinforcements duly arrived, and by December 1940 the odds against our Army in Egypt had been reduced to about two to one. General Wavell felt that this was good enough, and decided to take the offensive himself. The result was a resounding victory; the destruction of an Italian Army of nearly ten divisions; the capture of 130,000 prisoners, and a westward advance of 500 miles. It was our first military success of the war; the story rang round the world, and the prestige of the British soldier was restored. Best of all, the soldier himself became imbued with a new spirit of confidence and will to win.

It was a truly auspicious beginning, but much had to happen, and many vicissitudes of fortune be endured, before the final victory. More than once during those years, it will be remembered, our desert forces were pressed back, after a successful advance, to the Egyptian frontier—at one time the catch-phrase of the moment was 'Benghazi and back!'—for not only had our War Cabinet considered it necessary, for political reasons, to divert the greater part of General Wavell's victorious 'Army of the Nile' to the assistance of Greece (General Wavell himself being transferred to India), but the Germans had taken over the direction of the North African campaign from their incompetent Allies. In due course Marshal Rommel, with his formidable Afrika Corps, fully motorized and well supplied with the most modern tanks, regained all, and more, than the Italians had lost.

So serious did the situation become that in the summer of 1942 the British and Dominion forces were compelled to retire to El Alamein, a prepared defensive position lying within Egyptian territory, between the impassable Quattara Depression and the sea. Here they stood fast, repelling every attack, while at home in Britain the munition factories worked night and day to equip our new divisions, and transports, in an increasing stream, conveyed men and munitions round the Cape and up the Red Sea.

In Egypt General Alexander, the newly appointed Commander-in-Chief Middle East, was achieving a miracle of reorganization, while General Montgomery built up and trained the Eighth Army—destined to achieve enduring fame in the years to come.

By October 23rd, 1942, all was in readiness, and Montgomery struck back at Rommel. The rest is history, for after the opening victory of El Alamein the Eighth Army, supported throughout by the coastwise aid of the Royal Navy, swept the enemy out of Libya and Cyrenaica in an advance of some 2,000 miles, which never ceased until Montgomery had joined hands with Anderson and the First Army in Tunisia, on April 7th, 1943.

Such, in brief outline, was the pattern of that immortal campaign. Let us now consider the service rendered therein, and some of the adventures encountered, by our Army Nursing Services.

III

A Nursing Sister's expectation of adventure in the African campaign depended very largely upon two factors—in which period of that campaign she served, and where she found herself stationed.

Nursing units had arrived in the Middle East as early as 1936, in company with troops sent out from home to deal with any emergency that might arise from Italian designs upon Abyssinia or with Arab unrest in Palestine and Transjordania; but it was not until late 1939 that Q.A.I.M.N.S. arrived in any considerable numbers. Most of them were posted to hospitals in Cairo, or, a little farther afield, in the Nile Delta and Suez Canal Zone. They had no call to penetrate westward, for uneasy peace still reigned between ourselves and the Italians.

Here is a picture of a typical General Hospital of the Middle East at that time—No. 6 General—situated near Quassaseu in the Canal Zone, and opened in early 1940. It stood in a large military camp where troops were being assembled, trained, and equipped against the moment—the inevitable moment, all felt—when they would be dispatched to deal with an Italian invasion. It was also employed later as a rest-camp for troops who had been in action.

At first the hospital was composed mainly of tents; the permanent buildings were in course of erection but not yet completed. It was designed to accommodate 1,200 patients, and be capable if necessary of expanding to 2,000. In total war no one can foresee the extent of casualties: the safest plan is to overestimate them.

Besides the tents there were a number of Nissen huts—those useful arched structures of corrugated iron which were to become such a familiar feature of every British theatre of war. These held twenty-four beds apiece, or could be divided up into smaller and separate rooms for the accommodation of isolation cases. They also housed the operating theatre, the X-ray department, and the laboratory. At first the only internal illumination was from hurricane lamps, as in the days of Florence Nightingale: in due course, however, electric lighting was laid on throughout.

Nissen huts were employed in various other ways. One served as a dining-hall for convalescent patients, and for the giving of entertainments. Another was the Hospital Chapel, and much loving attention was lavished here. At first there was no altar —merely a wooden table—but later a quite ornate structure of bricks and concrete was set up by Italian prisoners. Chairs were contributed by British Red Cross and the Order of St. John of Jerusalem. The Sisters themselves helped to make the curtains and altar-cloths.

Each of the hospital tents accommodated twenty patients, and was sunk about five feet into the ground, as a precaution against bomb-blast. At first the floors were composed merely of the sand and rock of the desert: later, concrete roofs and bomb-proof walls were added.

The Sisters themselves lived in square tents, sunk as usual some feet into the sand, furnished with camp equipment, and accommodating two or three. For their meals and recreation they were provided with one of the invaluable Nissen huts.

Presently the hospital was in full operation, for Mussolini declared war in June, and desert fighting began at Mersa Matruh, just beyond the Egyptian western frontier.

Towards the middle of October [one Sister tells us], we began to receive, nightly, small convoys of surgical walking cases passed on from Casualty Clearing Stations and Base Hospitals nearer to the north coast. These men travelled by ordinary passenger trains, often taking two hours for the journey and making at least two changes *en route*. Accommodation was very limited, and they seldom got a seat. They were met by trucks at the nearest halt, and conveyed to the Hospital.

About this period, and always in the early morning hours, we began to get air-raid alerts, and the men had to be guided and put to bed in complete darkness.

Towards Christmas 1940 a fresh variety of patient was introduced into the hospital, in the persons of a large number of prisoners of war. Many of these were Italian-trained native troops: they spoke no language but their own, and were disconcertingly allergic to the niceties of European civilization. Bedclothes and pyjamas were a complete mystery to them. Blankets they came to understand, but not pyjamas. In every case the patient insisted upon wrapping these round his head and keeping them there. The explanation, when discovered, was simple enough. A member of this particular tribe, it appeared, could not, upon religious grounds, go bareheaded—hence the pyjama swathings. Soon turbans were devised from towels, and all was well.

The behaviour of the next contingent of prisoners was even odder, though these should have known better. They were Italian officers, and were convinced, to a man, that Q.A.I.M.N.S. were out to poison them. Such is the power of propaganda. Over and over again a Sister was herself compelled to take a sip out of a medicine glass, as a guarantee to a resisting patient that the potion it contained was not lethal.

As for the Italian rank-and-file, once they had been persuaded that they would not be poisoned or handed over to a firing-squad, they were happy enough. None of them seemed to take the slightest interest in the war, and turned with relief and efficiency to such congenial jobs as cooking and waiting at table.

Presently General Wavell launched his great offensive, and casualties began in earnest. Fortunately the hospital was now fully prepared for them. A very efficient system was organized to get the men to bed as quickly as possible: after food and a cigarette they soon fell asleep. Besides being wounded they

The Hospital Ship *Leinster* at Akureyri, Iceland, March, 1941

Serving patients' meals in the ward, No. 94 General Hospital, North Algiers, November, 1943 (*Imperial War Museum*)

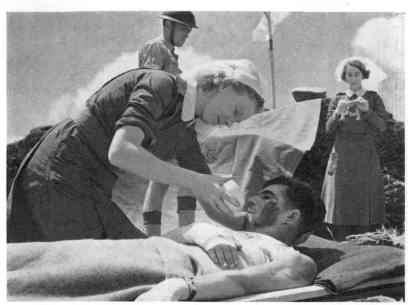

British Red Cross nurses in Sicily, one hour's ride from the front line
(*Imperial War Museum*)

"Q.A.s" in Normandy, July, 1944. With R.A.M.C. orderlies, carrying out a
patient after the operation (*Photographic News Agencies, Ltd.*)

were dead tired, but wonderfully cheerful under the stimulus of victory. It should be added that these patients, in time, included representatives of almost every one of the Allied Nations and British Empire—not only from the great Dominions and India, but from Greece, Poland, Czechoslovakia, Mauritius, Malaya, China, Free France, Syria, Palestine and Malta.

A word may appropriately be said here regarding the immense strides made in recent years in the treatment of wounds and of sickness arising from active service conditions, especially in hot climates.

First came the miracles performed by blood-transfusion. This was a very highly organized service, for its success depended largely upon prompt action. Special orderlies were trained for it, and there were 'Central Blood Banks', where blood could be obtained as required. In the forward areas special tents were set aside for purposes of reception and resuscitation. Abdominal cases, which usually involve great loss of blood, were received into previously warmed beds, where the transfusion was given at once and the patient treated, at the same time, for shock. The operation was performed as soon as the surgeon and anæsthetist pronounced him fit. In former days the man would probably have died from loss of blood and shock.

Chest and facial wounds were treated with the same care and modernity of method. For chest cases oxygen was always available, and the surgical staff in the facial-maxillary centres always included an experienced dental surgeon.

Incidentally, the principal Chest Hospital for the Middle East Forces was situated upon the summit of Mount Scopus in Palestine. It was originally a palace, built for Kaiser Wilhelm, possibly in anticipation of the day when he should feel qualified to proclaim himself Spiritual Overlord of Christendom. He never occupied it.

On the medical side, the principal menace of the serving soldier in the Middle East were dysentery and malaria.

The treatment of dysentery had been revolutionized by the use of the drug Sulphanilamide, coupled with careful dieting, rest, and isolation. Much, too, was achieved by rigid preventive

N

methods. Some of these, as we know, dated back to Florence
Nightingale—*Sanitas Sanitatum! Omnia Sanitas!*—but they were
now rendered trebly efficacious by the systematic elimination of
flies, thorough washing of all fruit, and the use of no drinking
water other than that approved by the medical authorities.

Malarial fever was now diagnosed and dealt with far more
accurately and scientifically than before. In many cases the attack
was recurrent, and in former days had been treated by dosing the
patient with quinine until he recovered. Now more scientific
methods were employed. As soon as a man was thought to be
suffering from an approach of malarial fever, a blood-slide was
taken, and repeated every two hours until the diagnosis was confirmed. Then followed the appropriate treatment, dependent
upon the type diagnosed. The patient was kept in bed for at
least four days, and treated with plenty of fluids, together with
glucose, salt, and alkali. Aspirin, unknown a generation ago,
was available to relieve the inevitable severe headache.

Such were a few of the benefits bestowed upon the modern
soldier by scientific research. They had certainly improved a
sick or wounded man's expectation of life out of all knowledge.
In the great General Hospital just described, only six patients died
during the first year.

IV

Let us pass now to the other end of the scale, by advancing
from the base to the front and studying the activities of what
was known as a Mobile Military Hospital. We must advance,
too, a year or more in time, for these institutions did not come
into being until El Alamein and General Montgomery's subsequent triumphal progress to Tripoli and Tunis.

The earliest, and perhaps the most famous Mobile Military
Hospital—or 'Freak Unit', to employ the sobriquet so un-
gallantly bestowed upon it—was No. 1. It came into active
existence in the autumn of 1942.

Early in October [we are informed by the Sister who tells

the story] rumours began, since we had discharged but did not immediately re-admit. We were quite sure that an Army move was impending, and that we should move forward to deal with direct battle casualties.

It was an exciting prospect, but the rumours received no encouragement, and presently died down. But they began again towards the end of the month, following upon a notable increase in the number of British bombers passing overhead nightly. Then—

> One morning the Commanding Officer told me that when the Eighth Army advanced we might reasonably expect to go with it !

This was tremendous news indeed, and was confirmed by an official intimation that the Sisters must provide themselves with some different uniform than grey cotton frocks and scarlet capes. The reasons for the order were obvious.

> The frocks were thin, and would be very cold in the winter in the open. The Air Force, moreover, complained that they were too easily visible from the air. We would have practically no laundry facilities. Dresses of any kind are not suitable when nursing stretcher cases. (We had found in Belgium that the men were very embarrassed when the Sisters were attending to a patient on a stretcher next to or near-by.) As we should be travelling in lorries or ambulance cars, dresses were not practical.

The upshot of it all, of course, was service slacks and battle blouses, and thus sensibly arrayed Q.A.I.M.N.S. advanced into action.

But not immediately. The Battle of El Alamein had begun upon October 23rd, and the Eighth Army was somewhere far beyond the desert horizon by the time our impatient Freak Unit was called upon to make a move. This was on December 4th, when the Sisters were embarked at Alexandria upon the Hospital Ship *Llandovery Castle*, to find themselves two days later at Tobruk, which had fallen to the enemy six months before and had recently been recaptured, after hard fighting, by the Eighth Army.

Needless to say, that historic seaport showed considerable signs of wear and tear.

I myself counted 72 partially sunk ships in the harbour, and was told that there were many more sunk out of sight. Not one building seemed to be intact, but on one less damaged building proudly flew the White Ensign that denotes Navy House.

We disembarked in barges, which carried us to a badly shattered jetty—merely a series of planks laid over old oil barrels and stretching out into the harbour. Along these planks we walked slowly and carefully, carrying our suitcases in one hand and balanced on the other by our ever-present respirators and steel helmets.

Two days later the Sisters left camp and set out (under the envious glances, we are told, of the Sisters of No. 14 Casualty Clearing Station, who were still clad in grey and scarlet) in full pursuit of the Eighth Army.

Two Sisters travelled in each ambulance. During daylight and while on the move, both sat in front with the driver.

We wore our anti-gas glasses to protect our eyes from sand, but that did not prevent a layer from adhering to our faces.

At night they slept inside the ambulance, each on a stretcher. Each Sister had her bedding-roll, suit-case, and two-gallon water container—this last for the purpose of her rather sketchy ablutions.

On they went, day after day, through Derna, over Halfaya Pass, and finally to Benghazi, where they found that they had overtaken the Eighth Army at last and that their hospital was all set up and waiting for them. They had already covered 650 miles—eight days of travel by sea and road—a very fine road, constructed by Italian engineers.

The hospital tents, they found, contained some 300 patients, all bed cases. The walking wounded were taken charge of by a neighbouring field ambulance.

The patients were amazed to see us. We were the first white women most of them had set eyes on for many months. We heard many comments to the effect that now all would be well—that the Army *couldn't* retreat now that it had its Sisters up in the forward area.

No. 1 remained at Benghazi for another five weeks, which included Christmas and its accompanying festivities. Thanks to N.A.A.F.I. and the Red Cross, there were presents for all.

On Christmas Eve, when we could hope that all the patients were asleep, the Quartermaster and I loaded one of the cars with Christmas stockings, and set out to do a round of the hospital. At each ward tent we left a filled stocking for every patient, and either a pipe and tobacco or cigarettes. The stockings contained a piece of soap, a pair of socks, writing-paper, envelopes and a pencil.

Christmas Day itself the Sisters celebrated by discarding their slacks and gum-boots *pro tem*, and returning to their grey frocks and white caps.

Early on Boxing Day, however, came a sharp and sudden reminder that a desert campaign is not all composed of parties and presents, and that the desert itself is not invariably a region of sand and sunshine.

I awoke feeling that something was wrong. Looking out of my tent, I saw that the entire camp was under water. I sat up in bed and turned back the blankets and put one foot on the ground, meaning to rescue my clothes before they became soaked. Alas, instead of encountering the usual hard floor, my leg sank half-way to my knee in mud! With great difficulty I extricated myself and got into slacks and boots and proceeded to the hospital.

Torrential rain had flooded the camp so completely that it was found necessary to evacuate almost all the patients. The ground, moreover, had become so soft that none of the motor ambulances could reach the tents, and every patient had to be carried a distance varying from a quarter to half a mile to ground sufficiently hard to accommodate the ambulances. In one ward-tent the ground was so soft that the beds sank until the mattresses were level with the floor.

For some days the Sisters went about their duties without stockings, in their gum-boots, wearing their trouser-legs turned up above the knee. It was a thoroughly unpleasant experience, but a useful hardening process for even more strenuous adventures.

v

The forward march was resumed on January 10th, 1943. The convoy moved in three sections, with the Sisters in the second section.

The routine was always the same. Up at 6.0 a.m. and over to the cookhouse with tin plates or mess-tins for breakfast. At 6.30 the engines were warmed up, and by 7.0 we were on our way. We halted about 10.0 for a brief rest for the drivers, when cook always had a welcome cup of tea ready. Then on again until midday, and an hour's halt for dinner; then on until 4 p.m. when we camped for the night. The halt had to be made at this early hour so that a meal could be eaten, all vehicles overhauled, and the next day's water ration given out, as no lights could be shown after nightfall.

This water ration varied in quantity, and was seldom sufficient, despite recent floods. At one time it fell to one half-pint a day for personal use.

First in priority came the vehicles, then the kitchen, then the operating theatres and wards, lastly unit personnel.

One small bowl of water was put out in the ward in the morning for surgical purposes. When washing patients, we took it in rotation which bed to begin with, as we could not afford fresh water for each patient. Head cases were welcomed, as they meant less washing!

We developed a special technique for washing-up dishes and cutlery. These would be plunged first into the sand, thereby removing most of the débris. When any tea was left over, this was utilized for dish-washing, to save water.

The convoy was close on the heels of the Eighth Army now. They were skirting the Gulf of Sirte and arrived presently at Sirte itself, which the Eighth Army had captured only the previous day. Here they camped beside the New Zealand Casualty Clearing Station, and took in some casualties from a recent tank engagement.

These men, in addition to wounds, were also badly burned. They were very plucky, and never made a murmur of complaint.

On the road to Sirte the convoy had received a gruesome reminder that they were now well within the battle zone.

By now the way was well posted with notices not to leave the roads, because of mines. A few days later I saw the result of not obeying the notices. A truck just ahead of the car in which I was travelling left the road for a small oasis, perhaps ten yards away. It had not gone five yards before it went over a mine. The driver was killed outright, and the man beside him received terrible multiple wounds: of the men in the back two died before we could get them out, and a third before he reached hospital.

Progress after Sirte was less rapid, for now the main road was periodically abandoned in favour of desert tracks. The pace of the convoy sometimes dropped to less than five miles an hour. The weather, though dry, had become bitterly cold, and a rum ration was regularly issued. The Sisters, we are told, were accustomed to 'camouflage' theirs with cocoa.

They were constantly passing old battlefields now, littered with the débris of conflict, including many tanks, overturned or blown to pieces. The swastika and the red, white, and blue circles lay side by side. On the edge of the field two sets of graves could be seen, one for the enemy and one for friends.

The fighting ahead grew fiercer, and casualties were coming back daily, to be evacuated eventually to Egypt by air. (Tobruk Harbour was not as yet regarded as safe for hospital ships.) Many of the wounded begged earnestly not to be sent back to rest: all they asked was to be patched up sufficiently to enable them to participate in the capture of Tripoli.

On January 23rd came the news that the great event had taken place. The road was crowded with traffic of all descriptions— artillery, tank-transporters, ration and ammunition lorries. There was little or no 'convoy distance' now: everything seemed to be moving engine to tail and wing to wing. All concerned were delirious with excitement at the thought of their state entry into the captured city.

The excitement even spread to the animal kingdom. Some time previously, in an abandoned village on the line of route, the Sisters had adopted a female pie-dog—or rather, the animal had adopted them. They christened her Bessie, and took her with them. Bessie's contribution to the great occasion took the form of no less than nine puppies, born, during the convoy's actual entrance into Tripoli, in a wooden box at the feet of a Sister in the leading ambulance.

No. 1 Mobile Military Hospital entered Tripoli at 10.30 a.m. on January 24th, feeling justly proud to be the first British medical unit to achieve such distinction. Our eight Nursing Sisters had been the first British women ever to make a desert crossing as part of an Expeditionary Force. They had covered 1,221 miles in seven weeks, and had stood up to their duties as stoutly as any man.

VI

With the capture of Tripoli and the occupation of Tripolitania, the Eighth Army were accorded a well-earned 'breather'. They were in great heart. Rommel and the Afrika Corps were still in full retreat, and the old unhappy routine of 'Benghazi and back' had been relegated to a memory of the past.

General Montgomery set up his headquarters in a field on the edge of the desert, with his men disposed about him for rest, refreshment, and re-equipment. On Sunday, January 30th, he held a Church Parade, followed by a review of the troops which had taken part in the capture of Tripoli.

> One of the Sisters and myself went down to the sea-front as spectators. While we were standing waiting for the march past, General Montgomery drove up. On getting out of his car, he walked across the road to shake hands and express his approval of the presence of the Nursing Sisters.

And this was not all. Four days later Mr. Winston Churchill himself paid a visit to Tripoli and reviewed the Eighth Army. This time all eight of the Sisters were present, as privileged spectators, on the steps of the Castle, and heard the Prime Minister, in a truly characteristic utterance, congratulate the troops on having 'nightly pitched their moving tent a day's march nearer home'!

No. 1 remained in Tripoli for six weeks, and then, having handed over to a base hospital which had now moved up, moved on to the Tunisian border, where they established and maintained a hospital of some 400 beds during the heavy fighting on the famous Mareth Line.

While in Tripoli they had at last succeeded, after endless applications to the D.D.M.S. Eighth Army, in getting themselves issued with some sort of standard headgear, to go with their slacks and gum-boots. These took the form of black berets, hitherto the property and prerogative of the Tank Corps. Previously the Sisters had 'made do' by cutting off the tails of their shirts and twisting them into some sort of turban.

The Mareth Line Hospital housed patients of all nationalities, both Allied and enemy. No special supervision was exercised over enemy patients, except that it was deemed advisable not to place Greek and Italian prisoners in adjoining beds. The Germans, as usual, were chiefly concerned with themselves. One group had been told, and believed, that we wired the mouths of all prisoners to prevent them from talking!

The presence of the Sisters themselves in so advanced an area was still a source of wonder, incredulity indeed, to the troops.

> In many cases we had to remove our head-scarves before the men would believe we were really women.

Their work during the Mareth Line fighting was heavy in the extreme. On April 7th, at the climax of the battle, the record number of 1,269 casualties passed through the unit; yet every man was fed, and all were washed and either received theatre treatment or had their dressings renewed.

A week later the unit handed over to a South African Casualty Clearing Station and entered Tunisia on their way to a hospital west of Gabes, on the Tunisian coast. (*En route* they crossed a small stream—the first running water they had seen since Alexandria.) Their stay at Gabes was comparatively brief, but during that period they had the misfortune to lose the Sisters' Mess Tent, by fire, and with it their furniture, china, and a very precious sewing-machine.

Luckily, on their way through Sfax, they encountered a 'Mobile Officers' Shop', a novelty of that time—a lorry fitted up with shelves and cupboards containing shirts, socks, and the like. Its custodian possessed few articles of feminine attire, but was always prepared to take orders and execute them promptly.

From Sfax they proceeded to Sousse, and were in Sousse when

the African campaign came to its triumphant conclusion. The triumph was complete—so complete that enemy prisoners swamped their captors, and had to rove about in their own transport looking for the cages.

Peace reigned once more, from Casablanca to Cairo.

The quietness of that first night was most uncanny. It was here in the hospital at Sousse that we nursed the most severe cases. As there was no longer need to evacuate in order to have empty beds for further casualties, we were able to keep our cases until they were able to stand the trip back to Tripoli, or even right back to Alexandria.

On May 21st the unit handed over the hospital and its patients to a field ambulance of the First Army, and set out on the return journey to Alexandria, its task completed.

It should be noted that the First and Eighth Armies, together with the Americans and Free French, had joined hands on April 7th, and that now all the forces concerned had been amalgamated into the 18th Army Group, under the supreme command of General Eisenhower. Thus the long and happy association of No. 1 Mobile Military Hospital and the Eighth Army had come to an end at last, to the genuine regret of all concerned.

CHAPTER 14

MIDDLE EAST: FARTHER AFIELD

To recount the experiences of all the hospitals and casualty clearing stations in North Africa and Middle East during the Second World War with the fullness that they deserve would be impossible within the limits of the present volume. Their several sagas must await the time when all can be enshrined in a full and official History.

However, the mention of certain hospital names and numbers is permitted. It will awaken memories both pleasant and poignant in the hearts of those who served in the hospitals and casualty clearing stations concerned.

There was No. 6 General, for instance, whose adventures have already been described in some detail; No. 19 General, in the Canal Area; No. 27 General, at Tel-el-Kebir (scene of a famous battle in the 'eighties of last century); No. 58 General, situated some seven miles from Ismailia; and, perhaps best remembered of all, No. 64 General, in that most ancient and beautiful of cities and seaports, Alexandria.

Then there were the General Hospitals in Palestine, notably No. 62 General in Jerusalem—already mentioned as having been erected for an entirely different purpose by Kaiser Wilhelm. Jerusalem, incidentally, was a favourite leave centre of Q.A.I.M.N.S.; from here they could visit Nazareth and the Sea of Galilee.

The nursing at No. 62 General was not confined to British and Dominion cases. There was a whole ward for Indian casualties. These patients, we are told, were remarkable for the quiet and uncomplaining fashion in which they bore their sufferings. The chief difficulties to be overcome in their case were those arising out of their diet, the peculiarities of which had to be tackled by a special Indian cook.

In direct contrast was the behaviour of the French wounded. These were divided into de Gaullists (or Free French) and Vichyites, and so heated did their political debates become that it was found necessary to relegate the Vichyites to a separate ward.

In Jerusalem too there was a Sick Sisters' Hospital.

> What a joy it was [writes the Sister in charge] to see the expression come over the sick Sisters' faces when they were put into a little room to themselves, and a bed with a mattress! A lot of them were very ill, in fact dangerously ill, with dysentery, malaria, sand-fly fever and operations; but I am glad to say that, thanks to the ever-ready help I had from Matron and the C.O., and very pleasant, competent junior Sisters, the sick people recovered, and were able to rejoin their units.

Mention must also be made of the Polish hospitals in the Middle East.

The first was established at Alexandria in 1941, with 200 beds. It was equipped throughout by the British Government, but the entire staff were Polish. There was also a special department attached to No. 12 British General, in Palestine, for Polish patients. The nurses were Polish: they shared quarters with our Sisters. Both hospitals were exceptionally bright and comfortable, we are told.

Somewhat different were the conditions prevailing in the Military Hospital at Geniefa, a typical desert station situated some thirty miles from Suez. Climatic variations could be trying in the extreme. Sand-storms left a film of sand over everything—beds, food, and clothing—while rain-storms were frequent and the nights bitterly cold.

By contrast with the sand, mention must be made of a certain casualty clearing station in Egypt, which appears to have been subject to a different kind of visitation, as the following extract from a Sister's personal narrative will attest.

I had had a busy night, and was preparing to go off duty when a patient called me and said there were 'things' crawling all over his badly burned leg. On investigation I found almost a complete ants' nest in the bed! The ants, one of the very small brown kind, had come in by the ward window and climbed up the patient's Balkan beam, and got into his bed despite the fact that the legs of the beam had been well saturated with paraffin. It took me nearly three-quarters of an hour to remove every ant and redress the leg.

II

Let us now travel a thousand miles south of Cairo to the Sudan, and visit No. 32 General Hospital at Khartoum. This done, we will proceed a few hundred miles eastward, to Eritrea and the shores of the Red Sea.

The Anglo-Egyptian Sudan and the Italian colony of Eritrea furnished the theatre of our first encounter in 1940, with the Italians, who were at that time arrayed in overwhelming strength against General Wavell's slender forces. After the defection of France and the occupation by the enemy of French Somaliland in August, the garrison of British Somaliland had no choice but to evacuate too. But they hung on resolutely to the Sudan, and in the end, following the final expulsion of German and Italian alike from Tripolitania and Tunisia, occupied Eritrea and Italian Somaliland. In consequence, the long-exiled King Haile Selassie found himself once more seated upon the throne of Abyssinia.

The buildings forming No. 32 General Hospital, just outside Khartoum, had originally functioned as a college for Sudanese boys, and the large classrooms made most serviceable wards; but, lying as far south as it did, the hospital was uncomfortably isolated, and matters were not improved by the difficulties of approach. The roads converging on Khartoum were mere rocky tracks, with the result that transport usually broke down, and the personnel of a medical unit had occasionally to spend a night under the desert stars.

Casualties were conveyed by Nile steamers, to save them from insufferable jolting over the so-called roads. Even this method of transport was by no means ideal, for convoys were frequently stranded on shoals or sandbanks wherever the river sank low, as it frequently did, upon important or critical occasions.

Our busiest time [a Sister tells us] was after the Battle of Cheren.

Cheren was a rocky fortress perched upon a mountain 6,000 feet above sea-level, whose defenders were accustomed to keep attacking forces in check by rolling rocks down on them.

We had our large ward full of Italian prisoners of war, all very badly wounded. The difficulty of language, with the patients' names and regiments in Italian, made this a really 'heavy' ward. Still, despite the long distance over which some of these patients had had to travel since being wounded, infection of wounds was not unduly serious, and we saw no gas gangrene—so different from the experience of some of us in France, where the highly cultivated soil often leads to virulent infection.

The heat is even greater than in Khartoum itself, where there are at least some trees and green spaces, instead of scrub and sand in all directions. Bedmaking in the wards merely consists of re-arranging two sheets. The heat is so intense that Sisters have been known to heat an iron in the sun to press handkerchiefs.

(This rivals the old story of the London stockbroker who won a bet by frying an egg on Finsbury Pavement during a heat-wave.)

Despite its remoteness from Cairene civilization, the amenities of Khartoum were pleasant enough. The Sisters had their own clubhouse, where games could be played and an occasional small dance held. There was a cinema show, out in the open under the African stars, three nights a week. The civil population were most friendly and hospitable. And, they were well out of range of the enemy.

III

In due course, as ever, the time came for the Sisters to abandon these pleasant surroundings and betake themselves elsewhere, to take over a hospital in Eritrea.

The journey itself presented the usual Sudanese obstacle-race. The rainy season had begun, and parts of the railway track had been washed away. (This was not altogether surprising, for it was a single track line, with the rails laid directly on the sand.) Consequently upon reaching Kassala, near the Eritrean border, it was found necessary to abandon a reasonably comfortable train and continue by lorry.

The next obstacle was a river in flood, so the lorries were left and each Sister carried across lying on a string bed, by four Sudanese bearers—a trying experience, for the current was swift and the bearers most uncertain on their feet. Once across, they were transferred to great troop-carrying lorries driven by coloured Cape Corps chauffeurs. After a nightmare journey of bumps and bruises they reached a small transit camp, so small and ill-equipped that it was close on midnight before the last of the party could be provided with a meal.

Twenty-four hours later they crossed the border and found themselves in Eritrea, travelling along the magnificent Italian roads which are Mussolini's sole bequest to Africa.

The hospital which they took over had originally been set up by the Italians.

It had been left with all its equipment. Indeed they evacuated in such a hurry that they left in the middle of an operation. What happened to the patient I do not know.

Their first patients were South and East African troops. Here,

June, 1944. The R.A.M.C. Sergeant, a hairdresser, is in great demand
(Imperial War Museum)

Below:

With the 5th Army in Italy. Sisters carrying Red Cross parcels to patients
(Imperial War Museum)

A cheerful party of "Q.A.s" with their baggage in Normandy
(Imperial War Museum)

Sisters in their beach-head hospital with the 2nd Army in France: smalls on the line *(Photographic News Agencies, Ltd.)*

in addition to the usual malaria and dysentery cases, they encountered tropical diseases wholly new and strange to them—Bilharzia, Kala-Azar, and Amoebic Hepatitis.

Being on night duty was a rather eerie experience, especially if one had to go from ward to ward, as out of the dark came strange noises from the baboons and hyenas in the surrounding hills. A large snake was killed outside a ward one night.

There were no recreations, except a cinema twice a week—a cinema provided with a number of old and scratched films and a debilitated projector of uncertain performance. The benches too had a habit of subsiding without warning.

The road to Asmara and the Red Sea was a remarkable piece of engineering, but it was addicted to hairpin bends and sheer drops on the open side. A dance arranged at Christmas was 'somewhat marred', we are informed, by a car full of guests going over the edge. 'It took three somersaults; then the roof came off, and the occupants were flung out. Fortunately no one was killed.' Despite the enforced absence of the enemy, life at Asmara could never be described as uneventful.

By way of variety, earthquake tremors were experienced from time to time.

Still our Sister sums up favourably enough—

The whole country is mountainous, having only the one plateau upon which Asmara is built, and there is only enough food grown in the country for its few thousand inhabitants. Any large hospital units are therefore dependent upon Army depots for food and other supplies. Provided these are plentiful and constant, life can be quite pleasant in this faraway isolated spot.

Mention has already been made of the evacuation of British Somaliland after the French collapse. The Colony was reoccupied after the defeat of the Italians, and by 1945 a particularly

o

interesting military hospital had been established there, at Mandera, housing 350 patients from all parts of East Africa.

These were Somalis, Ethiopians, Indians, and Italians. (There was a separate building for the use of eight British Officers and eighteen Other Ranks.)

There were the usual complications arising from differences of religion and, as an inevitable corollary, diet.

All our nationalities had separate kitchens, as their food had to be cooked in their own special way. At certain times of the year the Somalis, being Mohammedans, fasted all day and feasted all night, and sometimes the noise was dreadful.

This was the Festival of Ramadan, during which no member of the true Faith touches food or drink between sunrise and sunset.

All the Somalis, sick or convalescent, had what they called a Prayer Ring laid out in an open space in the desert. They bordered it round with stones and put up a pole in the centre. One morning I found the hat-stand from our postmortem room was being used for this purpose! How they managed to get hold of it I do not know!

Much tact and diplomacy were required to maintain peace among these temperamental invalids. The Indians looked down on the East Africans, and the East Africans despised the Somalis.

Somali dressers and orderlies were of course restricted to the Somali wards, and very good they were. But East African dressers had to be put into the Indian wards. One day an Indian patient complained to me that the dresser had refused to collect his food. The dresser's explanation was that the Indian had called him an animal—in other words, 'a dog'. 'Animals,' he said, 'do not carry food; they defile it.'

A good answer, was Sister's private verdict. None the less she employed the opportunity to give both disputants a salutary little lecture on the subject of live and let live, and that in any case matters of dispute must invariably be referred to a higher authority and not settled by single combat.

It was also part of the Sisters' duty to lecture to the dressers. Their pupils were genuinely anxious to learn, but some of their supplementary questions were apt to be embarrassing. One gigantic Somali warrior inquired anxiously whether, if one of his kidneys were removed, he would 'still be a man and have a baby'.

Another dresser bought an Ethiopian wife for £20. Finding that she did not measure up to his standard of perfection he returned her to her family and asked for his money back.

In the end [Sister tells us] he lost both wife and money.

Certainly in East Africa the life of a Nursing Sister was not lacking in variety.

IV

Conditions of service in the West African area differed from those in the Eastern in one important respect: the only fighting there was done by our medical services against the ever-present forces of disease and death. This is not to overlook the gallant service of the West African native troops, who fought stoutly enough, but that was elsewhere.

The three principal British Colonies in West Africa are Sierra Leone, the Gold Coast, and Nigeria. They may sound remote and unimportant theatres of war by comparison with Flanders and North Africa, but the Gold Coast is nearly as large as the United Kingdom and Nigeria is about twice the size of pre-war Germany. In any case it was vitally important that all three Colonies should be protected from enemy invasion, for any of them in German hands would have provided not only U-boat bases on the Atlantic coast, but a convenient jumping-off place for a German invasion of Brazil and Latin America generally.

So the three Colonies were garrisoned as strongly as our resources permitted with British and Empire troops, accompanied as a matter of course by their medical and nursing units.

Despite the fact that there was no actual fighting in West Africa, the Nursing Services were kept busy enough.

As usual, they had to begin by acclimatizing themselves to new and uncomfortable conditions. The first lesson which every Sister had to learn was that of taking every reasonable precaution against malaria herself. The West Coast of Africa was once, and not without reason, christened The White Man's Grave. If, thanks to modern prophylaxis, it is that no longer, it still offers every prospect to the unwary of becoming the White Man's (or Woman's) Hospital.

> Malaria [says one Matron's Report] is the Curse of the Coast, and oh, how difficult it was to make Sisters, abroad for the first time, 'Malaria conscious'. They just could not see the importance of wearing mosquito boots with thigh extensions, and long sleeves, after sunset. It took them time to learn that the ever silent *anophiles* is a ruthless opportunist, always on duty after dusk.

However, the Sisters soon learned their lesson, which was just as well, for there was plenty for them to do in the hospitals, where the prevailing cases were 85 per cent malaria, 10 per cent dysentery, and 5 per cent others.

The headquarters of the medical services in West Africa were at Accra, on the Gold Coast. The principal seaport was Takoradi, whence an interesting trip could be made by rail to Ashanti, the ancient capital of King Coffee. One of the coaches on the train was heavily barred for the conveyance of gold from the mines up country to the coast.

The first Q.A.I.M.N.S. party to land on the Gold Coast in 1940 numbered nine in all. As a British Colony the country was

already well provided with civilian hospitals both for the
European and native populations; but with the increase in
the military garrison, and the steady arrival of contingents of
wounded from East Africa and elsewhere, there was urgent need
for the establishment of several military hospitals. These were
forthcoming in due course.

Until our hospital was ready for patients [writes one
Sister], we helped at the European and African hospitals.
I had four weeks of valuable experience at the Gold Coast
Hospital. The patients were Africans of all ages, with a
qualified African male and female nursing staff.

Lots of young boys were being trained for the R.A.M.C.
They had received excellent theoretical training, and were
most anxious to learn practical nursing. Each boy seemed to
decide immediately they saw us which Sister he would like
for his 'Missus', and we could hardly get them out of our
sight.

There will be more to say about these young gentlemen later.

In addition to the care of the wounded, the Sisters were soon
fully occupied with malaria cases. Neither were they themselves
immune. Several went down with the disease, and there
was one serious case of dysentery. However, with the gradual
improvement in hospital accommodation and supplies, and
especially in the Sisters' own quarters (which had at first consisted of mud huts) the routine soon settled down to normal,
though it could never at any time be described as easy.

The surrounding country was beautiful, a land of fruit and
flowers, except during the rains, which were torrential and could
be accompanied by fierce thunderstorms; while the highly
organized social life of the little Colony offered pleasant society
and much agreeable (and unusual) diversion. On Empire Day
some of the Sisters visited Accra, to see thousands of school-
children march past the Governor of the Gold Coast to the usual
music ('Roll Out the Barrel' and the like) of innumerable
bands.

There were thousands of people as spectators, including many Chiefs, in their gay robes, under huge multi-coloured umbrellas.

V

We come now to Sierra Leone, whose capital Freetown possesses one of the largest natural harbours in the world, furnishing throughout the war an invaluable port of call and rallying-point for our Cape-bound shipping.

The town and native quarter are clustered together, forming an attractive combination of red roofs and green background, and are surrounded on all three sides by hills. Hill Station, on the right, stands about 500 feet high, and forms the European residential quarter.

No. 51 General Hospital arrived at Freetown in August 1940, bringing with it twenty-two Nursing Sisters and a certain number of hospital orderlies. Pending the erection of the hospital itself, temporary premises were secured in what had been the Officers' Quarters of the Royal West African Frontier Force, and work began at once. Here it was possible to accommodate 120 patients, including beds for ten officers and five Sisters.

This last provision soon proved its value, for no less than twelve out of our twenty-two Sisters succumbed at one time or another to malaria.

No. 51 General enjoyed the use at this time of the Operating Theatre and X-ray Department of the Freetown Civil Hospital.

By the end of December most of the new hospital wards on Mount Aureol were ready for occupation and were taken over by No. 51. Subsequently, however, these were handed over to No. 34 General Hospital, which had been organized to deal with native patients only: No. 51 found a new home on the crest of another hill, 900 feet high, farther from the town and in a much healthier position.

In due course the new hospital was completed and fully occupied. In addition to its admirable medical and surgical equipment it contained a library and large recreation hall for the patients, in which cinema shows, concerts, and even dances could be organized.

In less than three months [reports one Sister] we were functioning as if we had been there for years, and had our full complement of 200 beds, which were always filled and were still expanding.

The 200 patients were all Africans, of many different tribes, many of them conveyed to this safe haven from far-distant theatres of war.

They loved to tell us of their experiences of life in Burma, India, and the M.E.F.[1] How thrilled they were when they found someone with whom they could discuss similar experiences!
While waiting for artificial limbs to be fitted, Occupational Therapy proved a real boon to them. They knitted pullovers, plaited belts and made embroidered mats with gaily coloured wool. After a while they became quite experts in these arts: these I felt could be quite useful to them when they returned to their villages.

(For the materials for these invaluable exercises the Sisters were indebted, as ever, to the British Red Cross Depot.)
Of course everything was not all plain sailing. There was as usual a shortage of R.A.M.C. orderlies, who were urgently needed in less pacific surroundings, and this involved the training of African orderlies.

These [we are told] had previously been taught the rudiments of obedience, discipline, and general ward duties. We were to train them. They were of varying degrees of intelligence, but very keen, and in time became quite useful. As they were picked from fifteen different tribes, speaking different languages, we compromised by teaching them

[1] Mediterranean Expeditionary Force.

'pidgin' English, which sounded dreadful but was really quite effective.

The climate was a perpetual trial, but might have been worse: the shade temperature was seldom higher than 90 degrees. The atmosphere, however, was humid all the year round, and there were periods of torrential rain between May and November.

The humidity is greatest in July and August, when all one's clothes feel damp and smell mouldy, and green mildew grows overnight on leather shoes and suit-cases.

Other material and perpetual discomforts were furnished by the insect population. Some of the wooden huts had to be pulled down and rebuilt in stone within the first six months, owing to the ravages of the ubiquitous white ant. These it was found impossible to exterminate altogether, though their activities could be checked to a certain degree by treating the wood with creosote. But—

Our main menace from the livestock point of view, besides ants on our dining-table, were huge cockroaches, which ate holes in our silk underclothes, and all the gum from stamps, envelopes and bottle-labels. It was no uncommon experience to open a trunk and find some of these creatures having a meal off one's best pyjamas.

Also, huge bats with a wing span of fifteen inches used to fly about our sitting-room in the evenings. We were used to them, but one evening we entered the Mess to find four senior members of a hospital, newly arrived visitors, sitting with cushions on their heads!

But the summing up, as usual, is pleasantly philosophical.

Life here is indeed very full, and one certainly needs a complete sense of humour and the spirit of an ambassador thoroughly to enjoy nursing in these tropical countries.

Much has been done to eliminate malaria and yellow fever, and with marked success, by spraying from the air and by wearing of protective clothing by all ranks.

Our tour of service here is eighteen months.

And quite enough too, one might suggest.

VI

We come lastly to Nigeria, and the experiences of No. 56 General Hospital, which arrived at Lagos, after a narrow escape from a German bomber—two near-misses—in the North Atlantic in May 1941.

The Sisters' Nigerian experiences did not differ greatly from those of their colleagues in Sierra Leone and the Gold Coast— the climate and the insects, ants and mosquitoes, in particular. The heavy rains bestowed upon the local grass a Jack-and-the-beanstalk rate of growth—two and a half inches in twenty-four hours—so keeping it down provided continuous employment for a large number of coolies.

The hospital itself, however, was ready, and all the huts had been thoughtfully provided with concrete foundations and floors. The standard design was a 40-bedded ward, with its own small ward-kitchen, Sisters' duty-room, and sanitary annexes at each end. The Sisters worked hard to render the interior of the wards attractive, and since each bed sported 'a pretty blue blanket', the general effect was highly decorative.

There was the usual difficulty in training native orderlies. The Nigerian variety possessed characteristics all his own. He was a man of some erudition, being ineligible for ward duties unless he had passed the Sixth Educational Standard. This meant that he spoke tolerably good English, though of an archaic, almost Shakespearean stateliness. He was studiously inclined, but, as is so often the case with an undeveloped intelligence, found it easier to memorize a passage than to understand or paraphrase it. It is regrettable to have to add that when up-graded he frequently became 'conceited, lazy, and important in his own estimation'—a failing, incidentally, not entirely confined to the Sons of Ham—'throwing his weight about among his juniors, whom he was inclined to regard as his personal attendants'. Ward Sisters were constantly called upon to arbitrate personal differences and settle small rows.

Most of these orderlies were Christians, and the fact was responsible for a certain Biblical flavour in their official reports, thus: 'Bed 20 went to his Heavenly Home at 11.25 p.m.'

But for all their undoubted virtues they were for the most part incapable, as ever, of appreciating the difference between *meum* and *tuum*. A careful watch had to be kept upon all drugs and hospital supplies, especially those of a saleable character. Certain Sixth Standardists were found to be running a highly profitable black market in such commodities as 'M & B', at one shilling per tablet; while Sisters administering the drug to pneumonia patients had to dissolve the tablets in water; otherwise they would never have reached the patients.

The majority of the patients in the hospital wards were suffering from malaria, to which unseasoned troops were highly susceptible. Tropical ulcers and pneumonia had also to be dealt with.

Africans rarely fall victims to that dread disease blackwater fever, but there was a constant risk that it might superimpose itself on a European malaria case. A 'Blackwater Team', therefore—one medical officer, two Sisters, and one R.A.M.C. orderly—was always kept in readiness to proceed at short notice to a patient too ill to be moved to hospital. Many lives were saved by this precaution.

It was an exacting existence for all concerned, especially since the Nursing Sisters on this particular station were themselves unusually susceptible to attacks of malaria. Thanks however to the good offices of the A.D.M.S., they were provided with excellent quarters, and the usual recreational facilities were not lacking.

Perhaps the high-spot among all the social activities of the Nigerian station was reached at Lagos during Christmas 1946, when the war itself was over. This took the form of a full-scale pantomime—*Aladdin*. Both principal boy and girl were played by members of the Nursing Services, and the script was written by an R.A.M.C. major. The excellence of the performance moved *The Nigerian Daily Times* to the following panegyric:

> For sparkling wit, scintillating brilliance of costume, and quality of production, there has never been such a show in Lagos, or in West Africa for that matter.

The proceeds amounted to £137 odd, and were handed over as part of the Nigerian contribution to the British Empire Nurses' War Memorial Fund.

CHAPTER 15

MEDITERRANEAN ADVENTURE

So much for the manifold and variegated experiences of our Nursing Services on the Continent of Africa. We pass now to a brief review of their activities on the northern coast of the Mediterranean and some of the islands adjoining.

Let us deal first with the unhappy history of British intervention in Greece in the early part of 1941.

The German High Command, impressed by the ignominious failure of their Italian allies not only against General Wavell in Libya but against the Greeks in Albania, had decided to intervene in the Mediterranean theatre on their own account. The Greeks, realizing that however successfully they might hold Italians in check they were in no position to withstand an all-out German *blitzkrieg*, appealed to Britain for aid.

The British Government had a hard decision to make. No troops could be spared from Britain itself, where the threat of invasion still loomed large and the training and equipment of the new divisions was in any case far from complete. The only army in being was the Army of the Nile, at present recovering from its tremendous exertions against the Italians, and doing its best to repair and replace the losses in armour and equipment inevitable in a campaign stretched over 500 miles of desert.

Were these troops to be allowed, after due recuperation, to complete their triumphant desert victory, or be diverted, in part at any rate, to the assistance of Greece?

Plainly the troops available for the purpose could not constitute much more than a token force in the face of German Panzer divisions and overwhelming infantry strength. Worse still, we would be unable to afford adequate fighter protection to these troops against enemy bombing.

The whole problem, needless to say, aroused considerable controversy, but the British War Cabinet adhered to their decision, and the Expeditionary Force was dispatched.

It was accompanied—preceded, in fact—by a British medical unit from Palestine, which arrived in Athens in the middle of November 1940, having been dispatched thither to aid in nursing Greek troops wounded in fighting against the Italian and Balkan armies.

Their reception was embarrassingly enthusiastic; they were clapped and cheered in the streets, patted on the back, and presented with flowers.

Presently they were enabled to settle down in their hospital at Kephissia, a quite considerable establishment.

> The hospital [reports the Matron] consisted of a private house for offices, the Aphergis Hotel for Medical Cases, the Cecil Hotel for Surgical Cases, and the Olympus for Reception, M.I. room, dental, ear and eye department. The two top floors were used as a special treatment centre.
>
> This was the primary arrangement, but with the advent of the wounded Greeks, and later the rush of our own wounded, other arrangements had to be made.
>
> The nursing staff were housed in three private hotels. We were really very comfortable, except in the early days, when we were entirely without heat of any kind and the weather was bitterly cold.

The hospital opened on November 26th, 1940, with accommodation for 110 patients. The beds were not all occupied at first, and there were opportunities for social relaxation. The Matron enjoyed the distinction of being the only lady guest at a reception arranged in honour of the King of Greece, the Crown Prince, and the Prime Minister General Metaxas. The Medical Faculty of the University of Athens also gave a dinner in honour of the unit.

But after the British troops arrived and began to take part in the battle there was little time for such agreeable exchanges. The number of patients in the hospital increased steadily, and by the beginning of April 1941 600 beds were occupied; and as the German attack developed and intensified, the casualty list mounted day by day.

The day after hostilities commenced we had 709 patients. In the course of time we had them lying everywhere—on mattresses on the floor, on stretchers, and in any odd corner.

It soon became obvious that the combined British and Greek strength was totally inadequate to cope with the German invasion. Despite the stubborn gallantry of our troops, it was a losing battle from the start, and the end could only be a matter of time. In one single day 300 British soldiers were received into the hospital and 400 evacuated to a hospital ship. The hospital orderlies, we are told 'were marvellous', carrying on through continuous periods of stretcher-bearing with the shortest of breaks. But the end was at hand.

On April 21st I received a message that 25 Sisters were to be ready for evacuation. The following day I was awakened at 3 a.m. *All* the Sisters were to be ready for evacuation, hand luggage only.

The situation was evidently deteriorating rapidly, as was indicated by the number of orders and counter-orders issued at this time. The main difficulty was to find accommodation for the Sisters in the crowded ships, and at the same time to get them on board without danger to themselves, for the ships were under constant bombing.

On April 23rd there was a message to say that all the Sisters were to stay in Kephissia. Another message at 3.45 p.m. said that there were a few seats available in a ship, if any Sister wished to leave. Eight Sisters left in an hour.

On April 24th the D.D.M.S. told me that it was considered wiser for us to remain, rather than risk a getaway. . . . There were air-raids all day. . . . A certain number of walking cases were discharged at intervals: many of these returned to us several times before they finally got away.

How real the danger was is indicated in the following passage:

About 2 p.m. the Commanding Officer and Registrar left, and a number of walking cases left too, to travel in the same ship. At 7 p.m. we received a message that the ship had been hit, and that the C.O. was among the casualties. She had received three direct hits and was ablaze immediately.

It was really pathetic to see the lads we had discharged a few hours previously returning to us with fresh wounds. Their spirit was magnificent. The C.O., mercifully, only had a large scalp-wound, and he started off the same night.

By this time the situation was such that the Sisters in the hospital seemed to have no alternative left but to stay where they were and be taken prisoner. But deliverance was at hand, almost at the eleventh hour.

On the morning of April 25th the D.D.M.S. rang up to say that a destroyer might be laid on for us later in the day, and that I was to confine the Sisters to barracks, with a view to laying hands on them at short notice. In the evening a further message informed us that we were to be ready to start in three-quarters of an hour. Some Greek nurses had kindly volunteered to take over the nursing in the hospital.

The party set off in lorries at 7 p.m., pausing to pick up forty Sisters from the Australian Hospital. The journey occupied five hours, in complete darkness and over unspeakable roads. Finally they reached the port of embarkation, a small jetty projecting into the sea. The promised destroyer had not materialized, but a ship of sorts was available, and in her they contrived to cross to Crete at 5.30 p.m., fortunately with only one casualty (a ship's officer). Here they found the eight Sisters who had preceded them on the previous day.

They were kept in Crete for only two-and-a-half days, and were then evacuated in comparative peace, except for two bombing raids and an uncomfortable E-boat scare during the hours of night.

> I am glad to have this opportunity of telling you how well the Sisters worked. Their behaviour, especially on the boat to Crete, where the noise was indescribable, was beyond praise.

It certainly must have been, and the report gives us but an average picture of the courage and endurance of all the Nursing Sisters concerned in this nightmare adventure.

So ended our Grecian crusade. The effort had cost us dear, both in Greece and Crete, but the account was not altogether on the debit side. Had it not been made, Hitler might have penetrated unopposed through Palestine and Syria to India and the East.

> The attempt to save Greece [adds General Wavell], though unsuccessful, undoubtedly frustrated the plan for future enemy operations, by destroying so large a proportion of his airborne troops. The total enemy losses were at least 12,000–15,000.
>
> The defence saved, in all probability, Cyprus, Syria, Iraq, and perhaps Tobruk.

II

Tucked away in the north-east corner of the Mediterranean lie the island of Cyprus, forty miles from Asia Minor and sixty from the coast of Syria—a position admirably adapted to the strategic needs of the Allies in these waters.

The island is a large one, with an area of some 3,500 square miles. It is a comparatively recent acquisition to the British Empire, and owes its place therein to the foresight and initiative of a British Prime Minister, Benjamin Disraeli, who, having in 1878 purchased for the sum of four million pounds a controlling interest in the newly opened Suez Canal, leased the island from the Turkish Government as a convenient base from which to guard the approaches thereto. At the outbreak of the First World War, when Turkey joined the Axis powers against us, Cyprus was automatically annexed to Britain, and in 1925 became a Crown Colony.

In consequence, when the Second World War broke out in 1939, and Hitler occupied Greece and Crete eighteen months later, we were in possession of a valuable barrier against enemy penetration into Palestine and the oilfields of Iraq. A strong military garrison was installed there, accompanied by the usual medical services.

The population was mainly Greek and Moslem, and the languages spoken were Turkish and Modern Greek. Most of the educated classes spoke English, a distinct boon to Nursing Sisters struggling with the routine difficulties of hospital organization amid strange surroundings and unfamiliar tongues.

The heat in the plains, where the troops were first quartered, was very great, and the health of the men suffered considerably. Matters were aggravated by an almost complete lack of sanitation. In due course, however, new and healthier quarters were established in the hills, while a campaign of sanitary reform, which would have earned the warm approval of Florence Nightingale, gradually reduced the death-rate to average level.

Cyprus, more fortunate than Malta and Greece, was practically free from major enemy operations throughout the war, and the energies of the Q.A.I.M.N.S. representatives could in consequence be concentrated on the building up of an adequate nursing service.

The task was by no means easy, and the personnel of No. 23 Scottish General Hospital, which arrived in late 1940, had plenty to occupy them.

P

They began in a small way, with a staff comprising an Assistant Matron and four Nursing Sisters.   Their first hospital was a large private house, recently the Italian Embassy.   The Sisters were billeted in a hotel close by.   They had some thirty-six patients, half a dozen of whom were Cypriots.

With the coming of spring and the arrival of additional troops the nursing establishment was considerably increased.

> Our first real war casualties [writes one of the Sisters] were Naval ratings from a destroyer which had been bombed off the coast. Road accidents became more numerous, and we had occasional air-raid casualties.
>
> The arrival of a field ambulance unit relieved the situation, and they started work at various centres.   One company opened up a small hospital at the Hill Station, and we took it in turn to go up there, and thus got a change from the intense heat of the plains.
>
> The orderlies had been well trained in field dressings and as stretcher-bearers, but were inexperienced in ward work; but they were all very keen and most enthusiastic.

Down in the plains, however, matters were growing serious. Dysentery had broken out among the troops, and for lack of proper equipment tents and even outhouses had to be used as wards.   The average number of patients in the island hospitals had now grown to 100, including some ten to fifteen officers.

The work was obviously growing beyond the capacity of an Assistant Matron and four Nursing Sisters.   In April 1942 the situation was materially eased by the arrival of sixteen Sisters and an Assistant Matron from Egypt.   The Matron had arrived a few weeks earlier.   It was decided to close down the existing military hospital and erect a new one of a more modern type on a more suitable site.   This was to consist of 400 beds, of which 200 were for Indians.

> The Hospital [reports the Matron] was built on the semi-dispersal plan and consisted of stone huts, capable of taking

twenty-five beds at each end, with a Sister's duty-room, dressing-room, ward-kitchen and linen-room in the middle. The wards were very wide and had plenty of windows, but unfortunately there was no glass in the island. Eventually we managed to have fly-netting fixed in, but this did not prevent great discomfort when a dust-storm was blowing.

As the wards of the new hospital were completed the Sisters took them over, having first successfully evicted an Indian casualty clearing station which had somehow got possession.

Needless to say, the usual delays and difficulties inevitable in the setting-up of a new hospital in an out-of-the-way island had to be faced and overcome.

We were rather held up for want of medical equipment, which had to come from Egypt. We could not open the operating theatre, as we had no table, autoclave, or trolleys. We eventually borrowed these from the C.C.S., and the Red Cross gave us a case of instruments. On this equipment we managed to carry on quite well until our own arrived. The Red Cross were always helpful, but they had very little stock, for all of which they depended on Egypt, and shipping was not too plentiful.

Indeed it was not, for at this period enemy submarine and bombing activity was at its height throughout the Mediterranean. Convoys to Malta were being decimated, while in the summer of 1942 the *Ark Royal* and *Barham* had recently been sunk and the *Valiant* and *Queen Elizabeth* lay stranded in Alexandria Harbour, disabled by limpet bombs.

Towards the end of May a convalescent hospital was opened in the hills, and this was staffed partly from our hospital. It was a great boon to the patients, and also gave all Sisters and R.A.M.C. personnel in turn an opportunity of getting out of the heat.

The flies were a perpetual pest, and until we got the fly-netting the wards were black with them. Our cases were nearly all medical—malaria, dysentery, and lung conditions.

On June 3rd we moved into our own Mess. The Sisters were most appreciative of the fact that each had a room to herself. We got some old mosquito nets, cut them up, and the contractor fixed these into the window-frames. We were now fly-proof and mosquito-proof, but not, alas, dust-proof.

In our Mess we had an R.A.M.C. cook and four Cypriot maids; we had found it impossible to get a Cypriot cook at anything like the pay allowed. The maids were excellent workers, and three of them lived in.

It was difficult to buy anything on the island and though we had an officers' shop in one of the towns, uniform was seldom available. It took nearly two months to get anything from Egypt.

From the above clear and dispassionate narrative the reader will gain an interesting and rather unusual picture of the administrative side of Army nursing on active service. In most cases the narrative has inevitably been interrupted and obscured by operational details: here, in the comparative tranquillity of an unbeleaguered island, the domestic pattern has an opportunity to emerge.

But if the dangers were less than usual, discomfort and worry were not. The climate, the flies, the perpetual strain of nursing, the shortage of supplies of every kind, above all a sense of remoteness and isolation from the outer world—these had all to be reckoned with.

Nevertheless, life was never dull, and recreation and small excitements were not lacking. The climate in spring was delightful, and cycling, tennis, and walking were available for all. Sea-bathing was a special delight, especially to Sisters who had come from other and sterner periods of service elsewhere.

There was also the great occasion upon which His Excellency the Governor formally inspected the completed hospital, and the occasion, greater still, when H.R.H. the Duke of Gloucester visited the island, and Matron represented the Sisters at an official reception given in his honour.

III

Our three principal strongholds in the Mediterranean in 1941 (apart from those of the North African littoral) were Gibraltar, Malta, and Cyprus.

Gibraltar, the key to the Mediterranean, was never seriously attacked; for that we were indebted to General Franco and his dogged determination to keep Spain out of the war at any price; otherwise Hitler would undoubtedly have made Gibraltar, and after Gibraltar Algeria and Tunisia, one of his major objectives.

But Malta was in a very different case: its possession was an almost indispensable adjunct to the command of the Western Mediterranean. That fact had been fully borne out by its history. Throughout the centuries the island had been occupied and employed as a naval base, in turn, by the Phœnicians, Carthage, Rome, Arab pirates, and the Knights of St. John of Jerusalem. Napoleon took it in his stride in 1798, on his way out to Egypt and thereafter to the Battle of the Pyramids and the destruction of his fleet by Nelson in Aboukir Bay.

The British expelled the French from Malta two years later, and remained there ever after, at the express request of the Maltese people. Upon the face of a tablet over the Main Guard Room, opposite the Palace of Valetta, a Latin inscription was set up, cut deep and bearing the date A.D. 1814:

> *The Love of the Maltese People* [it runs] *and the Voice of Europe, Have for Ever Entrusted the Guardianship of These Islands to Great Britain, the Unconquered.*

In 1940 that trusteeship was to be put to a test unknown even in the stormy history of Mediterranean warfare.

Malta lies some sixty miles south of Sicily, and is about the same size as the Isle of Wight. It possesses a magnificent deepwater harbour at Valetta, and in normal times is the headquarters of our Mediterranean Fleet.

Obviously, here was a prize of inestimable value to an enterprising enemy. But although Mussolini declared war on the British Empire in June 1940, he made no direct attempt to occupy this vitally important base and stronghold, lying only sixty miles away. He contented himself with futile air-raids, on no particularly heavy scale, and the dropping of incendiaries. It was not until December 1941 that matters became serious, for now Germany took over. Hitler had invaded Russia that summer, and now that the Russian winter had brought the campaign to a temporary standstill his heavy bombers, particularly his dive-bombers, were available against the Maltese.

Fortunately full preparation had been made for these visitations. Malta is composed mainly of limestone rock of a type so soft that it is not difficult to cut it with a knife; and this rendered it possible to construct subterranean shelters on a most elaborate scale, to which the civil population could betake themselves in time of need. By the end of the siege the greater part of Malta, especially round the Grand Harbour, lay in ruins, but the Maltese were for the most part safely housed underground.

As a result of these measures the civilian casualties during the devastating months which followed, considering the density of the island's population, were surprisingly small. Indeed the great majority of them were incurred in that first German raid in December 1941. In all 1,493 civilians were killed. The actual population was about 307,000, or 2,500 to the square mile. Those most exposed to danger were the troops defending the island, and the dockyard workers in the Grand Harbour.

The Military Hospital, a permanent institution regularly employed in peace-time, stood on top of a bare and rocky plateau overlooking an aerodrome. In such a small island it was quite impossible to site all the hospitals in positions out of range of military targets, and the Military Hospital suffered accordingly. The aerodrome was bombed regularly day and night.

The enemy [we are told by one of the Sisters] appeared regularly at 7 a.m., at midday, and at 6 p.m. The first raid we watched as we were scrambling to get dressed for breakfast; during the second you were either in the theatre or the mess, according to whether you went to first or second lunch; the third raid, at 6.0, served as an accompaniment for tea.

Before the Spitfires came[1] the Messerschmidts used to play hide-and-seek up and down the blocks of the Barrack Hospital, and machine-gun bullets used to fly.

As an emergency measure a small underground theatre was hewn out of the rock, and here operations could be performed if the situation overhead became too hot. It possessed only one water-tap, but was otherwise as fully equipped as any other theatre. It was not often found necessary to use it, which was just as well, for during night raids the electric current invariably failed, and work had to be carried on by the light of torches and hurricane lamps.

The main handicap of the medical services in Malta was shortage of supplies, for everything had to be transported by sea, and the island was so thoroughly blockaded by submarine and bombing activity that it was only at rare intervals that a convoy got through, and then only as a fraction of its original self. And the shortage was not confined to medical supplies. Everything—food, fuel, ammunition, and military stores had to be strictly rationed, and by the end of the siege the situation was precarious in the extreme, as we can gather from the following characteristically restrained statement:

Of course we were a bit hungry at times, and it was a bit unfunny when it came to counting out the slices of bread for breakfast and tea. But we had a little more to eat than

[1] The Spitfires, incidentally, were a long time in arriving, for their short flight-range made it necessary to ship them in an aircraft-carrier; and it was not until May 1942 that the first contingent arrived. Their intervention reversed the air-situation almost entirely.

the civil population, which really did starve—one tin of bully beef per family per fortnight, and nine ounces of bread per day.

Supplies of almost everything needed in a busy theatre were woefully short. We were rationed to one pint of spirit per week and one gallon of Dettol per month. Test-tubes, rubber gloves, catgut, certain drugs, quick-drying plaster bandages and X-ray films were all rationed monthly. We used to do minor operations without wearing gloves, in an effort to conserve our dwindling stocks.

Needless to say, the Sisters had their ration of casualties too.

Almost the last raid we had was when the Sisters' Mess was straddled and hit at 5.0 a.m. No one was killed, but two Sisters were badly injured, and we had to dig a couple more from under the debris.

Amid all the wreckage and mess a printed motto still hung, though a little askew, on the wall of Matron's damaged bedroom, triumphantly claiming—*Don't worry; it may not happen!*

On another part of the island a General Hospital was destroyed by direct hits. The Sisters incurred some considerable shock, but were uninjured. Some of the R.A.M.C. personnel received fatal injuries.

Still, as all the world knows, Malta weathered the storm, and had the unique distinction, conferred by the King upon the island as a whole, of the George Cross, formally and publicly presented to the Lord Chief Justice of the island by Lord Gort, V.C., Governor and Commander-in-Chief.

Here is one Sister's final comment upon the record of Q.A.I.M.N.S. in Malta:

I must emphasize that not one of us thought at any time

that we underwent hardships and difficulties greater than those experienced by other Sisters on active service elsewhere.

Nevertheless, a full share in the glory of the George Cross was theirs alone.

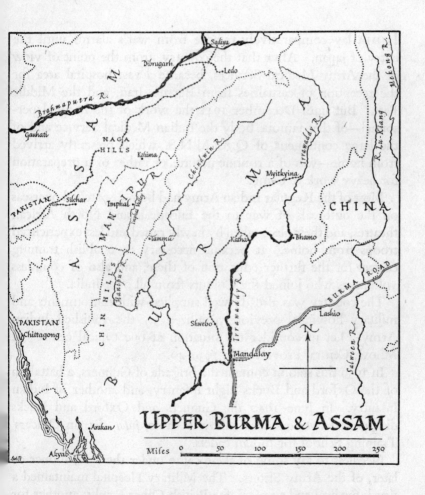

UPPER BURMA & ASSAM

CHAPTER 16

FAR EAST: INDIA AND CEYLON

INDIA lay comparatively remote from war's alarms until the entry of Japan. After that the country, from the point of view of the Army Medical Services, became a vast hospital area for the reception of casualties from Burma, Iraq, and the Middle East. But until December 1941 the work of the hospital personnel—of that famous body the Indian Medical Service and of the large contingent of Q.A.I.M.N.S. which presently arrived from home—was of a routine nature, or rather of a preparation for heavy work to come.

Most of the Regular Indian Army had been dispatched overseas on the outbreak of war to the European and North African theatres, and their place taken by newly raised and less experienced troops from home. It became necessary to establish training centres for the further education of these, and also of countless volunteers who joined the Colours from all over India.

The country was already well supplied with cantonments and military hospitals, previously utilized by the vanished Indian Army. Let us consider the situation at one typical centre—at Mhow, Central Provinces, in 1939-40.

In 1939 this station contained a brigade of Gunners, a battalion of the Oxford and Bucks Light Infantry, and another of Indian Infantry. In June 1940 the Gunners and Oxford and Bucks disappeared overseas, and Mhow became, *inter alia*, an Officers' Training School for Indian cadets.

Needless to say some of these came under the care, sooner or later, of the Army Sisters. The Military Hospital maintained a ward, medical and surgical, for British Other Ranks, another for Indian cadets, an Officers' ward and a small operating theatre.

There was also a Military Families Ward, for the wives and children left behind by the Regular units of the Indian Army which had departed overseas.

The Nursing Sisters had prepared themselves as far as possible for their new duties by acquiring a smattering of Urdu with which to make themselves understood in the wards, but they were not long in discovering that they had many other things to learn. The cadets came from all over India—teachers, lawyers, book-keepers, some of them mere boys. They were of various races and creeds, with strong religious views on diet. The food of the Hindus and Moslems had as usual to be specially prepared, and cooked in separate kitchens. Beef was *tabu* in any case.

The hospital patients also had their own standards of personal dignity, and held strong views on the sanctity of the human person (which in the case of the Moslems is purdah from neck to knee). The Sikhs, as we have already seen, attached considerable importance to their heads.

> I learned [one Sister tells us] when helping a Sikh patient to sit up, never to touch his head. They also objected to wearing pyjamas instead of a dhoti, but they got used to this in time.

The Indian Medical Service was itself enlisting recruits, and a contingent of I.M.S. lieutenants came to Mhow for a course. They were of all types and ages. Here is the tale of one of them, and of his subsequent military record.

> He was already a doctor, married, and with many children. He was admitted to my Officers' Ward. He sat up cross-legged in bed in a dhoti, and I am afraid he spat. On manœuvres in the Station he refused to ride a bicycle, because it was 'against the teachings of God'. He admitted that he had not been at all keen to join up.
>
> Ultimately he was sent to Malaya as M.O. with an Indian regiment. One day in the jungle they found them-

selves cut off and without ammunition. The M.O. took a brief lesson in how to control a Bren-gun carrier, then drove it alone through the Japanese lines, and came back with the ammunition. He was subsequently killed, with most of his battalion.

As regards Indian hospital buildings in general, these, the Sisters soon found, varied greatly in size and importance, and all were very different from those at home. There was in the early days little attempt at modern sanitation, and water was not invariably laid on. Hill stations had no electric light. Owing to the rigidities of the caste system, too, various duties could only be performed by orderlies of various grades. Ward-boys cleaned the wards; water was brought by a water-carrier known as the *Bhisti*, while the sweepers, the Untouchables, performed all the more menial and least pleasant jobs.

Some of the lower-grade Indian hospitals must have been conducted upon somewhat happy-go-lucky lines.

The first hospital I served in [one Sister tells us] was of the '3rd Class' variety. The operating-room had a fire-place and a fire-screen of casement cloth, on which the anæsthetist hung his coat. The instruments were of a weird and wonderful variety.

We had an emergency appendix one day, and in the middle of the operation it became very dark—a dust-storm. Suddenly, with a fearful noise, a pigeon arrived down the chimney, covered with soot and dust. It flew round the theatre twice, and then settled on the screen, where it remained cooing softly to itself for the rest of the operation.

From which the reader will gather some idea of the amount of improvisation and make-do devolving upon Q.A.I.M.N.S. until reasonable standards of good order and hygiene could be attained, especially in certain of the up-country districts.

Besides the cadets, the Sisters had other patients, especially

British soldiers newly out from home. As usual they were a cheerful and friendly crew, and immensely appreciative of all that was done for them.

II

With the entry of Japan into the war in late 1941, the long period of peaceful routine came to an abrupt end, and all India awoke with a shock to the realities of total warfare, and immediately sprang to active life as an evacuee area for casualties from all the neighbouring theatres of war—Burma, Malaya, Iraq, North Africa, even Madagascar. It was safer and more convenient to evacuate these to India rather than ship them back to overcrowded and bomb-smitten Britain. Not that India herself was entirely free from bombing, but this was only intermittent in character and spread over a wide area.

Two types of Indian Military Hospital were available, British and Combined. The first took care of British troops only, the second had both a British and Indian Section, the Indians preponderating. The purely Indian nursing staff came from many different Provinces and from as far as the Burma border. Many did not understand one another's language, but fortunately all could speak English, but the difficulties of the Matron and British Sisters in reconciling so many different temperaments, religions, and points of view may well be imagined.

Trained R.A.M.C. orderlies were no longer available, for all as usual had been spirited away to various theatres of war, and it was necessary to make do with Sepoy orderlies. These were efficient and friendly, but as usual, owing to caste distinctions, were in the habit of delegating to unqualified menials duties which their dignity precluded them from performing themselves.

The patients were much more satisfactory to deal with.

We enjoyed nursing Indian Sepoys [writes one Sister]. They were mostly bright-eyed recruits, sons of smallholders from native villages, who convinced one of their intelligence and charming unspoilt natures despite their inability to speak English. These lads seemed to be so grateful and surprised at having women to do things for them.

Some of the British patients were in a very different case. They had been conveyed from various battlefields, largely by air, with the dust and dirt of battle still upon them—from Eritrea and Abyssinia in the beginning, and now from Burma and Malaya.

With the help of the local St. John's Ambulance Brigade they were put to bed and made comfortable and fed. The majority of them wanted only to be left alone to sleep; but next morning, after washing and shaving, they looked quite different men. How pleased they were to find their own countrywomen round them!

There was at first a considerable shortage of nursing staff. The Sisters however received much welcome aid from the 'abandoned' wives of British officers, who helped in the library and the management of the wireless and gramophones, besides organizing entertainments for convalescents and taking them to the cinema. In due course, too, a number of the V.A.D. became available, and proved a great help.

Accommodation for ever-fresh arrivals furnished a continual problem. After the fall of Hong Kong drafts of British officers, 200 at a time, arrived to be seconded to Indian units, but stayed at Mhow and elsewhere to learn the language. This involved an increase in officers' accommodation and wards. The arrival of a small party of Nursing Sisters from Malaya, after dreadful experiences, did little to help at the time, for they had lost everything they possessed and had to be sent on leave, to rest and refit. However, a large contingent of Sisters arrived from England shortly after, and the situation was eased, not only at Mhow but at various other important stations.

In the great cities of India, such as Bombay, the problems of Q.A.I.M.N.S., as may have been expected, sometimes took a different turn. Owing to shortage of accommodation, whole barracks had to be converted into hospitals and the barrack-rooms into wards destitute of furniture, save perhaps for a single cupboard.

As in most urban communities, too, the atmosphere was impregnated with politics.

On Saturday evenings Gandhi's followers had a habit of throwing home-made bombs into the *café* frequented by British soldiers in Bombay. That wrecked the *cafés*, and four or five soldiers usually came to us for small repairs. Whenever Gandhi was having one of his fasts, our troops were kept standing by, on the look-out for the activities of 'Congress Wallahs'.

To perform works of Necessity and Mercy under such conditions must have cast an added strain on the labours of our Sisters —though the situation fortunately was not without its element of humour—if to be assailed with bombs by the people one is fighting for can be reckoned as a really humorous experience. At any rate Thomas Atkins thought so.

The United States, too, now wholeheartedly committed to the common cause, was beginning to contribute to the Indian hospital services.

Among Matron's many duties in Bombay outside her work, she was asked to go down with Headquarters Staff and greet an American convoy bringing three General Hospitals. We lunched on board: it was a pleasant outing for us and they seemed to appreciate our visit.

III

During 1944-45, with the Burma campaign at its height, a novel and congenial form of hospital duty—congenial to those Sisters who did not object to comparative isolation from the rest of their kind—came into being in the form of the 'Indian Hospital River Steamers', a flotilla of eight flat-bottomed vessels, of the 'showboat' variety, which plied up and down the great Brahmaputra river, conveying sick and wounded from the Burma front down to Dacca, in Assam.

Each hospital steamer was a self-contained unit, with a medical officer, usually an Indian, in command; two Q.A. Sisters, one British orderly, and a staff of Indian nursing orderlies. The life of this little community alternated between three strenuous days and nights spent in tending a packed shipload of patients, and three days of perfect peace and *dolce far niente* during the return trip upstream to collect the next consignment.

One Sister has left us a lively account of life on board her own particular showboat.

The master of the vessel [she tells us], a Mahommedan from Chittagong, governed his motley crew by the judicious use of loud, insulting epithets in every known dialect East of Suez.

There was a sort of brotherhood amongst these masters; indeed, I believe most of them were closely related. They all looked like Old Testament prophets, with their long white flowing beards, snowy garments, black-embroidered waistcoats, and little red fez. Our master was the eldest of two others, and it was common knowledge that whenever this old rascal encountered his youngest brother at a common port of call, he used to give him a good beating as a prospective inducement to good behaviour. Incidentally the youngest brother was about sixty years of age!

All the same, the master seems to have been a companionable old fellow. He was never too busy to point out to the Sisters places of interest *en route*—those districts where the inhabitants still went in for head-hunting in a big way; the place where one of the steamers had turned turtle in a particularly severe monsoon gale; and, last but not least, the paddy-field in which another hospital steamer was left high and dry in the night, the Brahma-

putra having, with characteristic irresponsibility, suddenly
changed its course.

Most interesting of all were the various types of patient carried.
At one time they were all Indians, at another a party of Chinese,
at another a trainload of the famous 'Chindits', of whom there
will be more to say presently—Orde Wingate's 'Phantom Army'.

Pathetic it was to see these men, bundles of skin and bone,
riddled with dysentery and malaria, trying to eat the good
meals we provided. Their poor stomachs just couldn't cope
with anything stronger than milk.

Last, and in increasing numbers as the war progressed, came
the Japanese—sick and wounded prisoners of war.

These men were put in a caged room on the deck, more
for their own protection than to keep them from escaping.
The Ghurka patients used to threaten them through the bars
with their *kukris*,[1] and say: 'When we are prisoners you
starve us: when you are our prisoners you eat our rice!'

This was followed by a realistic pantomime of throat-
cutting on the part of the Ghurkas, whilst the terrified
Japanese cowered.

I felt certain that one morning I would come on duty to
find a cageful of dead Japs and a bunch of Ghurkas doing a
sword-dance over their corpses. Fortunately for the Japs,
the cage was as strong to hold men out as it was to keep
them in.

The lower deck of the steamer held livestock for consumption
during the voyage. Thus, apart from the throbbing of the
engines, the rhythmic chanting of the crew, and the cry of the
man whose duty it was to take periodical soundings with a long
pole, there appears to have been a perpetual chorus of squawking
hens, quacking ducks and bleating goats.

[1] A particularly unpleasant curved knife.

Q

There was one goat in particular, a pet of the crew. He must have been a redoubtable animal. He was about the size of a Shetland pony, we are assured, and was a perpetual source of uneasiness to the Sisters, who had no desire to be butted overboard. As it happened, that indignity was reserved for the ship's cook, who had to be rescued from the waters of the Brahmaputra and plied with raw brandy, much to the distress of his strict Mahommedan soul.

In the end it was the goat which perished, of pneumonia, despite four-hour doses of M. & B. magnanimously administered by the Sisters. Great care had to be taken after his decease to ensure that he was safely committed to the bosom of the Brahmaputra, and not incorporated in the ship's catering arrangements.

Of course these voyages were not always plain sailing.

The Monsoon season was a bad time of the year to be out on the river, even in a flat-bottomed steamer. In a severe gale the ship rocked alarmingly, and the waves grew dreadfully high. Remember that Indian rivers are so wide in places that the banks of either side cannot be seen, and you will appreciate our nervousness. We might as well have been on the high seas.

Then there was the usual trouble with representatives of the insect world, both creeping and flying. They appear to have been of an unusually repellent type, even for the tropical East.

On very hot nights we slept out on the little deck, with mosquito nets to protect us from the queer insects that paid us a visit, attracted by the beam of the searchlight. Like Heinz sauces, there were at least fifty-seven varieties. The most fearsome were armoured flying creatures, as big as frogs. We called them Flying Frogs, and kept a baseball-bat handy for the sole purpose of dealing with them. There was another insect which left a smarting blister if it settled on one's skin: the mark it left we called a 'Spider's Lick', but I have never met anyone who could describe the insect that caused it. So there is at least one mystery of the East left unsolved!

These intrepid Sisters seem to have explored most of the others.

IV

With the intrusion of the Japanese into the war, the people of Ceylon, who during its earlier stages had lived a comparatively tranquil existence, were now awakened to stern realities. They were soon to realize that their island was actually within the zone of active hostilities, to an extent not experienced by India, most of which lay too far north to be affected greatly by enemy action.

But the position in Ceylon was different. The Japanese were in practical control of the Bay of Bengal, and the island soon found itself within range of Japanese submarines and bombing aircraft.

Nevertheless, Ceylon was a much safer area than Malaya, and soon became the haven of casualties and evacuees from Singapore and Kuala Lumpur.

But not safe enough, as was soon to be made plain. Here is an illuminating extract from a hospital Matron's report:

Patients were arriving all day and night by ship and plane. We were very crowded and there were many serious cases; but all was in fair running order until Easter Sunday morning, about 7.30 a.m.

This was Sunday, April 5th, 1942, some six weeks after the fall of Singapore. The actual scene was Colombo.

I was returning from Church in a rickshaw when I heard explosions much too near for my liking. There were no shelters or slit trenches in our boarding-house, and a nurse and myself took refuge under the stairs.

We looked out presently and saw an enemy plane shot down. Our lads were twisting their tails good and proper. The staff had left for the hospital, which was some distance away, in a bus, and had had to take cover *en route*. I followed them to the hospital as soon as I could, and found great excitement. Our Singapore patients were thrilled to see so many R.A.F. planes in the sky, and remarks such as: 'We hadn't anything like that to put up in Singapore!' were heard. From that morning Ceylon was war conscious.

The chief preoccupation of the medical services in Ceylon from this time on was with the provision of further hospital accommodation, and of sufficient staff to operate it.

The island already possessed a military hospital, No. 55 Indian General, and two more General Hospitals now arrived from India. Unfortunately they brought no Nursing Sisters with them, so the D.D.M.S. made a broadcast appeal for helpers, whether trained or untrained. The first recruits in Ceylon itself were five Nursing Sisters from the Colonial Nursing Service and one refugee Sister from Cyprus.

No. 55 General Hospital (which had combined itself with the Regular Military Hospital) had found excellent quarters in the Royal College opposite the Race-course, but to find accommodation for the two new hospitals from India was another matter, for Ceylon is a small island, and the usual battle royal was in progress between the Navy, Army and Air Force for accommodation of any kind. Our Navy has a gift for allotting First Priority to itself upon these occasions, and the Q.A.I.M.N.S. were soon made aware of the fact. Hospital accommodation had been provided for their patients, but they were sorely in need of living quarters for themselves, for thirty more Sisters had arrived from Singapore, and some of these were in a sadly exhausted condition.

The boarding-house [we read] was not very comfortable owing to shortage of food and servants—many of these had run away on Easter Sunday—and the Sisters were anxious to have their own Mess. So we went house-hunting.

There were many empty houses owing to the blitz, but none were suitable.

Directly opposite the Convent I saw a lovely big house, shaped like a wedding-cake, with a well-trimmed garden. I made inquiries and found the Royal Navy was occupying it. We probed further, and found it was used for stores! I reported to the C.O., and he succeeded in getting it for us by coming to an agreement with the Navy that they were to share half the back premises. It made a lovely Mess, and we were very happy there for two years.

Australian Red Cross were our very best and loyal helpers from the start. Nothing was a trouble to them, and everything was done with a smile. They were very kind to the sick troops.

CHAPTER 17

FAR EAST: BURMA

EARLY on Sunday morning, December 7th, 1941, the Japanese Air Force descended from the blue over Pearl Harbour, in Hawaii, and put the greater part of the United States Pacific Battle Fleet out of action in a single raid. The two countries were at peace at the time, and the American ships were lying at anchor in close formation, totally unprepared for action. Indeed, large numbers of men were ashore on week-end leave.

From that day and hour all the world was at war, and with the entry of the United States, fighting mad, on the side of the Allies, the ultimate issue of the conflict had become practically a foregone conclusion. But years of hard and desperate fighting had yet to be faced.

The entry of her new and immensely powerful Ally brought no immediate relief to Britain: indeed it doubled her responsibilities; for until America's vast resources in men and munitions could be effectively mobilized, Britain was compelled to face both Germany and Japan single-handed. True, Russia could now be reckoned as an Ally, for Hitler had invaded Russian territory six months previously; but that fact brought little comfort to the already overstrained British Navy, or to the all too few British troops available for the defence of our Far Eastern territories against Japanese aggression.

The main theatre of our land campaign against Japan was Burma. Burma itself is about the size of pre-war Germany. Its capital is the city of Rangoon on the Gulf of Martaban, in the Bay of Bengal, and its most important city is Mandalay, lying in the centre of the country on the great River Irrawaddy, flowing from north to south. Indeed, practically everything in Burma runs from north to south—the hills, the valleys, the rivers, and the railways. This meant that British troops advancing eastward out of Assam were perpetually travelling, as it were, against the grain of the country.

This was the terrain in which General Wavell, Commander-in-Chief in India, was called upon to operate with such forces as he could muster—a theatre of the highest strategic importance, for through Burma lay the only route by which the Armies of our Chinese Allies could be kept supplied, and bases stocked for Allied air attack on Japan itself.

To add to General Wavell's transport difficulties, there existed in 1940 no direct east-west road from India into Burma. Between the basin of the Irrawaddy and Assam itself stretched some 200 miles of trackless mountain and jungle.

The Burma War, which lasted from 1941 to 1945, fell into three phases, of a pattern not unfamiliar in British military history. The first consisted of a series of rearguard actions by totally inadequate forces against an enemy advancing in overwhelming strength, especially after the fall of Singapore in February 1942, and ending, after the loss of Rangoon, in the complete evacuation of our troops into India.

Secondly came a period of stubborn resistance along the Indian and Assam frontiers, accompanied by perpetual guerrilla warfare, commando raids, and other devices to hold the enemy at bay until the necessary reinforcements, both on the ground and in the air, could be assembled.

The best-remembered features of this campaign, in the public mind at any rate, were the exploits of Orde Wingate and his famous Chindits, who instituted a system of long-range infiltration through and over the enemy's lines by small detached bodies of troops, fed from the air (or 'down the chimney'), and maintaining a hand-to-mouth existence in the depths of the jungle.

In 1943 the tide began to turn, and by the end of 1944 the enemy had been ejected from India; by January 1945 the road to China was open again, and our forces had joined hands with those of Chiang Kai-shek; and by the autumn of the same year our 11th Army Group, consisting mainly of the Fourteenth Army had almost completely destroyed the Japanese forces and liberated Burma.

II

We turn now to the experiences of the nursing units who served through this most trying of campaigns.

We will begin, as a typical example, with No. 66 Indian General Hospital, situated on the lines of communication running roughly from Gauhati on the Brahmaputra river to Imphal, in Manipur State, upon the eastern border of Assam.

It was a very different establishment from that to which the newly-arrived Nursing Sisters had been accustomed. Here are the first impressions of one of them:

> Fresh from home, with its well-equipped modern hospitals, Nurses' Home, clinics and the like, this amazing cluster of bamboo huts, interspersed with rough reeds, seems more like a native village in a jungle clearing than a busy hospital treating some 100 or more patients, both British and Indian. The wards are long thatched bamboo erections without windows or doors. The main buildings—namely theatre, laboratory, and equipment stores—are all built of asbestos sheeting with corrugated iron roofs, imposing but incongruous by comparison. The hospital itself is divided into two sections, one British and one Indian. Each ward is joined to its neighbour by covered ways of bamboo pole and thatch, so necessary during the monsoons.

The old Florence Nightingale 'Pavilion' lay-out, in fact.

The turnover of patients at No. 66 General was very large, and at times enormous, for the Japanese were at this time making a desperate effort to break through Assam into India, and heavy fighting was in progress round Imphal and Kohima in Manipur State; and since the hospitals lying farther forward had perforce been evacuated, the strain upon No. 66 was heavy. The total number of patients treated here in 1944 was no less than 51,000. At times as many as 300 patients were passing through the Sisters' hands in a single day, and the operating theatre was open all round the clock.

> The ambulance trains evacuated hundreds of patients daily, for prolonged treatment was impossible to give here.
>
> Some of our very worst casualties had to be operated on by the light of hurricane lamps and torches, and many of the patients received all their primary treatment on stretchers placed end to end in an already overflowing ward.

The climate too was a perpetual drain upon human energy. The monsoon in these regions breaks as a rule in May and continues until November. The rains brought some relief from the intense, humid heat, but they were of too short duration to be of much help. Their general effect was to convert the ground into a sea of mud, to break down flimsy thatched roofs, and compel the Sisters to go about their duties in rubber boots and under umbrellas.

Mosquitoes too were a perpetual pest and menace as breeders of malaria. Every possible precaution was enforced against these. Mosquito nets were rigidly inspected: specially detailed anti-malaria units sprayed ditches, wards, and quarters daily, and the Sisters were compelled to wear long sleeves, high necks, slacks and thick socks in the evening.

> Malaria here is always regarded as a rather criminal offence, so that we have to be over-cautious, even if it results in discomfort.
>
> The new suppressive Mepacrine treatment has proved very effective, and figures show a big decrease in malaria as a result.

Such was the picture in 1942. But there was a different tale to tell later on, towards the end of the war.

To end on an up-to-date strain; we are now proud possessors of big, airy, mosquito-proof brick wards and offices, with good metalled roads, and all the jungle cleared away from our back doors. Perhaps our biggest delight is the new Mess, complete with polished wooden floor for dancing, and the installation of loudspeakers to relay programmes to the patients.

III

But this is to anticipate: much had to be endured, right up to the end of 1944 in fact, before such civilized comforts could be achieved. Let us hark back to earlier conditions, especially those prevailing nearer the scene of active operations.

We will begin with certain extracts from a Matron's report, written at headquarters after her arrival in Assam, on the scenes during our evacuation of Burma in 1942. Notice to quit was short and the peril extreme, with resultant hurry and confusion. It was found necessary to evacuate the Sisters concerned by air.

I think all of us have lost everything, including bedding. Lives were the first consideration on the planes: all Mess books and the like had to be left behind. I had to leave my precious ledger of my staff in Burma. I am doing all I can to keep some sort of record, but it is not easy.

I think the evacuation is over now, but it is all so sad. The rains have broken, and it is coming down in torrents. I managed to get a pair of men's strong shoes today, and am thrilled. I never thought I could be so delighted about such a thing, but such is life!

There are several Burmese and Anglo-Burmese Nurses of my staff here, on their way to India, and I fear they will feel very out of place in every way. I do hope someone will look after them.

Doubtless someone did.

Mention has already been made of the Chindits, and the *modus operandi* of these gallant men outlined. They carried their personal effects on their backs. For months on end many of them lived under conditions of squalor sufficient to sap the manhood of the most insensitive. They could seldom wash, they never shaved, their clothing was in rags, and their food was primitive in quality and uncertain of arrival.

Later, these operations were carried out on a greatly enlarged scale, by glider, far behind the enemy's lines. In either case the orders were, when all had done their utmost, to return as best they could, singly or in groups. Special preparations were made to meet and greet them on their arrival, and accommodation was kept constantly prepared for them at the Combined Hospital at Panitola. Every day a fleet of ambulances was driven by Sikh soldiers to Dinjan aerodrome, whither they were to be conveyed in the final stage of their journey, by air. At first the ambulances returned empty, but at last, on June 7th, 1944, the first contingent arrived and continued to come by the hundred, night after night.

Poor, emaciated men in dirty, torn uniforms, with long hair and beards, joking and laughing as only B.O.R.s[1] can —bless them!

We had converted one of the long *basha* huts into a reception ward. The walking cases sat down at long tables as soon as they arrived, and drank with great relish large mugs of hot sweet 'char' and ate real bread-and-jam, so appreciated after months of K rations. At first we gave them stew and beer, but it made them sick. The less ill boys came over from the wards, and there were some grand reunions. After they had been seen by the M.O. they went to the adjoining *basha*, where all our available tin baths had been filled with hot water by the *bhisti*: they threw away their ragged clothes and were given clean pyjamas from the wards.

The stretcher cases were put on beds in the same reception room, and were treated for shock or given blood plasma

[1] British Other Ranks.

where necessary.   They were then sent straight to the theatre and from there to the wards, where the Sisters washed them and made them comfortable for the night.

The theatre itself worked night and day until the relieving surgical team came two weeks later.   During these first weeks the day-Sisters were never off duty till midnight. Some of the convalescents would be up all night, sitting with the 'Dangerous' cases or carrying stretchers to and from the theatre, or making welcome cups of tea for the Sisters and doctors.

It was very eerie going round the B.O.R. ward at night. Most of the boys had nightmares, and kept shouting out about machine-guns and Japs.   One boy kept crying for his mother: he was only nineteen, and had a dirty gunshot wound in his chest, but he recovered.

I would like to take this opportunity to say how well the nursing Sepoys worked during this time.   When they saw the British Sisters doing everything, even sweepers' work, they forgot their caste and took their cue from us.

Then follows a somewhat unexpected postscript, illustrative of the extreme remoteness and isolation of this particular station.

I wonder if people at home can ever visualize some of the difficulties we had to put up with.   At Panitola it was cows! It was monsoon weather, and the cows came into the wards to shelter, and we could not keep them out.   Going round from *basha* to *basha* with a hurricane lamp, as often as not one would fall over a cow lying between two of the beds.

Perhaps it was not altogether surprising that some of the patients should have suffered from nightmares.

IV

Of course the Chindits were not by any means the only sick and wounded conveyed from the battle area by air.

By 1944 the British forces in Burma had been strongly augmented by fresh contingents from home. These were sorely needed, for during the previous year our troops in Burma had been in contact with the enemy on no less than four fronts—in Arakan on the Bay of Bengal, on the Chindwin River along the western border of Burma, in North Burma round Myiktilina, and in the Chin Hills north of Manipur.

The Japanese strength amounted to at least five divisions, and a new railway from Siam into Burma threatened to open yet another line of entry into the country. This railway, incidentally, was largely constructed by British prisoners of war, under conditions of bestial cruelty which have since become notorious, and for which full retribution was in due course exacted.

But in 1944, with the arrival of adequate reinforcements, a complete reorganization of the control of our land forces was rendered possible. An Army Group was set up—11th Army Group—largely on the lines of General Montgomery's 21st Army Group—under the command of General Sir George Giffard, who had recently rendered distinguished service in East Africa. A new Army, the Fourteenth, was created—an Army destined to win immortal fame under its commander Sir William Slim. Over all stood the Supreme Commander of the South-East Asia Command, Lord Louis Mountbatten, filling a role roughly comparable with that of General Eisenhower in Europe. An American general, General Stilwell, hitherto attached to the Chinese Army, was appointed his Deputy.

The new Supreme Commander brought to his duties the highest possible qualities. As a naval officer he thoroughly appreciated the value of Combined Operations, and lost no time in integrating all three arms under his command. He was a man of inspiring presence and direct speech. In addressing the troops he laid special stress on two points—firstly, that he expected them to fight all the year round and not merely in the dry season—a battlefield is not a cricket-pitch, he pointed out—and secondly that they had now proved themselves at least a match for the Japanese soldier, and must act accordingly.

The campaign was thus renewed upon a revised and ordered

plan, in which the British soldier fought with a renewed courage and faith, conscious that he was now the attacking and not the defending party.

Victorious battles unfortunately mean heavy casualties, and our nursing services soon felt the strain; but by this time hospital accommodation had been greatly increased, and amenities improved all round. Moreover, as we have seen in the case of the Chindits, our increasing ascendancy in the air had made it possible to convey casualties to hospital by aeroplane direct, with enhanced saving of time and suffering.

A particularly busy hospital at this time was No. 49 Indian General, situated in a forward area at a convenient distance from the scene of active operations.

It was a Combined British and Indian Unit, with a staff consisting of Regular Members of Q.A.I.M.N.S., T.A.N.S., and Auxiliary Nursing Service, with British, Anglo-Indian, Sepoy, and West African orderlies—a truly Imperial combination.

The wards were of the usual *basha* type—plaited bamboo, with grass roofs and earthen floors, each large enough to hold twenty-four beds. There was also a large *basha* employed as a dining-hall for convalescents.

Here is a Sister's description of the daily routine at No. 49 C.G.H.

The day starts at 7.30 a.m., when day Sisters meet night Sisters in a Central Office to take the report. On arrival at her own section each Sister sees to it that the early convoy gets away, greets her patients, and returns to the Mess for breakfast. The rest of the morning is taken up with medical officer's round, clerical work and treatment, and probably the reception of a fresh convoy. We have to evacuate as many patients as possible every day: the longest time a medical case remains with us is forty-eight hours.

In the Indian Section we have two large wards for 'Dangerously Ill' patients, one of the Senior British Sisters being in charge, aided by two South Indian nurses, each capable of speaking several dialects. The Sister in charge of these wards is wonderful with the Indians, and sometimes says she would rather nurse them than the British!

One of the things that has struck me very forcibly is the patients' pleasure at being greeted on arrival by white women. Any spare moment I have I encourage them to tell me about their homes, and if possible give them any advice I can. It makes one feel very humble to have one's fellow-creatures trust one so implicitly.

Incidentally we have five small girls in the ward, victims of the Japanese. They are delightful little things, and by this time have become civilized in their habits. The whole ward resembles an entire wardful of children—all the patients are so easily pleased!

The adult patients too appear to have possessed one at least of the pleasing attributes of childhood: whenever medicine was administered in the ward, all present clamoured to be given a dose of it too, however unpalatable.

The general routine of No. 49, however, was not quite so smooth—Arcadian, in fact—as it sounds. The climate and the mosquitoes could never be entirely ignored. Indeed, the Sisters habitually wore slacks and bush-shirts with long sleeves after nightfall. And there were other inconveniences.

Towards the middle of June, at the height of the Monsoon, most of the *bashas* leaked through their thatched roofs and, the hospital being on low-lying ground, we waded through inches of water when going from ward to ward. With the moist, steamy heat one just dripped with perspiration all day and became covered with prickly heat.

After dark all patients were under mosquito nets, which made nursing and treating the serious cases not at all easy. To lift the net meant that a swarm of mosquitoes would get in, and if a single one was left inside, it would give the patient a restless night, as well as the risk of malaria.

And there was always the prospect of some other unwelcome visitation.

One day a patient spotted a snake coiled round a bamboo pole over someone's bed. In a second the ward was in an uproar, and those who could came rushing to me for protection. I hate snakes myself, but I just had to pretend that a snake over a patient's bed is practically nothing at all. By this time, however, help had arrived, and the snake was caught and destroyed.

v

This chapter would not be complete without some description of that invariable accompaniment of the military evacuation of a country—an unending procession of civilian refugees, such as we have already encountered, in more than one war, in France and Belgium. Let us hark back once more to 1942.

The reader will recollect that mention has already been made of the strip of mountain jungle, some 200 miles in width, lying mostly within Manipur State, which separated Burma from Assam, and that in 1940 it was pierced by no continuous road of any kind.

By 1942, however, such a road had been constructed. It was not by any means a first-class road, but it at least provided a direct channel of communication between the Imphal Valley, lying west of the Chindwin River, and India; and along this *via dolorosa*, between May and August, our sick and wounded were conveyed, accompanied by thousands of refugees.

Here is the scene, as described by a Nursing Sister.

The exhausted force lay in the Imphal Valley, and with the strain of fighting over for the time being, malaria and dysentery began to take fearful toll. At the same time thousands of Indian refugees from Burma were nearing the end of their amazing trek back to their native land. Day after day saw hundreds of these poor wretches, all on foot, struggling slowly and painfully down into the Imphal Valley, and on through the Naga Hills to India.

Survival of the fittest was the order of the day. At the

few hastily erected camps along the road only those with energy enough to fight their way near the cookhouse were fed. The nights, even in May, were bitterly cold, and about sixty miles of the road were over 4,000 feet above sea-level. When the rains started the plight of these people, with no more clothing than the flimsy rags they clutched about them, defies description. Every day dozens gave up the struggle and died where they fell by the roadside.

Then came the crowning tragedy. At Milestone 42, four miles from Kohima, a stretch of the road suddenly subsided and went sliding down into the valley below. The break thus created increased rapidly, and presently extended for more than 100 yards.

Desperate efforts were immediately made to check the landslide. Naga labour gangs, hundreds strong, were brought in and directed by a Field Company of Sappers. Assamese tea-garden labourers gave a hand. Channels were dug and mountain streams diverted. The men started at dawn, and built a path of logs across the soft mud; then, knowing full well that this temporary causeway would have slid down into the valley by the morrow, set to work to construct another, higher up the hillside.

Thus, by hook or crook, exhausted military units on their way to India from Imphal, with sick convoys numbering some 300 patients a day, and the never-ending, pitiful stream of refugees, contrived to struggle and slip their ways across some hundred yards of moving quagmire.

Towards the end of June the Army authorities decided to convey all the sick and wounded remaining in Imphal back to India, in two large convoys. This meant that on each of two successive days over a thousand of these had to cross the slide.

The convoy arrived late at night at Kohima, south of the gap, and at dawn next morning the lorries picked up their human cargo from the straw-hutted transit camp and conveyed them to within 400 yards of the landslide. Other

R

lorries were waiting about 400 yards beyond the gap to convey them to railhead in Assam.

Those two days were filled with the grimmest tragedy. Many never wakened on the morning when they were due to start on the last lap of their journey. Many more died in the space of that half-mile between lorries, while of those who survived by no means all lived to see their homes.

On each of these days I took down to the slide forty stretcher-bearers. Normally we had worked with a dozen or so, but this time every available man was needed, and needed badly. From dawn till dusk those Indian stretcher-bearers worked tirelessly and willingly to carry military sick and wounded across the gap. The numbers needing help were so great that only two men could be spared for each stretcher, the remainder helping those along who could just walk with a little assistance.

Sometimes the stretcher-bearers did not complete their journey: there was no need.

During all this time the flood of civilian refugees continued by night and day.

None who witnessed them can ever forget the innumerable scenes of individual tragedy. There were two children not more than eight years old, with abdomens grossly distended and the limbs of skeletons, trying to awaken a mother who had passed beyond human aid; there was a little girl of four or five having to be forcibly separated from her dead father, and an old woman who dropped exhausted by the roadside while her husband, reduced to a mere automaton with only the will to live, staggered on.

Some carried small bundles, and it was pathetic to see how they clung to the last to things that represented home—a brass flower-vase, a pair of ornate candle-sticks, and in one case an ancient gramophone.

It was three days before the last body could be buried, but by this time the worst was over. The convoys of sick and wounded had been conveyed across the gap, and the stream of refugees was dwindling down to a mere trickle. Best of all, by August 7th the landslide had consolidated itself and come to a stop, and by the fifteenth a new road had been laid down.

On that day the first lorry drove across amid cheers of jubilation. It is to the credit of those who made that road, that during the following year, in spite of a heavy monsoon, traffic was never again held up at Milestone 42.

But some of the credit was surely due to the Nursing Sisters and stretcher-bearers—and perhaps most of all to the invincibility of the human spirit when put squarely to the test.

VI

With the arrival of abundant reinforcements, rendering it possible, as already noted, for the Supreme Commander to reorganize the Burma plan of campaign at long last upon an elaborate and effective scale, British forces were able to take the offensive on all fronts. Upon the tactical details of these operations there is no need to enlarge here. Contact with the Chinese Armies had already been restored, and by the end of 1944, as we know, victory had been achieved along the Assam border in Manipur State and the Chin Hills. It now remained to reoccupy Mandalay and, having liberated the Irrawaddy basin, to strike south for Rangoon.

Both operations were completely successful. Mandalay was retaken on March 8th, 1945, and Rangoon fell to a combined sea-air attack early in May, just before the monsoon broke. The road to Singapore lay open at last, and Singapore itself was reoccupied without resistance on September 9th.

Three days later the Japanese Commander-in-Chief in Malaya, Java and Sumatra, signed the surrender of all Japanese armed forces in South-Eastern Asia, and so far as the British Army was concerned the Second World War was over at last.

Many members of Q.A.I.M.N.S., however, remained long after this in Burma, Malaya, China, even Japan itself, nursing the sick and wounded back to complete recovery.

VII

Mention of China reminds us of the fact that the first Q.A.I.M.N.S. Sisters ever to become prisoners of war were the staff of the British Military Hospital, Bowen Road, Hong Kong, who were captured as a unit by the Japanese upon the surrender of the garrison, on Christmas Day, 1941.

For the next eight months they were imprisoned in the hospital itself, surrounded by the usual electric fence. Nevertheless they were able to continue nursing the battle casualties and the sick brought in from adjacent concentration camps.

In August 1942 they were removed from the hospital and sent to Stanley Gaol, where they remained in internment until victory dawned in September 1945.

CHAPTER 18

SINGAPORE AND AFTER

MENTION of Hong Kong gives us an appropriate opportunity to outline the tragic story of what had been happening farther down the coast, along the Malay Peninsula and in Singapore.

Singapore is one of the strategic and commercial key-points of the world. It lies at the southernmost point of Asia, where the Indian Ocean merges with the Pacific, midway between India and China. It has been a British possession since 1826, and has grown from a small island, inhabited only by a handful of fishermen, into a city of nearly one million inhabitants, largely Chinese.

Between the wars Singapore had been converted into a great naval base. This was to protect Australia, and generally, in view of growing Japanese aggression, to defend British interests in China and the Pacific. The defences had been greatly strengthened, and were regarded as impregnable against attack from the sea.

On the land side there seemed to be no particular cause for apprehension. Singapore was itself an island, separated on the north side from the State of Johore by half a mile of water, but joined to the mainland by a causeway. Beyond Johore, stretching northward for more than 500 miles, lay the Malay Peninsula, mainly composed of the Federated Malay States of the British Empire, and ending at the borders of Siam and French Indo-China. Siam was a friendly neutral and France was our Ally, so all seemed well.

But with the collapse of France in 1940 the whole situation was revolutionized, for Japan, upon entering the war in 1941, promptly occupied both Indo-China and Siam, and thus established a base for a landward approach down the Malay Peninsula towards Singapore.

Singapore itself was sadly unready to resist such a challenge. The troops available were inadequate in numbers and quite un-used to tropical jungle warfare, at which the Japanese were past masters. The enemy enjoyed the additional advantage of being able to subsist on handfuls of rice. They were also over-whelmingly strong in the air. As a crowning disaster our sea-ward defences received an early and crippling blow in the sinkings of the new battleship *Prince of Wales* and the battle cruiser *Repulse*, both of which had gone into action without air cover.

The final result was almost a foregone conclusion. Let it suffice here, without going into operational details, to say that Singapore, with its docks, military stores, and garrison, fell to the enemy on February 26th, 1942, less than three months after Japan's entry into the war.

II

We come now to the experiences of our Medical Services, and especially of the Nursing Services, amid the chaos and devastation of that trying period. Singapore, one may note, had been under continuous bombing for some time before the actual invasion took place—almost ever since Pearl Harbour, in fact.

The purely military hospitals in Singapore consisted of the Alexandra, No. 1 Malayan General, No. 17 Combined General, and No. 20 Combined General. All were ultimately concen-trated in Singapore itself: previous to this Nos. 17 and 20 had been posted in Malaya, behind those forces putting up what resis-tance they could against the Japanese advance down the Peninsula. The hospitals conformed perforce to the movements of the troops, and this involved perpetual uprooting and retirement.

After a stand, first before and then in rear of Kuala Lumpur, the capital of the Federated Malay States, followed by a series of further hurried withdrawals, No. 17 C.G.H. found itself on the southernmost extremity of Malaya, at the edge of the narrow strait dividing the Sultanate of Johore from Singapore Island. (The view, one Sister tells us, with commendable detachment, was very like the view from Netley Hospital across Southampton Water.)

But they did not stay there long, for by this time the situation on the mainland had deteriorated so seriously that both these hospitals and their staffs had to be evacuated to Singapore.

Not that they were any safer there, for the Japanese were soon in the city.

The fighting line [reports the Matron of No. 20 C.G.H.] was daily growing nearer. So near, one could hear rifle and pistol shots in the lull of the deafening roar of bombing and gunfire. One after another the hospitals were hit, and the wards still available were full to overflowing. Eventually No. 20 (ours), Alexandra and No. 1 Malayan General were the only Military Hospitals functioning.

No. 17 C.G.H. (which like ourselves had been moved to Singapore) had been bombed and evacuated; also an Indian General Hospital, with fearful casualties.

My recollections of the next few days seem just a hazy memory of wounded pouring in, and of helping in the wards where I thought I was most needed; and through it all of the dispiriting thought that however much one was able to do, it was all so little in the mass that must be done. The blowing up of the Johore Causeway depressed me fearfully, but fortunately one had no time to think.

As for the bombing, here are the recollections of a Sister in No. 1 Malayan General. (Needless to say the Japanese Air Force took not the slightest notice of the Red Crosses freely displayed upon hospital roofs.)

They usually came in a formation of fours, with twenty-five planes in each. On Saturday, 7th February, they got a direct hit on No. 17 C.G.H., which lay on the very edge of Singapore Island, within direct range of a small island where the Japs were. The patients were transferred to us and to Alexandra Hospital.

Our turn came next day, when the night Sisters' quarters got a direct hit.

And so it went on. On Monday the Sisters were transferred to some barrack blocks, only to be bombed out again.

The Officers' Mess had a direct hit, and the place was a shambles.

By this time, when the alarm whistles went, everyone just jumped under the nearest bed or table. Even the very sick patients didn't want to be helped. The more I think of how they managed to get out of bed the more amazing it seemed.

Plainly Singapore was doomed, and it was not altogether a matter for surprise when, upon the morning of February 13th, the Commanding Officer of No. 20 Combined General Hospital informed the Matron that the Sisters were to be evacuated to Java, and safety, forthwith.

The Sisters' reception of this announcement was the very reverse of what might have been expected.

The news [the Matron tells us] was so unexpected and dire that at first it was difficult for me to grasp the meaning of it. We were to *go*—go in half-an-hour's time—and leave behind all our patients and our hopes of being able to help them! How to break it to the Sisters, who had worked so bravely and untiringly through our many moves, I did not know. It was a comfort to think that our C.O. and M.O. and all the orderlies who had done such splendid work would, we hoped, be left to look after them.

We left that evening, Friday the 13th, on board the ill-fated *Kuala.*

Friday the 13th proved an ominous date, as we shall presently see.

Meanwhile it should be explained that there were in point of fact not one but two evacuations of nursing personnel from Singapore, upon successive days. The Sisters from No. 20 C.G.H. were actually the second contingent to leave: No. 17 had preceded them on the previous day, February 12th. Let us tell of their adventures first, as seen through the eyes of one of the Sisters.

She begins quite frankly:

It actually is incredibly difficult to describe *anything*, as events were so rapid and momentous that one can easily leave out important details. But I will try to give you as much detail as I can.

Her story begins with the departure of the Unit at dawn on February 12th, on board a small and densely crowded ship, carrying Air Force and Australian units and many civilian passengers, including babies a few weeks old. The Sisters were allotted space in one of the holds, which they shared with some Australian Sisters. They slept on bare boards, using gas-capes, steel helmets, or gas-masks as pillows.

They were not permitted, however, to depart in peace, for their vessel was dive-bombed continuously from 8 a.m. until 2 p.m., and several of the lifeboats were put out of action. No one appears to have had a life-belt. There were several casualties, and a number of Sisters from No. 17 C.G.H. established a casualty clearing station in one of the cabins, from which the patients were transferred to a small hospital in the hold, improvised by the Australian Sisters.

Many men were blown overboard, plus 12 killed and 26 injured. Most of us had a fair supply of morphia in our pockets, which was most useful.

After our C.C.S. had been started the ship received four direct hits, and the stern caught fire. But it still sailed on. Had it not been for the Captain and staff of that merchant ship, we should never have reached Batavia at all.

Throughout all the racket and confusion of that terrifying voyage the Sisters maintained their heroic labours, and in due course all came safely, almost miraculously, to Batavia, the capital of Java, the following evening.   Needless to say they were not expected, and had to remain on board with their patients for another night until quarters could be obtained for them.   Ultimately they were accommodated in the Princess Juliana Convent, where the nuns 'were very kind to us'; and next day thirteen of them were put on board a ship bound for Ceylon.

They were thankful to be on their way back to British soil, but the voyage does not appear to have been a particularly pleasant one, to judge from the terse postscript with which our Sister concludes her narrative.

> Conditions on board this evacuee ship, which could not be helped, resembled those of an emigrant ship of the last century.

After a voyage of seven days all came safe to Colombo.   Here the D.D.M.S., as soon as he was apprised of their arrival, came on board to greet the Sisters and make provisions for their comfort.   They were dispatched up country to Kandy for a sorely needed rest of seven days; at the end of which, indomitable as ever, eight of them returned to Colombo for temporary duty with a Combined General Hospital.

In Colombo they encountered those colleagues, or as many of them as were left, who had sailed from Singapore in the second contingent upon Friday, February 13th, on board the *Kuala*. Here is their story.

III

On that morning these Sisters had been collected in the pavilion of the Singapore Cricket Club, ready to be conveyed aboard ship.   They were a large party, some fifty in all, and included most of the senior members of the Service, among them Miss Jones, Principal Matron, from Alexandra Hospital, Miss

West, Matron of No. 1 Malayan General, Miss Spedding, from 20th C.G.H., and Miss Russell from No. 17 C.G.H., together with Miss Coward, Home Sister at Alexandra.

The voyage did not begin too auspiciously.

We were all taken down to the Naval Dockyard at about 4 p.m. [one of the Sisters tells us]. An air raid started while we were there. Some of us had got safely on board the ship; others, including myself, were in the launches, on our way out. We were machine-gunned. The casualties were mostly minor, but two civilian Sisters were killed by splinters.

It should be mentioned here that the party included other nursing units apart from Q.A.I.M.N.S.

We had on board about 400 women and children evacuees, 300 Public Works Department officers, and our own crowd. There was just standing room for all on board.

We sailed about 7 p.m., and anchored the following morning at a small island south of Singapore.

(The island in question must have been situated somewhere in the Straits of Malacca, which separate Malaya from the great island of Sumatra.)

The unhappy *Kuala* was not allowed to lie at peace for long. Six Japanese bombers came over that morning and scored a direct hit, through the bridge, on to a cabin which had been allotted, a few minutes before, to Miss Jones and the other senior officers previously mentioned. Of these gallant women Miss Jones, Miss West, Miss Russell and Miss Coward were never seen again, for the ship itself rolled over and sank almost immediately.

In the next instalment of our Sister's narrative (which is naturally somewhat elliptical at this point) we find her struggling, with everybody else, in the sea, with the Jap bombers still at their congenial task.

They came over four times while we were swimming in the sea, and did dive-bombing and machine-gunning. The death-roll was something enormous, as there were only two life-boats and insufficient life-belts to go round. The land was about a quarter of a mile away, but there was a very swift current, which kept sweeping people either back to the ship or out to sea. That was why everybody got taken to various islands in the vicinity.

The last statement alludes to the fact that most of the survivors —not 'everybody', alas!—were ultimately able to take refuge on one or other of the islets which dotted the Straits. Their privations were extreme, but they received much help from friendly Chinese junks, which collected isolated groups from the islets and conveyed them to a larger island from which they were ultimately enabled to reach Sumatra itself. Two British naval vessels also visited the islands and took off survivors.

In course of time some of these Sisters found their way right across Sumatra (one of the largest islands in the world) to Pedang on its western coast, where they were fortunate enough to encounter some British naval vessels which had put in to refuel after the Battle of the Java Sea, and these evacuated them to Bombay.

Some of them, however, preferred to disembark at Colombo *en route*, and it was their arrival which is mentioned in the narrative of the Sister who had described for us the voyage of the first contingent of evacuees, via Batavia.

Others of the *Kuala's* ship's company were less fortunate. They were compelled to remain in Sumatra, with the result when the Japanese occupied the whole island in April, they were interned as prisoners of war.

We come lastly to the experiences of the largest contingent of all—a party of some 250 women and children, including eight Q.A. Sisters. Having survived the sinking of the *Kuala*, these were re-embarked two days later upon a small steamer, the *Tanjong Penang*, and were dispatched to Sumatra. They never got there, for a Japanese destroyer intercepted them by searchlight that night and sank the *Tanjong Penang* with a few salvoes.

The subsequent experiences—almost incredible experiences—of the survivors of that outrage must be described in greater detail, for this is perhaps the most memorable and poignant story of the Second World War.

IV

For a long time the fate of the *Tanjong Penang* was wrapped in mystery, and in due course she was given up for lost, with all her crew and passengers.

But one passenger, and one alone, survived to tell the tale in full—a tale as vivid and moving as any in the long and heroic record of Q.A.I.M.N.S.

The passenger in question was one of eight Nursing Sisters. Here is her story, which loses nothing of its effect from the composure with which it is told.

> We settled down to sleep on deck for the night, when suddenly a searchlight shone on us, and without any warning a shot was fired, and then another, both hitting the ship. When they stopped shelling I found myself beside Sister Le Blanc Smith. People were lying dead and wounded all round us, but there was little we could do for the ship was sinking rapidly.
>
> We both stepped into the water, and presently managed to pick up a small raft. Then we came across some other people with a raft. We joined them together. During the night we picked up more people: in the end there were sixteen of us holding on to the two rafts—including six children, two being under one year old.
>
> We lost one or two the next morning; they just could not hold on, despite our attempts to bring them back. Sister Le Blanc Smith died that afternoon, after being terribly brave. Two more also drifted away. What with the tropical sun beating on us, and at other times terrible storms, and no food or water, it was not very pleasant.

Understatement could no further go.

On the second day the children went mad, and we had a difficult time with them. We lost them all.

That night I found myself alone with one other woman, so we got rid of one raft and just used the small one. We could see small islands in the distance, so next day we tried with our hands to paddle towards them, but the current was against us and we just had to go round in a circle. That afternoon the other woman went off the raft, leaving me quite alone.

I was picked up on the fourth evening, February 21st, by a Japanese cruiser, and taken to Muntock on the island of Bangka. Then I was put in a place which before had been used for Chinese coolies.

The island of Bangka lies off the east coast of Sumatra, some 200 miles south of Singapore. It appears to have been used as an assembly-point for British and Dutch prisoners of war.

Our Sister was now to discover that she had been delivered from the blind forces of nature only to be submitted to the calculated ferocity of the human animal.

The place consisted of about eight huts, with stone slabs all round the walls and an open square in the centre. Here I found Service men and civilian men, women and children, interned—about 600 or 700 of us altogether. We were overcrowded, and sanitary conditions were poor. Most of us had nothing to sleep on or to cover ourselves with. Our food consisted of two rice meals a day. Once we got a bit of dried octopus.

In April, however, these prisoners, including all the Sisters, were transferred to a permanent place of internment at Palembang, the capital of Sumatra.

Here the female internees were separated from the men. There were some 700 of them in all—two-thirds Dutch and one-third

British. There was a hospital some two miles away, and most of the trained nurses in the camp volunteered to serve there, but this they were not allowed to do; so they devoted themselves to taking care of the sick people in the camp itself, cooking and collecting the rations. This for the most part meant carrying heavy sacks of rice and collecting and chopping logs of wood for cooking purposes. As if the conditions under which they existed were not sufficiently trying, their custodians made a practice of inventing superfluous and humiliating jobs for them.

> Whilst we were at Muntock camp one of the things the Japs made us do was to catch flies—the men were supposed to catch 100 and the women fifty each day. Anything, in fact, to cause the proud British to 'lose face'—especially the women. Still——
> Looking back on those early days, they were in a sense luxury days compared with what we had to put up with later.

At first they were not too heavily supervised or overworked. Those with any money could buy such small luxuries as sugar, coffee, and curry-powder, to help the rice down. Some in their spare time even played bridge with home-made cards, or mah-jong with pieces laboriously carved out of wood. Others established classes for learning French or Malay. They even organized humble little debates and concerts, and attended a Church service on Sunday mornings, conducted by one of the missionaries.

After six months, too, the Japs, finding themselves short of hospital staff, raised the ban upon British nurses working in a native hospital close by, to the extent of two civilian and two Q.A. Sisters, of whom latter pair our own particular Sister was one. This gave them congenial occupation, and they had no special cause to complain of their treatment. Their lives were anything but happy, but they were now beginning to be buoyed up by the hope, hitherto remote, that they would be able to 'stick things out' until the war ended.

That hope was not entirely vain.   She came through, though the other Q.A. died there.

On April 16th, 1943, we were all told to report at the Civilian Office at noon.   When we arrived we were kept waiting for two hours, and were then taken to the Kempital, the office of the Military Police.

There the only words addressed to us by the Jap officials were: 'You blue-eyed English—ugh!' After that they talked to our Dutch doctor for a long time, and then started beating him up—also his wife, who went to his assistance.

After they had finished their 'fun' they told the doctor, Sister Cooper, and myself, to go back to the hospital.   They took the doctor away again that night.

Then followed a typical display of the Japanese sense of humour.

Next morning the Japanese doctor asked us if we would like to continue working in the native hospital or go back to our friends in the camp.   Of course we said we would prefer to go back to the camp, and they said they would come and fetch us at 1.30 p.m.   This they did, but instead of taking us to the camp they took us to the gaol!

We were searched, and then had to wait whilst they turned some natives out of a cell to put us in—just with what we stood up in—no change of clothes, no towel, nothing to cover ourselves up with.   We just sat on a stone slab, behind bars and the door padlocked on us.   We were allowed out twice a day for four minutes, to wash.   Our food was passed in to us—two meals a day; either cold tea or cold water to drink.

That was the beginning of the longest six months of my life.

Needless to say no reason or excuse for this imprisonment was ever vouchsafed to the two Sisters, and they did not ask for one.

With their usual philosophy they simply made the best of the situation—took it in their stride, in fact.

Our fellow-prisoners in gaol were murderers and thieves —and they became our friends. They spoke to us when able to, and sometimes passed through the bars black coffee in an old cigarette-tin. They were certainly good to us, especially the Chinese. If they had been caught they would have got into serious trouble.

However, the six months ended at last, and our two Sisters were restored to a measure of freedom, for they were sent back to their internment camp. The camp had been moved, and the women were now living where the men had been, in wooden huts shut off completely from the outside world. A given number were allotted to each hut, and quarters were terribly close.

The actual space that we were each allowed was 27 inches wide, and in this we had to keep all our personal belongings —not that they were many—and some women got annoyed if one was an inch over the allotted space. We were all living in such close proximity and under such trying conditions that I am afraid tempers did get frayed a bit. But still the Japs could not get us down. They hated the British. They could not understand why we went about smiling and singing at our work. They said we should be serious, for there was a war on!

Time marched on, with leaden footsteps, and once again the situation deteriorated, this time to an almost unendurable degree. After April 1944 the military authorities took over. Rations were cut, and grew less and less. Concerts and other forms of recreation, however modest, were rigorously suppressed. Hard and humiliating tasks were imposed on the women prisoners.

There was a large area in the centre of the camp which was really hard clay. We had to dig that up, to plant
s

vegetables. We also had to tidy up the roads outside including the gardens of the Japs' houses, even clean out their drains. This was all done during the heat of the day.

Water was terribly scarce. We asked if we could fetch some from a hydrant half a mile down the road. Whenever we were allowed to it was in the heat of the day, and when we got back to camp with our full bucket we would be told to go and fill up the baths in the Jap houses. We had to make several trips to do this. If we, the British, protested —nobody else did—we were punished.

In September 1944 the women internees were moved to yet another camp. It was roomier than the last, but was infested by mosquitoes, with resulting malaria, beri-beri, and dysentery. There was a hospital, always full, and here British and Australian Sisters found some relief from their own troubles by working side by side with the regular staff—a party of Dutch nuns.

But it was a hopeless kind of nursing: people dying every day, and sometimes two or three a day. There was no cemetery, so we had to make our own—and dig the graves and bury the dead.

Most of us managed to be cheerful, and did not doubt for a moment that Britain would win the war—but hoped it would be soon!

And deliverance was nearer than they thought, for it was now the spring of 1945, and the Allied invasion of France and the Continent of Europe was in successful progress. Word of all this was penetrating into Japan, and the Japanese knew full well that if their ally Hitler was finished, so were they. So they changed their tune, even in far-distant internment camps. Gone was the brutal, bullying, sub-human animal, and in his place there appeared the smiling, ceremonious, almost servile Oriental of an earlier day.

There was no definite news of victory as yet, but everywhere throughout the Japanese occupied areas the same change of atmosphere and relaxation of camp discipline was perceptible. The average Jap gaoler seemed to be trying to 'work his passage' towards lenient treatment in the event of the present situation being reversed. So, thousands of prisoners and internees in Malaya, Burma, and the Dutch East Indies began to lift up their hearts—and their heads.

And then, on May 15th, we were told that we were to have a Japanese military band to entertain us! We were not very keen to hear their band, but they more or less chased us there at the point of the bayonet. Actually it was a very good band.

We really thought the war must be over when, on July 10th, they brought fourteen live pigs into the camp for us. Of course we had to kill them ourselves, but my word! we had a great feast that day.

Still, nothing more happened for a while, until that great day, August 15th, 1945. We were all called to a meeting at 3 p.m. and told by the Jap Commandant that the war was over—*so we were no longer enemies but friends!*

CHAPTER 19

THE PERILS OF THE DEEP

SOME of the experiences of Q.A.s by sea during the First World War have already been described.[1]

The main difference between conditions in the two wars was, firstly, that during the First War the danger zone, so far as troop-carrying vessels and hospital ships were concerned, was limited in the main to the British sea-coast and the Mediterranean. In the Second War the danger zone was world-wide.

The other difference was that by 1939, and upon an ever-increasing scale thereafter, it had become possible not only to sink ships by U-boat attack from below the surface but by precision bombing from the heavens above. The most notable instance of the success of this form of destruction was the sinking, already mentioned, of the *Prince of Wales* and *Repulse* off the Malayan coast in February 1942.

The reader will thus realize that the perils to which Q.A.I.M.N.S. (in common with other serving units) was subjected during the Second World War were incomparably greater and more numerous than those of the First, as may be gathered from the study of a few typical examples, culled from a very large number of personal narratives.

As usual, the Nursing Sisters who travelled overseas were serving either in hospital ships, hospital carriers, or troopships. The first were regularly equipped floating hospitals, the second were merchant vessels only roughly fitted out, and employed to convey the largest possible number of casualties in the shortest time from the port of evacuation to the nearest hospital base. We have already encountered such vessels in 1915, transporting

[1] See Chap. 13, Secs. iii and iv.

great numbers of men from the dressing-stations on the Gallipoli beaches to the hospitals at Mudros.

In like manner, during and for some time after the Dunkirk evacuation in 1940, hospital carriers were kept plying ceaselessly between the ports on either side of the English Channel, maintaining what practically amounted to a shuttle service night and day in the face of all that hostile submarines and aircraft could bring against them.

Many old friends of peace-time were engaged in that work, friends with names familiar to every holiday passenger to and from Calais, Boulogne, Dieppe, or elsewhere—*Isle of Thanet, Isle of Guernsey, Maid of Orleans, Maid of Kent, Worthing, Dinard, Paris*, and others. Not all of these survived their gallant exertions.

II

The German invasion of Belgium began upon May 10th, 1940, and from that time convoys of wounded men began to arrive at the Channel ports in ever-increasing numbers. Matters reached a climax when the Dunkirk evacuation itself began.

The following condensed diary, or log, kept by a Sister on board the *Isle of Thanet* during the height of the evacuation, will give the reader some idea of the astonishing closeness of the timetable to which these hospital carriers contrived to adhere. (Times are given on the twenty-four-hour scale.)

> *May 23rd.* Sailed for Dover 00.20 hrs.: arrived off the Downs about 04.30 hrs.
> Sailed from Dover 11.20 hrs.; arrived Dunkirk 13.45, with the *H. C. Worthing*, escorted by Destroyer *L.O.2*. Air raid at 14.50 hrs. (Oil and petrol dumps burning furiously.) Commenced to embark 275 casualties from No. 13 Ambulance Train. Completed at 10.10 hrs. Sailed at 20.47 hrs. Arrived Newhaven 03.50 hrs., with all wounds dressed.
> *May 24th.* Disembarkation completed 06.00 hrs. Wards ready, and all soiled sheets and blankets changed, 07.20 hrs.

Sailed from Newhaven 11.25 hrs. to Dover. At 15.50 hrs. received orders to proceed Dunkirk. When opposite Dover Patrol Memorial at Calais came under shell-fire, falling about 100 yards away, starboard side. Took on 800 casualties at Dunkirk. (Our capacity, 255!) Continuous bombing.

May 26th. Tide receded and embarkation delayed. Gangway would not fit; walked over planks instead. Got off at last. Arrived Newhaven 07.45 hrs.

May 27th. Sailed from Newhaven 01.15 hrs. At Dover ordered to proceed to Dunkirk. Shelled by shore batteries off Calais. (Saw nine dive-bombers attack a trooper.) Recalled to Dover for some fresh charts. At 13.10 hrs. sailed Dover to Ostend, then back to Dunkirk, arriving 19.00 hrs. Dunkirk ablaze.

May 28th. Arrived Dover 02.40 hrs. Collision with pilot boat. *Isle of Thanet* bow knocked in. Towed into Newhaven 15.00 hrs.

May 30th. Sailed from Newhaven 06.00 hrs. Arrived Southampton 15.10 hrs., and dry-docked.

Sisters and personnel, 7 days' leave, at 24-hours' recall.

A study of the foregoing breathless record reveals to us that, despite the fact that she was hung up for twenty-four hours in Dunkirk Harbour by an exceptionally low tide between May 24th and May 26th, the *Isle of Thanet* crossed the Channel nine times in seven days—on one occasion three times in twenty-four hours, under the perpetual menace of shell-fire and bombing; and that it was only that she became disabled in a collision which seems to have prevented her and her nursing staff from carrying on indefinitely. It should be added that she had begun this particular tour of duty on May 8th—nearly three weeks before.

Let us now consider in greater detail the experiences of two other hospital carriers during this period.

The first of these is the *St. Julien.* She sailed from Southampton to Boulogne the day after the launching of the German invasion of Belgium. Wounded were already pouring in. Many of the men taken on board had been wounded a second time by bombing while lying in hospital the previous night. All were conveyed safely to Southampton next day.

The next visit of the *St. Julien* to Boulogne took place a week later, and the Sister who tells us the story has occasion to remark upon the 'terrible changes' brought about in the port and town by merciless bombing. Apart from the material devastation, the civil population had succumbed to panic.

> Headquarters had been badly bombed, and there were a number of fires. The town and all roads round it were filled with French and Belgian refugees. We were constantly stopped by them, and asked the way to ships for England.
>
> There was a bad raid that night, and a number of fires. A larger number of the refugees gathered round, trying to board our ship, but we could not take them on board until we had our patients. However, we fed them with tea and soup and bread and butter and milk.

> Next day the ambulances arrived, and the wounded were conveyed on board.

> We took on some very bad cases: one man had to have his legs amputated immediately. We did two other major operations on board, all of which were successful, and the patients did well. We had no theatre.

It should be remembered that the *St. Julien* was not a regular hospital ship: she was merely an ordinary cross-Channel passenger steamer, but rudely equipped for major operations.

> We took on board 141 refugees, making a total of 407 in all.

The *St. Julien* duly disembarked her patients at Southampton, and sailed again next day. This time it was Dunkirk; and here we have a fresh picture.

It was a grim sight. Two ships had been sunk in the harbour, one of which, having gone down quite straight, was still flying the White Ensign.

We could not get up to the Quai Felix Faure, as there were ships there already. There was a hospital train on the quay, but no one answered our hails.

At this point came an attack by dive-bombers, and a salvo of bombs fell on either side of our ship. Pieces of bomb-casing and *débris* fell on the decks. We sailed away, as there was a risk of our blocking the harbour if hit.

No account seems to have been taken by the Sisters of the risk to themselves.

Next day the *St. Julien* returned to Dunkirk, under aerial escort, in company with the Hospital Carrier *St. Andrew*, and took on board 250 casualties, mostly badly wounded stretcher cases. Needless to say all this work was carried on under the ceaseless attention of the Luftwaffe and enemy coastal artillery.

We had to wait for the tide before sailing for home, and then had all lights on and markings plainly visible, until we were fired on by shore guns just south of Calais. This lasted for fifteen minutes. We were also bombed from the air, but not hit.

One of *St. Julien's* worst experiences seems to have been on May 31st, during the most hectic period of the evacuation.

We sailed at 5.30 a.m. on May 31st, and arrived at Dunkirk at 8.50 a.m. We moved alongside the Breakwater Mole. The quay was much broken and on fire in places. The patients were embarked with no gangway—just lifted over the ship's side.

The ship's officers and crew, stewards, and R.A.M.C. personnel all acted as stretcher-bearers, and carried the patients up the length of the quay under machine-gun fire from the air. The Naval Officer in charge on shore was so calm that one literally did not realize the aerial battle that was going on all the time.

We put the patients to bed as far as possible, and then made up beds on the floor. We did their dressings, which of course had not been done for a long time, made them comfortable, and fed them. They were a little shaken by some bombs that nearly-missed us as we were leaving Dunkirk, but they soon settled down.

We come lastly to the experiences of the Hospital Carrier *Worthing*, which in happier days had been in regular service between Newhaven and Dieppe.

The story this time is given not so much in the form of a continuous narrative, as in a series of disconnected incidents, described with complete detachment and *sang froid*.

In H.M.H.C. *Worthing* we made seventeen trips to Dieppe, whence we brought sick men to England from the hospitals in that area and from the hospital trains which had brought them from others. . . .

On our last two trips the 'alert' was pretty continuous. As we left Dieppe harbour on that Saturday evening the *Brighton* and the *Maid of Kent* sailed in. We heard later that they were bombed and sunk during the week-end. . . .

We made two trips to Dunkirk, and though our number of beds was 348 we brought back about 600 patients. We were usually shelled off Calais, and German planes came over and dropped bombs and machine-gunned the bridge. Fortunately no one was hurt. The Captain and ship's officers were wonderful.

We loaded each time under fire and bombs. On one occasion we had just taken in the gangway and slipped away when a bomb dropped exactly where the gangway had been, removing part of the quay-side. . . .

At one time we took on some Frenchmen who had been wounded when on duty on the quay. Some were badly hurt and died before we reached England. . . .

There was one young German, wounded in the back and looking terribly frightened. He inquired whether he would be tortured before being killed! On our assurance to the contrary he settled down and slept. . . .

It was extraordinary how perfectly safe the men felt as soon as they got on to the ship; and we did not disillusion them. . . .

We made one journey to Le Havre, and anchored just outside for seventeen hours, taking on what could be brought alongside by small boats, in spite of bombs and shelling. . . .

We started on a second trip to Le Havre, but were pretty badly shelled and had to turn round and go back. Portholes were blown in and steel plates strained, but again no one was hurt. We got the wheel-house fixed up like a pillbox, and were made seaworthy again in about four days. . . .

Shortly afterwards we went to Preston Docks, where, to our regret, we were disbanded.

This last statement will probably strike the reader as the most astounding of all.

III

Such were some of the experiences of Q.A.I.M.N.S. during the weeks of what is usually called the Dunkirk evacuation, though in point of fact evacuation of some kind was taking place, as we have seen, from almost every French port from Dunkirk to St. Nazaire.

Let us now turn farther afield, first to the Mediterranean.

Hospital ships and hospital carriers were much employed during the desert campaign in North Africa, being sent along the coast to the port lying nearest to our line of advance (or retreat) at the moment. Tobruk was the first of these, and it was from Tobruk that casualties from General Wavell's Army of the Nile were evacuated by sea to Alexandria in 1940–41. In the summer of 1942 Rommel counter-attacked heavily, and Tobruk was lost. It was regained later in the year, after our victory at El Alamein, and was once more employed as an evacuation base. Later, as the victorious Eighth Army continued to penetrate westward, Tripoli was employed for the same purpose.

Two of the best-remembered hospital ships of that time and theatre were the *Llandovery Castle*, an intermediate vessel of the Union Castle Line, which had been converted not into a carrier but a fully equipped hospital ship, and the regular Hospital Ship *Somersetshire*, affectionately remembered and described as the 'Old Tobruk Warrior'.

A visit to Tobruk at almost any time between the beginning of 1941 and the end of 1943 was always a risky undertaking, for the Luftwaffe were regular in their visitations, and for some months in 1941, when it lay entirely isolated on the land side, Tobruk was constantly under shell-fire. Here is a Sister's account of the first visit of the *Somersetshire* to Tobruk in December 1941, when the town was undergoing its long period of isolation and had in fact been besieged for some months by four Italian and one German Division.

We arrived at Tobruk Harbour on the morning of December 6th. It was the saddest sight, like a graveyard of ships, many listing badly and falling to pieces in rust; two or three large liners completely burnt out. Owing to the depth of water required by the *Somersetshire* we were only able to anchor within a mile and a quarter from shore. This meant that the embarkation of the sick and wounded was a long and very tedious task. We only possessed two motor launches, and these had to tow two or three life-boats to and from the jetty.

This jetty had been somewhat damaged, and in consequence each stretcher had to be lowered some four or five feet from the end of the jetty into the life-boat. Each boat could take nine stretcher cases and two or three sitters. On our first visit we embarked 540 sick and badly wounded patients.

So slow, unfortunately, was the rate of embarkation under the handicaps imposed that it was found impossible to transfer all of the 540 in a single day, and the *Somersetshire* had to lie off for the night, a circumstance of which the German gunners took full advantage.

What a night that was—nearly eleven and a half hours of bombardment! We had arranged that half the Nursing Sisters and half the R.A.M.C. orderlies should go to bed at 9 p.m. until 2 a.m., and the remainder from 2 a.m. until 7 a.m. However, I don't think any of them went to bed at all—certainly not to sleep.

By contrast, let us consider a later and more comfortable visit, a few weeks later.

On arrival at Tobruk on the morning of the 16th the O.C. asked me if I would like the honour of being the first woman ashore since the siege began.

Three of the Sisters went with me, and we paid a visit to the Base Hospital. Everybody seemed pleased to see us, and on our way back a laddie belonging to the Royal Tank Regiment came running out of a very shattered building and, touching me on the shoulder, said: 'You are a woman, aren't you?' He then stepped back and saluted, saying: 'I haven't seen a woman for over ten months!'

To round off, here is a description of what may be called an omnibus tour of duty on board the *Llandovery Castle*, starting in December 1942. By this time the victory of El Alamein had been won and Tobruk relieved.

The Sister who tells the story had joined the ship in November 1942 at Alexandria, where her first impression had been one of surprise and delight at finding herself in a vessel so lavishly equipped. There was no regulation Service austerity here, but all the comfort and luxury associated with an ocean-going liner.

No one who has not served in the field or in a converted

hospital for three years can realize with what joy I beheld the steam sterilizers and boilers, with an unfailing supply of hot water. The pantry was an even greater surprise: it appeared to be full of china. Actually cups, saucers, and plates sufficient for each patient! And the beds! Fitted with comfortable V-spring mattresses, so comfortable that one night, doing a late round, I found a patient sleeping on the floor with only the mattress beneath him. He assured me that after months in the desert he felt far too comfortable in bed, and begged to be allowed to stay there.

The *Llandovery Castle*'s first call was at Tobruk, whence she conveyed 715 patients to Alexandria. As each patient arrived on deck he was given a coloured tally denoting the ward to which he was to be admitted. The tally was given up on arrival at Alexandria.

A later trip was to Tripoli, now in British possession, where the Sisters were deeply impressed with the speed and efficiency with which the Royal Navy and the dock workers had as usual cleared the harbour of the obstructions left there by the retreating enemy. Six hundred and twenty patients were actually stowed on board in 2½ hours.

The year 1943 was now six months old, and the invasion of Sicily was imminent. An invasion flotilla set off from Tripoli, followed, to the deep concern of the Sisters on board the *Llandovery Castle*, by two regular hospital ships, the *Tarai* and *Talambo*. Was the *Llandovery Castle* going to be left out of all this? But no, all was well: she was duly dispatched the following day.

The *Talambo*, incidentally, was sunk on the way over, to the distress of the Sisters in the *Llandovery Castle*, who had many friends on board.

Their first patient on arrival in Sicilian waters was an airman who had just been picked out of the sea. They then proceeded to Syracuse, where, owing to the fact that the patients were brought to the ship's side in small gunboats lying low in the water, the task of hoisting them up proved a slow and difficult matter. However, soon 600 were eventually taken on board.

These patients were in a bad way, for the landing in Sicily had been a desperate and costly business.

> This [comments the Sister who tells the story] was indeed total war. I cannot describe the complete change ·of atmosphere in the wards. No laughter, greeting of friends, or exchange of hair's-breadth experiences. Each patient appeared to be more severely wounded and badly shocked than the last one; and as they were carefully lifted on to the beds they sank down and were asleep, in spite of their pain, before we could remove the tattered and dirty rags which were all that was left of their uniform.
>
> It required great control from many of us that day to restrain our tears as we went about the wards—something so new to us after our former cheerful patients, always ready for a second or third helping of food.

Upon their return to Alexandria the Sisters received the 'amazing news' that the next trip of the *Llandovery Castle* was to be for England and home. Soon they were filling up with convalescent patients, many of them old friends.

> It was good to see the pleasure with which these came aboard. Many of them, alas, had lost an arm or a leg, but all seemed quite happy discussing the merits of the latest artificial limbs; and, above all, looking so fat and well, compared with the wrecks we had put on the trains for the desert hospitals months before.
>
> One man confided to me: 'My girl says it's all right, Matron, me only having one leg.'

The voyage home, needless to say, was not without incident, especially in the neighbourhood of Gibraltar, but the *Llandovery Castle* came safely to England with all her passengers.

Other ships were not so fortunate. On October 26th, 1940, the 40,000-ton Canadian Pacific Liner *Empress of Britain*, with a full ship's company on board, was torpedoed and sunk while homeward bound from Alexandria, and when almost within sight of home. The seriousness of the loss of this great vessel was only comparable with that of the 50,000-ton *Britannic* in the First World War.

IV

Some of the most unusual and interesting 'adventures afloat' during those years were those of members of the Nursing Services, who participated in excursions to the remoter theatres of the war.

One unit was dispatched to Iceland on board H.M.H.C. *Leinster*, a Holyhead–Dublin mail steamer which had been completely re-equipped as a Hospital Carrier. She arrived at Reykjavik, the capital, in November 1940, and after a short stay proceeded to the unpronounceable port of Akureyri on the northern side of the island, almost within the Arctic Circle. Here she lay for the whole winter, with the Sisters quartered on board. Their duties were to render such hospital service as was needful to the British troops stationed in the island as a precaution against enemy occupation.

It was a peaceful, if unusual existence. There was no blackout, which was fortunate, for in winter daylight only lasted for some five hours. During January and February the ship was frozen in, and throughout the winter violent blizzards were frequent. The Sisters were issued with Arctic kit—leather jerkins, gum-boots, gloves and sou'westers. At the same time they found it was possible to indulge in a swim in a natural hot spring, with an outside temperature of 22 degrees below zero.

In the absence of more strenuous activities, training courses and lectures were organized, together with route marches and improvised 'schemes'. Nearly everybody learned to ski. Relations with the local population were most cordial, and it was with real regret that the Sisters separated in May 1941 for sterner duties. They took with them a number of men who had had toes or fingers amputated owing to frost-bite

There are many things one could write about the Ice-landers [reports one young Sister], their religious festivals and gala days, and the beautiful scenery; glorious waterfalls glistening like rainbows, sulphur springs and sulphur mountains, lovely lava deserts, the Northern Lights and the midnight sun.

My winter spent there and my first experiences of a Hospital Ship will always be a happy memory.

Q.A.I.M.N.S. was also represented in our brief and unsuccessful attempt to save Norway from German occupation just prior to the invasion of France and Belgium in the spring of 1940.

After an uneventful voyage, except for a few depth-charges, the Sisters found themselves in a fiord in Northern Norway, presumably in the neighbourhood of Narvik.

At the end of a week they were moved into a Norwegian ship, which they converted into a hospital carrier. Here they tended all the casualties which came their way, frequently under hostile bombing.

I remember [one Sister tells us] one occasion when the stretcher-bearers were bringing German wounded and the enemy came over. Our men showed not the slightest concern over the noise going on, but several Germans sat up with scared looks on their faces.

Throughout their sojourn in Norway the Sisters rendered yeoman service, moving in their peripatetic hospital carrier from fiord to fiord collecting wounded. Perhaps their most memorable experience during these brief weeks was when they steamed south from Narvik and took off naval casualties from two battleships.

The Norwegian Expeditionary Force, being 'too little and too late', had failed in its gallant purpose through no fault of its own, but its personnel had good cause to be grateful to Q.A.I.M.N.S., whose members, as usual, had not failed to win the affection and gratitude of the Norwegian civil population as well.

I hope to return in happier days, and shall always remember the kind and generous Norwegian people, who shared their homes with us and assisted us in many ways.

A characteristic postscript.

V

Yet another tour of Q.A.I.M.N.S. duty remains to be mentioned—in Madagascar.

After the surrender of France in 1940 and the setting up of the puppet Vichy Government, the large island of Madagascar, lying off the south-east coast of Africa, and hitherto part of the French Colonial Empire, immediately became an active menace to our sea communications, furnishing as it did a most convenient base for enemy activity against our vital shipping-lane between Durban and Suez.

The British Navy therefore convoyed an Expeditionary Force to Madagascar early in 1942, and a surprise attack was launched. Some extremely hard fighting was necessary before the island (which is two or three times the size of Great Britain) could be completely occupied by our troops.

As usual, the Force was accompanied by a unit of Q.A.I.M.N.S. Here is a brief record of the service rendered by those Nursing Sisters who reached Madagascar on May 5th, 1942, on board the Hospital Ship *Atlantis*.

Continuous fighting was in progress when they arrived, and casualties began to come on board the same night.

On the morning of the 7th [the Matron tells us] we sailed round the point to the harbour Diego Suarez, where more patients were waiting for us. Altogether we had about 200 casualties.

These patients were brought out to us in barges; and after crawling two miles through red dust, you can imagine what a state they were in. The theatre staff had very little rest for forty-eight hours, but stood up to it well. My very

T

good stock of Red Cross Stores came in so useful: I do not know what we should have done without it.

The Red Cross never seems to have failed, whatever the time or place.

Besides the accommodation for patients in the *Atlantis*, there was also available a French hospital of fifty beds, which after it had been cleaned up—it was in a shocking state—proved quite useful.

A startling episode of that particular visit was the torpedoing of two British ships in this harbour, late one evening. Fortunately the *Atlantis* escaped.

The *Atlantis*, whenever her full complement of patients was made up, conveyed them across to Durban and there discharged them, returning to Madagascar to load up afresh.

VI

One more ocean excursion of the *Atlantis* must be mentioned here, but in a very different connexion.

The year was now 1945, and the war with Germany was practically over. Germany itself was in course of occupation, but heavy fighting was still in progress, and our Allies, the Americans, who were by this time carrying a full two-thirds of the burden of the European campaign, had incurred heavy casualties. In these circumstances it was the proud duty of the *Atlantis* to convey a shipload of American sick and wounded back to their native land.

This was a novel and exciting assignment for the Sisters and R.A.M.C. staff in charge. Victory was already in the air, and the Atlantic crossing had by this time lost most of its terrors. Moreover, the ship was filled with American soldiers, so Q.A.I.M.N.S. had opportunity to make the acquaintance of that great person 'G.I. Joe'. Above all, the ship's destination, if all went well, was New York City, with its fabled wonders and delights.

The weather was not too kind—it was typical North Atlantic winter weather, in fact—and seasickness marred the enjoyment of the opening stages of what had promised to be something of a pleasure trip.   But these troubles usually pass quickly.

> We went swaying or staggering along [we are told], making every effort to keep vertical and carry on, until the pale and green faces gradually gave place to rosy complexions.
> During those early days we were especially grateful to the R.S.M. and the nursing orderlies, who never let the Sisters down, and carried on the routine of the wards until the new Sisters found their sea-legs.

But all these tribulations were forgotten as the *Atlantis* approached New York.   The first indication that the ship's company received that they were nearing the end of their journey was furnished by an American Coastal Patrol aeroplane, which appeared early one morning and circled over them as if welcoming them to the New World.
Then came the actual arrival, and the first glimpse of the 'cloud-capped towers' of Manhattan Island.

> Out of a clear pale-blue sky ahead on our starboard side, appeared pinnacles of grey, and we all watched the tall stately skyscrapers of New York come to reality.   On the left (port) side the Statue of Liberty broke into view, with the sun's rays gilding her spiked coronet.

It was certainly a different prospect and a different welcome from that which had awaited a good many of the ship's passengers on the Normandy beaches less than a year before.

> Down the gangway about twenty of us went, showing our passes to the N.P.A. police patrols, and out to the well-guarded dock-gates, where cars were awaiting us, driven by Volunteer Red Cross drivers.   This was the beginning of days of most generous hospitality.

It certainly was. From the moment of their arrival the Sisters seem to have been entertained or fêted from morning till night. They visited the Empire State Building, they shopped in Fifth Avenue, they were taken to parties and the Opera. They were even entertained at a specially organized 'English high tea', consisting of scrambled eggs, strawberry jam, and hot toasted muffins. Most gratifying of all, everyone they met agreed that the Q.A.I.M.N.S. grey and scarlet uniform was the smartest they had ever seen.

It is a thousand pities, incidentally, that that uniform was not seen more frequently in our own streets. But Q.A. Sisters are military officers, and like other British military officers prefer to appear when off duty in mufti.

Their professional interests were not overlooked, for they were taken to visit such institutions as the New York Medical Centre and Belle Vue Hospital. Altogether they seem to have crowded the maximum of instruction, amusement, and new and stimulating companionship into the few days at their disposal; and when at the end of their visit they gathered once more on board the *Atlantis*, to return to the stern realities of warfare not yet completely accomplished, it was with renewed energy and the happiest of memories.

CHAPTER 20

OPERATION OVERLORD

Now, at long last, all Allied commitments in other theatres had been successfully discharged, and the time had come for the supreme effort of the war. The Allied forces were approaching maximum strength, and munition output was at its peak.

The spring of 1944 was designated as 'target date', and the coming adventure was christened, not inappropriately, OPERATION OVERLORD.

The Allied plan of operations was very different from that anticipated by the one-track-minded Rommel, who was in charge of the French coastal defences. Instead of incurring heavy casualties in an attempt, possibly fruitless, to secure a French harbour as a base of operations, the Allies had hit upon the ingenious idea of bringing their own harbour with them. In point of fact they brought two—one for the British and one for the American landings. These floating 'Mulberry' docks were towed across the Channel in sections, and each section was sunk in its appointed position in the Baie de la Seine upon the Normandy coast, between the Cotentin peninsula and the River Arne.

The British and Canadian forces were to land on the left and the Americans on the right. The operation contemplated a great scythe-like sweep, first south and then east, by the Americans, while the British, acting as a hinge, kept the main enemy forces pinned down in the neighbourhood of Caen on the coast, drawing as many of Rommel's reserves as possible to the left (or eastern) Allied flank, and thus liberating the Americans, out on the right wing, for a rapid advance up to the Seine about Paris.

Of the brilliant and successful part played by the Americans in this elaborate plan there is no need to speak here. We are concerned solely in this narrative with the British 21st Army Group, comprising the Second British Army, the First Canadian Army, the British Airborne troops, and various smaller Allied contingents.

The American forces engaged were at the outset roughly of the same strength as the British, but during the months which followed, culminating in the invasion of Germany and the victorious ending of the war, the preponderance of American troops to British increased steadily—Britain had but few reserves remaining by this time, while the United States were just beginning to get into their giant stride—until by the end of the campaign the American battle-front was at least twice as great as the British. None the less the British contribution was at least of proportionate value. General Sir Bernard Montgomery commanded all the Allied land forces until September 1st, when General Eisenhower took over the Supreme Command himself.

The successful Allied landing on D-Day, June 6th, 1944, was the fruit of months of deep planning and close integration, in which all Arms played their part to the full. As a result, the problem of effecting a successful large-scale amphibious invasion of a strongly held enemy coast, which had baffled successively Philip of Spain, Napoleon Bonaparte, and Adolf Hitler, was solved for the first time in modern history.

II

The Armada which crossed to France on D-Day was unlike anything of its kind ever seen before. The troops and their equipment, including tanks and artillery, were carried for the most part in flat-bottomed craft specially designed for quick landing upon a tidal beach. They were escorted by ships of the Royal Navy and were accompanied by tankers, aircraft carriers, mine-sweepers, and store-ships. There were even cable ships contributed by the Post Office, to establish immediate and continuous communication between the home base and the beaches. One of these was mined and sunk with loss of life. There was also a contingent from N.A.A.F.I., ready to supply the material comforts of a campaign to the troops as soon as they should have established a footing.

The forces employed were for the most part composed of young soldiers, as yet untried in battle, but trained with an intensity hitherto unknown and equipped with every engine of war that modern scientific research could produce. In other words, our soldiers, after nearly four years of a constant struggle against odds, were at last prepared to undertake the offensive on a grand scale as the British Army of Liberation, or B.L.A.

Needless to say the invading flotilla was furnished with its full quota of hospital ships and hospital carriers, as well as store-ships conveying the equipment necessary for the setting up of field hospitals. The Nursing staffs of these hospitals did not accompany the first wave of invasion; their time would come when the hospitals were erected. Meanwhile they were assembled in marshalling areas at home, ready for immediate embarkation whenever the call should come. They had not long to wait, as we shall see. The majority of them were young and without previous experience of active service, and correspondingly eager, after the monotony of home training, to encounter the realities of their calling at first hand.

III

To disembark upon a hostile shore from a landing-craft is an experience in itself, as the troops on D-Day had already realized.

Their first discovery was that a Landing Craft, Infantry (or L.C.I.), though an admirable medium of debarkation on arrival, is a most uncomfortable vehicle in the process of transit, especially in bad weather. The weather on D-Day itself was atrocious, and it is to the lasting credit of those young soldiers who stormed their way up the beaches of Arromanches on that first morning that most of them had barely recovered from the prostrating effects of seasickness.

Nursing Sisters were protected as far as possible from this unpleasant experience by being conveyed across the Channel in hospital carriers, or other transport, and then transhipped off the Normandy coast into landing-craft; so their ordeal in bad weather was limited to the shortest possible period.

Here is the average itinerary of a Nursing Sister's progress from a Marshalling Area in the United Kingdom (disrespectfully alluded to by the Sisters themselves as a 'Concentration Camp') to a tented hospital ward behind the battle-lines in Normandy, probably in the neighbourhood of Caen or Bayeux, as described in her own words.

> At last the day dawned when we were actually to leave. We were called before it was light and climbed into troop-carrying vehicles and set off for the port. For miles the roads were lined by American troops on both sides, and they cheered us most enthusiastically. We were all going the same way!
>
> We set about going to war very comfortably, in one of our own hospital ships. The amount of shipping in the port was fantastic, and all the way across the Channel the traffic was unending. There was every conceivable type of craft as far as we could see. As we neared France, some floating mines had to be blown up, quite close to us.
>
> And then France came in sight. A church steeple in the distance, a solitary ruined house, and a beach where amphibious vehicles were busily running up and down. That was France.
>
> There came a terrific explosion somewhere inland, and a great column of smoke rose in the air. Further in the distance were flashes, and the sound of battle.
>
> We climbed down on to a Tank Landing Craft, counted our flock again, and set foot on the soil of France at Courseilles, up the coast a bit from Arromanches.

So far, so good—exceptionally good, in fact. But let us pause here to note that not all such passages were either so smooth or so pleasantly exciting. Here is another and different picture, derived from a less happy experience.

The party of Sisters upon this occasion numbered eighty-one in all, and were as usual conveyed across the Channel in a hospital ship. They arrived off the Normandy coast in the evening, and were informed that they could spend the night on board and would be landed by daylight in the morning.

Then, as frequently happens on these occasions, they were informed about 10 p.m. that plans had been changed, and that a Tank Landing Craft was on its way out to convey them ashore.

The Sisters were thrilled by the news, but Matron was not so sure; and her doubts were soon justified, for to descend from a tall ship on to an elusive landing-craft in a heavy swell and in pitch darkness is no mean undertaking, especially for a party of novices.

> The cable parted once, and we had quite a long jump. (We were all wearing slacks at the time.) Fortunately we managed to make it.
>
> When we shoved off, which must have been about midnight, the moon shone out in all its glory. The heavy swell and the standing and swaying on the open L.T.C. was too much for many of the Sisters, and they were violently sick.
>
> Suddenly there was great air activity. Shrapnel whizzed over our heads. 'Put on your steel helmets,' I called. We had to remain there in the open. Though terrifying, it was a grand sight—glorious sky and moon, hundreds of red lights, and a marvellous display of fireworks and droning planes.

But the troubles of this particular unit were not yet over. As the landing-craft entered the Mulberry harbour, a man emerged from the lighthouse guarding the mouth and announced firmly: 'Cargo cannot be landed tonight.'

> The answer to that one was: 'Cargo consists of eighty-one Nursing Sisters!' The word came back: 'Wait!' We went round in circles for ages, and still more Sisters were seasick.

The air fight overhead was terrific. Presently a young sailor came swaying along with a bucket of tea, saying: 'I thought you might like a drink while you are waiting.' How we enjoyed it!

The enjoyment was enhanced by the discovery of a bottle of brandy in a locker, a small dose from which worked wonders all round. Ultimately a landing was effected, and the Sisters subsided on to the sand-dunes until their land transport arrived, about 3.30 a.m.

The next stage in these journeys always took the form of a long and bumpy drive inland, over ground which had till recently been a battlefield, in search of one's hospital—or possibly hospital-site—as often as not through a military camp.

There were soldiers mending a road. I was struck by the amazing change in their expression when they saw the Sisters. Their faces lit up: they waved and cheered: one could hear them calling out: 'English girls!' English Sisters!

That fact made up, it seemed, for all previous tribulations.

We passed fields and fields of parked war equipment, and there was a ceaseless stream of lorries and the most weird and wonderful tanks and vehicles. By the roadside we saw numerous temporary graves, already decked with flowers by the French people. The roads were very dusty, and badly rutted. Here and there great wide by-passes were cut through the crops. Poor France!

In due course each unit reached its own hospital area. Sometimes several of these hospitals were grouped *pro tem.* in a single area, until the Commanding Officer should have selected suitable and more permanent sites.

There was one huge kitchen, in the open, for so many hospitals. We all queued up for meals, and most people squatted on the ground and picnicked. There were big marquee dining-tents near the kitchen. The Sisters lived in other marquees, twenty-five beds in each. Their laundry fluttered from the tent-ropes; they washed their hair and dried it in the sun. It was a gypsy life. Water had to be fetched from a distance and heated on open fires. Terrific air-fights continued at night.

Meanwhile the hospitals were going up. There was desperate need of those, for the enemy were resisting strongly in the neighbourhood of Falaise, and casualties were heavy. Here is one account.

One morning Matron and I went to see the site of our hospital, five miles away. It was a beautiful summer's morning that shone on these fields marked with our own hospital number. There were four cows grazing peacefully, who stopped to gaze at us curiously, while some wobbly geese took their way across the field in front of them. All round were thick hawthorn hedges and tall trees. It seemed impossible to believe that a fierce battle, where men were being wounded, and dying, was raging not ten miles away.

Presently our C.O. arrived, with the officers in charge of the Medical and Surgical Division, and planned out the details. That clump of thistles would be the theatre; the surgical block could be where the geese were. Medical Division in that field; offices here. The Sisters? Well, what about that orchard, under the cider-apple trees? Good! Officers' Mess next door.

And so it was planned, just standing there, visualizing 1,200 beds.

After that events moved rapidly. The relentless bulldozers got to work, and the sylvan beauty of this little corner of France vanished for the duration. Concrete was laid for the operating-theatre and X-ray. Tented wards sprang into being. Cookhouses were constructed. Beds, and other equipment which had arrived on time from the beaches (despite the fact that the last desperate battle for Caen was in progress, and a complete armoured division had passed by the hospital site, bumper to bumper, for thirty-six hours), were unpacked, scrubbed, and made up. After only four days of strenuous preparation, Hospital Headquarters were able to announce that they could 'take patients tomorrow'.

And they did. The first convoy of 400 ambulances began to arrive at 3 p.m. next day, and continued until 3 a.m.

How everyone worked! No longer a rural scene; only the intense activity of a large working hospital. Surgeons, Sisters and Orderlies were working eight-hour shifts in the theatre. A dynamo had been set up and was just able to produce enough light for the operations, but that was all. In the wards and reception tents we worked with two lanterns apiece, in strict black-out. There were enemy raids, and shrapnel from A.A. guns coming down. Sometimes when we did get to bed in the orchard, we would leap out again when an apple fell on the tent with as much noise as the shrapnel itself!

And so it went on, day after day. The pressure at this time was extreme, and young Sisters who had but recently finished their training in hospitals where there was every convenience and everything laid on for their use, learned in a day, we are told, to improvise and make-do, continuing at their work until they were ordered away from the wards and bidden to get some sleep and rest.

And the emotional strain was considerable, even for the most experienced.

The wounds, especially the burns, which were frightful, the wonderful bravery and cheerfulness of the men—these were things which, try as one might, made it impossible to remain altogether unaffected. Emotion, on the top of hard physical work and mental concentration, is apt to form an additional drain upon one's stock of vital and precious energy. Yet these young Sisters stood up to the strain of those days unfailingly.

In due course General Montgomery's scheme for rounding up the enemy in the famous 'Falaise Pocket' was successfully achieved, and wounded German prisoners of war came pouring into the hospital.

Among them were two German nurses. They had only what they stood up in—pink-and-white check uniforms and white aprons. We kept one small tent for them, and although unhurt they were much shaken by their experiences and cried easily. They were not keen to do any work among their own wounded, either. They stayed about ten days.

In one ward we had only one prisoner who could speak English. He had lived in Manchester until 1938 and was an S.S. sergeant. I asked him to explain to the other P.O.W.s what was expected of them with regard to ward discipline. What he said or did to them we never knew, but in two days the other Germans were so cowed that he had hastily to be returned to the Prisoners' Cage!

With the clearance of the Falaise Pocket and the onward sweep of the 21st Army Group the pressure of work in the hospitals round Caen began to slacken, as did the excitement of sustained effort. Autumn too was approaching, and the weather became cold and damp. Sleeping in tents under apple-trees began to lose something of its romance. The problem also arose of keeping the patients in the marquees and the Sisters in their Mess tent reasonably warm. Was it possible to install any kind of heating apparatus, within flimsy canvas walls, which would be both effective and safe?

The Pioneer Section of the Royal Engineers were more than equal to the occasion.

Next day, when I returned to the hospital, I found several Pioneers outside the marquee, busily mixing mud and empty oil-drums. The Sisters had given them cigarettes and beer, and they seemed in great form. Next day the fire-place was finished and in place, with a glorious fire in the grate. The whole thing was made out of oil-drums and mud, *with* a mantelpiece. The front was painted to repre-sent a brick fireplace of green tiles!

With the setting in of autumnal rain and mud the inestimable Sappers placed the Sisters still further in their debt by an overhaul of the rather sketchy sanitary arrangements which had been made to suffice during the summer months. This provided not only protection from the elements but a welcome increase of privacy.

The outstanding handicap in these tented camps was, as ever, a perpetual shortage of water. The arrival of the water-cart, we are told, was the event of the day. Laundry was always a diffi-culty and baths almost an impossibility.

The hospital lay somewhat remote from the nearest town, and the Sisters had no transport of their own. But this mattered little, for the art of hitch-hiking is easily acquired on active service.

One got lifts [we are told] on anything from a sand-lorry to a Staff car. No one was ever refused.

Presently it became obvious that the hospitals in the Caen area were beginning to outlive their usefulness. The time was fast approaching when some of them at least must uproot them-selves from their present surroundings and follow the flag farther afield—across the Seine, across the Somme, into Belgium and the Low Countries, whither the 21st Army Group had already penetrated, on the road to Arnhem and the Rhine.

Accordingly a certain number of the hospitals received orders to move. The remainder were transferred for the winter into Nissen huts.

It was bitterly cold, and rained for days on end. The

mud thickened and deepened. There were nights when we were flooded out of our tents, when the mud got under the tarpaulin or the ground became a squelchy mess; days and weeks of wearing gum-boots that were sometimes sucked off.

We stayed taking patients until the other hospitals were settled for the winter, until at last our orders came to move: and the packing of equipment, beds, lockers, store kettles and medicines, with the striking of tents and the loading of eighty lorries, began.

Once we went to visit a site where another hospital had stood. Somehow it seemed to be full of ghosts. A water-tap and a slab where the theatre had been; a road overgrown with weeds—these were all that was left of a place where so much had happened. And yet, all the life and death, all the drama, all the mingled sorrow and laughter of the place —somehow they were still there, in those empty fields.

And now we were to leave *our* fields, on Tuesday morning.

IV

In June 1944, as already noted, the Nursing Services landed close on the heels of the B.L.A. The first hospitals to arrive after the invasion were the 81st and 86th British General, of 200 beds each (tented), on June 9th and 10th respectively. These had been preceded by their casualty clearing stations.

The first contingent of Nursing Sisters landed on June 16th at 9.15 p.m., and were at work next day.

These, as usual, had received intensive training in their 'Concentration Camps' at home, including instruction in such matters as gas-drill, marching, saluting, tent-pitching, and the carrying out of elaborate large-scale operational schemes.

As D-Day approached they were moved first to Brasenose College, Oxford, and then to a camp in the New Forest, near to their port of embarkation.

The camp [one of the Sisters tells us] was run jointly by

British and Americans. The food was typically American. Peaches and cream three times a day proved almost too much for us!

The D-Day boys had already gone, but they had left messages for us chalked up on the walls: *'Good luck to the girls!'*

It should be added that on their arrival off the Normandy beaches a few days later, the Sisters were greeted by a chorus delivered through megaphones from a neighbouring L.C.I.: *'Nursie, Come over Here and Hold my Hand!'*

Other hospital units followed, and soon everyone was hard at work. As already noted, the great majority of the Sisters were young, and were facing active service conditions for the first time. Their first reaction, naturally enough, was of pity and compassion.

> I looked round the wards. Rows of stretchers, all occupied by poor boys, blown about, disfigured, maimed for life some of them, in the bloom of youth. I felt like choking; a few tears came into my eyes.
>
> But this was only momentary. Immediately I was off with my jacket and set to work—dressing, blood transfusions, penicillin injections; but most of all a cheery word here and there.

With the fall of Caen the hospitals began to move forward in the wake of the Army—'leap-frogging through France'. One unit found itself in Rouen. Here the hospital had been set up in a substantial brick building—a hotel—accommodation which, after months of tent-life, appeared positively luxurious. The premises had been occupied by the Germans up to the moment of their retreat, and they had left some of their wounded there, in charge of nine German nurses.

In Rouen, too, our Nursing Sisters had their first opportunity to meet their French 'opposite numbers', besides enjoying a good deal of purely civilian hospitality.

Several French ladies, introduced by the Mayoress, visited the hospital each week, bringing fruit and flowers for the patients; their whole attitude was one of friendliness and a desire to help. One of these, the Matron of the *Hospice Générale*, invited us to tea one day, to meet some French nurses. It was most interesting to talk with them and hear their views on the different branches of the service. Some of them had attended the International Course of Lectures in London before the war, and knew many of the leading hospitals and members of our nursing world.

With them we stood on one of the hospital balconies and looked down on the scene of devastation about us. They told us that a few weeks ago they had stood and watched the fighting from this very window, and how great their excitement and relief had been when suddenly they saw the French flag float up to the roof of a neighbouring building, giving them the wonderful news of their liberation.

By this time the British hospitals had become an established feature of most of the French landscape. There was considerable employment of French civilian labour. Many French civilians worked as stretcher-bearers between the wards and the operating theatre—and thereby hangs a tale. Let the Sister concerned tell it herself.

Among our Surgical patients was one with a twisted cartilage of the knee, whom we had prepared for the operating theatre. When he was ready the French civilians whom we employed as stretcher-bearers were summoned. After putting the man on to the stretcher I turned to the bearers and gave the order, 'Theatre!' '*Oui, oui!*' they replied, and marched off.

Imagine our surprise when, half an hour later, a theatre orderly arrived in the ward to inquire about this particular case, as he had not yet been brought to the theatre and everyone was waiting. After a diligent search of the hos-

U

pital we finally located our patient, thoroughly enjoying himself at an 'Ensa' show in the concert-hall at the top of the building.

v

Such were some of the experiences and achievements of Q.A.I.M.N.S. during OPERATION OVERLORD. Here are the impressions of the Matron-in-Chief, Dame Katharine Jones, D.B.E., summarized by her in a broadcast in July 1944, after a flying visit to the B.L.A.

It was a flying visit in all senses of the word. I went by aeroplane, and I stayed only four-and-a-half days, but I saw the whole set-up of the treatment of the wounded, from the time when they reached the first units in which Q.A.I.M.N.S. Sisters are working (about five miles from the front line) to the planes and hospital carriers on the coast, waiting to bring them home to the hospitals in the United Kingdom.

Up the line there is the whole magnificent R.A.M.C. Organization, which rescues a man from the actual battle-field and performs the most urgent operations. Then, when he gets to a casualty clearing station, the Q.A.I.M.N.S. take over and begin their work.

Watching the convoys of motor ambulances, loaded and driven with the utmost care and consideration, I noticed some marked with a large card hanging on the radiator: 'Urgent Case'. These are given priority on the road.

Dame Katharine went on to describe the work in the casualty clearing stations, and the closely integrated team-work of the Medical Officers, the Sisters, and the R.A.M.C. Orderlies, in the theatre, the resuscitation tent, and the wards. Many of the patients were soon ready for evacuation to areas farther in rear; but there were always some who had to be tided over a serious period of collapse, exhaustion, or hæmorrhage, by being put into real beds for a period of real rest.

As for the patients themselves:

I saw patients of all kinds. It was a grim sight, but in all my tour I only saw one man in acute pain. It is a blessed thing that there are in these modern days means of controlling the pain of body injury, both in peace and war; these means are always at hand in our casualty clearing stations and hospitals.

For their comfort and protection all the Sisters now wear khaki battle-dress blouses and slacks; they nurse their patients on stretchers for a great deal of the time, and facilities for laundry are very scarce. But whenever possible they will wear their grey-and-scarlet indoor uniform again.

Dame Katharine also visited various hospitals, both 200- and 600-bedded, and paid tribute in her broadcast to the astonishing speed and dispatch with which our Pioneers and R.A.M.C. workers could clear an entire hayfield and erect a tented hospital on it in something like forty-eight hours.

I saw the first 600-bedded hospital that had arrived in this country, now fully established. It was at this hospital that I saw the trench in which fifty Sisters had slept for the first few nights after their arrival, with enemy action overhead.

General Montgomery had visited this hospital two days before, and the Sisters lined up at the entrance to wave him good-bye as he went. He shook hands with every one of them, and their pride was immense.

In these bigger hospitals the wards really looked like wards. Except for the canvas walls, the patients might almost imagine themselves in hospital in England—beds, with sheets and clean blankets; lockers with a space for the little belongings each man needs to keep near at hand; the gifts he has received in his Red Cross bag, or those 'souvenirs' he has contrived to bring back with him from the front line.

Dame Katharine also described the relief afforded to a broken man by encasing him in plaster, and thus saving him from the jolting and jarring inevitable in a long ambulance journey over a rough road.

On these plasters the history of the wound is written in bold letters, so that each Medical Officer may know whether further medical treatment is required. In this way the patients are cared for by the team-work of Medical Officers and Sisters miles apart.

Last of all came the Central Evacuation Point, whither all the casualties were brought on their stretchers for evacuation in Hospital Carriers—a never-ending task, it seemed.

The cook said that he had cooked on one day for 1,600 people; and the Officer Commanding told me that a Hospital Carrier was loaded daily.

The Matron-in-Chief concludes with a warm tribute to the devoted service of the Nursing Sisters.

It was an inspiration to see it all for myself; and it will remain with me as a precious memory of the Military Medical Units on active service.

These words were broadcast upon the actual day of Dame Katharine's own retirement from the post of Matron-in-Chief, after a lifetime devoted to the service of her King and Country.

CHAPTER 21

ON TO THE RHINE

WITH the Falaise Pocket disposed of, the road now lay open to Belgium and the Rhine. Q.A. Units were everywhere warmly welcomed on their journey north, and the farther north they progressed the more enthusiastic grew their reception.

> In Belgium, in small villages as well as large towns, the reception given us was splendid. Unlike Venice, with its Battles of Flowers, ours became a Battle of Fruit. We were just drowned in it: grapes, pears, apples, peaches, tomatoes were all thrown to us.

The immediate destination of this particular hospital was Diest, to the north-east of Brussels. On their way the Sisters had passed through Rouen, Amiens, and other familiar-sounding towns and villages. Their first stop was at Aubigny, a village not far beyond Falaise. Here they attended to numerous French civilians who had incurred bodily injuries in the fighting. One Sister was called up in the middle of one night to perform what was under these circumstances an unusual task—that of assisting a French baby into this world—an event which created a feminine flutter of excitement throughout the hospital.

At Amiens they remained for a week or more, and took over a section of a French hospital recently occupied by the Germans and, as usual, left in a filthy condition. Cleaning operations were barely completed when a heavily loaded convoy of wounded arrived, and for three days everyone was working overtime.

Presently they were off again, traversing a road trodden by

the feet of thousands of British soldiers in two wars—Arras, Lille, and Douai. Vimy Ridge was visible in the distance. Lastly came the excitement of crossing the frontier into Belgium, where their reception has already been described. Some of them were greeted as *les femmes soldats*.

On the way out of Brussels towards Diest their lorries passed under some railway arches, to the appropriate accompaniment of Flanagan and Allen's famous 'signature tune', 'Underneath the Arches', proffered in chorus by a contingent of British infantry passing by in troop-carriers.

It was all in harmony, and was really magnificent.

The hospital at Diest proved a sad disappointment, for the enemy had done all damage possible, putting the gas, water and electricity supplies out of action before evacuation, besides planting various booby-traps in the hospital and its immediate neighbourhood. However, five days of hard scrubbing by the Sisters and repair work by the Engineers restored some measure of order and cleanliness, and the wards were open to patients.

This was what may be called the Arnhem period, in the late autumn of 1944, which witnessed the great British effort, aided by two American Airborne Divisions, to overleap the triple barrier of the Maas, Waal, and Lower Rhine—each a separate mouth of the Rhine itself—into Holland and Northern Germany. The attempt just failed, a circumstance which made it clear that the war could not now be won before winter set in. This was doubly unfortunate, because the inhabitants of London and elsewhere were at this time enduring the unremitting attentions of the Vi bomb.

II

A military setback always means a heavy casualty list, and some of our hospitals in the Low Countries soon found themselves promoted from 'Bed and Breakfast Hospitals' (merely treating cases for immediate evacuation to the United Kingdom) to fully employed General Hospitals dealing with innumerable serious casualties, some of them of a new and unfamiliar type.

Here, for the first time, the Sisters had an opportunity to study, in full detail, the progress achieved by modern scientific research in devising ever fresh methods of mutual extermination.

Some of the most appalling injuries to be dealt with had been caused by burns. With flame-throwers both sides had been made familiar in the First World War, but with the advent of the tank, and the risks attendant upon fire or explosion within its confined space, together with the wholesale employment of the petrol engine in place of the horse, this particular horror had been increased tenfold. A single sample will probably be more than sufficient for the reader.

One day at lunch-time we received without warning five cases of burns, as a result of a tanker blowing up in harbour. These were fifth and sixth degree burns, involving faces, heads, necks, hands and legs. It seemed impossible to find a corner which was not burned. From the moment of their arrival these men had to be treated with the utmost care. Air-beds, cradles, and every device to keep them warm, and yet not to allow anything to touch them, were brought into service. For the first eighteen hours they were too severely shocked to receive any treatment at all, except to be given morphia, hot drinks, and local application of heat.

The remains of their clothing were cut off, for they were soaked from having been thrown into the sea; some indeed had no clothes left on them at all. Their poor faces were swollen and their eyes closed; they could hardly open their lips, and so began to contract acute dyspnoea. The tracheotomy set was got ready, but, thank God, we did not need it.

The first night, to our great distress, we lost one man, but the others began to do as we had expected. Two men were given saline baths in the wards and had their backs and thighs painted with silver nitrate: their faces, hands and arms were treated with sulphanilamide cream. One of them

was sent to the theatre to be scrubbed and treated normally:
he was the only one considered fit for anæsthetics.

A few recovered quickly, but the others remained in a
critical condition for several weeks. They could neither
speak nor move: we fed them through fine rubber tubing.
We spent hours reassuring them, and planning with them
what they would do when they were better, and helping
them to use their hands and fingers—literally nothing but
bits of charred bone.

That any of these men should have recovered at all speaks
volumes, firstly for the devoted care with which they were
tended and coaxed back to life, and secondly for the astonishing
resilience of the human frame and the invincibility of the human
spirit. But it was a trying experience for the Sisters, and indeed
for all who witnessed the sufferings of their patients.

One day the Captain of their ship came to visit them.
The Sister in charge of their ward interviewed him and
warned him that they were unrecognizable. However, he
still said he wished to see them. Within five minutes of his
entering the ward the Sister had to bring him out again,
for he had just collapsed into her arms. He was given hot
sweet tea, but it was some time before he could control his
tears.

Cases of this kind, it need hardly be said, were by no means
exceptional. Presently, with the launching of the attack on the
Dutch island of Walcheren by the Canadian Army, their number
increased.

The family of burns increased by leaps and bounds, mostly
fifth and sixth degree burns, incurred from flame-throwers
or in blazing ships on the beaches.

Yet the majority of these men recovered, though the process
was slow and painful. The Sisters worked unceasingly to restore
their bodily strength and mental balance. They held their

cigarettes for them while they smoked; they kept moving their bodies into fresh positions, an inch or two at a time; they bathed hands and soaked eyes; they even encouraged them to play an imaginary piano to keep their fingers from stiffening.

And they had their reward. As the days passed, new skin began to appear under the crusts of the sulphanilamide cream, and the men began to open their eyes and look about them. They were greatly interested in one another's appearance, and this fact rendered a patient less concerned with his own. 'I don't look as bad as he does, Sister, do I?' was a constant query. Some of their accustomed cheerfulness came back to them. They sat up in bed and took an increased interest in all that was going on, even chaffing the Sisters—an infallible sign of approaching convalescence.

One of the most astonishing recoveries in this hospital was that of a patient who was ultimately (and rightly) christened the Miracle Man. Here is a *résumé* of his history sheet.

He came to us a week after being wounded high up in the chest. Two days later, to our dismay, he started discharging undigested food through his chest-wound. This, to say the least of it, was alarming. X-rays were taken, and that evening he was conveyed to the theatre, where it was discovered that he had had a piece of shrapnel through his lung, through his diaphragm, into his stomach.

Every attempt was made to remove the shrapnel, but in vain, and he returned to the ward in a most critical condition. Two days later he had a severe hæmorrhage, and three days after that another; then another, after a further two days. He was again taken to the theatre, and this time the shrapnel was recovered, together with a large piece of battle-dress!

Now he is walking about the ward, very thin, but recovered. His appetite is phenomenal; his great weakness is ice-cream, with a glass of champagne. He certainly deserves both, for he is the bravest man I ever knew. Until evacuated, he was our ward mascot.

Grim though the experiences were of many of the men wounded in the Second World War, their sufferings were to a great extent offset and mitigated by the progress, *pari passu* with the technique of slaughter and disablement, of the art of healing and, above all, of the alleviation of pain.

Mention has been made more than once in these pages of the incalculable benefits conferred by blood-transfusion, intravenous injections, penicillin, and the like; but perhaps the greatest boon to the sufferer himself has been the progress made by modern science in the employment of quick-acting anæsthetics and sedatives. Florence Nightingale's Crimean patients, as we have seen, were accustomed to be operated on without anæsthetics at all. In the South African war the use of chloroform had become universal in major operations, but chloroform, though an undoubted boon, is not a mixed blessing so far as its actual administration and immediate after-effects are concerned. To-day a patient can be plunged into complete unconsciousness by the prick of a needle; while such sedatives as morphia have brought relief and comfort to innumerable beds of pain.

Above all, Florence Nightingale's simple gospel of absolute cleanliness or, to employ a more pretentious title, the universal employment of antiseptic treatment—has in these days reached complete fulfilment and saved thousands of human lives.

III

One of the most tragic features of intensified modern warfare has been the dire result, in certain cases, of its impact upon the human mind.

In the First World War we used to speak of 'shell-shock cases' —men who, though unwounded, had been mentally prostrated for the time being by their battle experiences, and must be soothed, comforted, and rested until nature had resumed control and restored to them their normal faculties.

Various specifics were tried, not unsuccessfully. I (the writer) retain a vivid recollection of a vast dock-shed in Southampton in

July 1916, crowded from end to end with stretchers containing the first contingent of wounded from the First Battle of the Somme. In one corner, somewhat apart from the rest, lay the shell-shock cases. They were being attended by a professional mesmerist, who had been called in to lull their wandering, unhappy minds, if he could, to some sort of restful oblivion.

We have progressed since then, and the study and care of what are now known as psychiatric casualties has become an important item of medical research. In 1944 a special unit, the 32nd British General Hospital, was sent out to Normandy for this purpose.

Here are the observations of a Sister engaged in this particular hospital.

To those of us who had never seen acute battle-exhaustion cases before this new experience was intensely interesting. The symptoms were such that it was obvious to all that nursing care was urgently required. The majority of patients were admitted on stretchers and needed assistance with washing, shaving, and general care. Many of them could not walk, talk or feed themselves. They required sedatives at night; and even so, their sleep was frequently disturbed by battle-dreams. They required constant re-assurance, especially when any noises, such as gunfire, or aeroplanes overhead, could be heard.

On October 21st, following the advancing armies into Belgium, we again opened this hospital, in quarters architecturally beautiful, spotlessly clean, and pervaded with the atmosphere of welcome.

On admission, a personal greeting and introduction to fellow-patients help the patient to accept the idea that hospital treatment is really necessary for him. In this introduction the Sister plays an important part: the patient becomes aware in his immediate surroundings of a sympathetic and reassuring authority, and one in which he has confidence.

Selected cases, usually Anxiety States and Depression, are

given deep sedatives in a quiet ward set apart for this treatment. Here the patients are kept from three to five days, during which they need constant care and attention, having to be washed, shaved and hand-fed. Many re-live their battle experiences during this period.

As soon as these days of sedation are over, the patient returns to his own ward and takes part in the ordinary hospital routine.

In due course came the period of convalescence. Upon reaching this the patient was put back into normal khaki and marked for what was known as Grade I or Grade II training, consisting for most part of organized games under the supervision of N.C.O.s of the Army Physical Training Corps. Occupational Therapy was encouraged, under which the men learned to enjoy the pleasant distraction of turning out useful or ornamental articles, including various types of embroidery, some of it of surprisingly high quality.

Thus, though sometimes by slow degrees, the patient was brought back to his normal workaday self. The basis of the cure lay in the scientific consideration of each particular case, with appropriate treatment.

Still, when all is said and done, psychiatry is still in the experimental and tentative stage. What really sets a battle-shocked soldier on his feet again is the sympathetic understanding and unremitting care of the Sister in charge of him. It is the human touch that counts most, and always will—and in Q.A.I.M.N.S. that touch, as we know, was never lacking.

IV

Medical units toiling along in the wake of an invading army have a strenuous time of it, as was soon realized by the nursing staffs of the hospitals trying to keep pace with the B.L.A. during its victorious advance through France and Belgium in the autumn of 1944. They were constantly on the move, and systematic control of transport was difficult. Frequently personnel would arrive at a new station some way ahead of their hospital equipment, with resultant vexation and delay in getting to work.

In these pioneer days [one Sister tells us] each hospital, large or small, was a front-line unit, acting solely as a casualty clearing station. On one occasion we got into action just in time to make history, by opening in under twenty-four hours to admit the largest convoy of wounded on record—over 600 strong.

Far into that night of feverish preparation we had toiled—the ward personnel, the officers, 'Q' and his minions, the Steward's Store, the Field Cookhouses, the R.E., the Pioneers—all the complex machinery of a vast hospital creaking into action.

Much of our equipment had not yet arrived, and at every turn we were beset by difficulties, petty in themselves, but productive of endless trouble. The stationery was missing; there was hardly a book in the place. The dispensary had medicines enough to cure the whole British Army, but no bottles into which to put them. Essential types of medical stores were buried under mammoth packing-cases. The theatres were still in the hands of the Engineers: we worked by the light of hurricane lamps.

But—when those ambulances came screeching down on us, we were ready!

Then, after a description (with which the reader must by this time be tolerably familiar) of the various types of case to be dealt with and their appropriate treatment, comes a reference to the patients themselves.

The patients were superb, as front-line casualties almost always are. They begged for sleep and water: they bothered us for little else.

Sometimes they obligingly indicated bleeding points to us, either their own or their bed-fellows'! They assisted us wherever it was possible for them to do so, though usually that was impossible, for ours were all major cases. Most of them must have been suffering great pain.

They shared everything they had, particularly cigarettes and soap, for some of them had come in without a possession in the world, and some indeed lay naked in their blankets.

But after forty-eight hours, if they remained so long, they began to revive, and talk; and the accustomed chaffing of the nurses began. After a further forty-eight hours, according to their various natures, they were preparing to become either ward nuisances or good 'kitchen men'.

Naturally, these scenes of suffering were periodically brightened by a gleam of unexpected humour. There was the case, for instance, of a stretcher-bearer who, disgruntled by having everlastingly to carry other people about, surreptitiously deposited himself, wrapped in a blanket and ticketed *X-ray Examination*, on an unoccupied stretcher, and waited hopefully for 'Evacuation to U.K.' He was detected, unfortunately, at the eleventh hour, harshly restored to the perpendicular, and returned to duty.

Many German wounded were brought in during the advance. They did not create a favourable impression.

They were starved and they were filthy, with the filth of long unwashed humanity, as opposed to the mud of the British Tommy. Their wounds were nauseating, and the German surgery had either been unskilled or desperately hurried. Their mental outlook was sullen with perplexity and, doubtless, fear. What they had expected from us was evidently anything but what we gave them.

We on our part were frankly revolted, not only by their evil condition, but their manners. They lifted not a finger to assist us in our labour for them. They spat anywhere and everywhere on the floor, and their other personal habits were equally disgusting.

We treated them as we had treated our own men; and yet, out of the lot of them, only one young boy turned to thank us.

v

In due course the Seine and Somme were crossed, and the B.L.A. penetrated into Belgium, so close on the heels of the enemy that one hospital unit, taking over new quarters in Antwerp, found the city still flag-bedecked and the inhabitants still celebrating their deliverance.

The hospital buildings now taken over had been occupied by the Germans until a few days previously. Its design was unusual and not entirely convenient. There was a large number of small wards, holding from two to seven beds—an unsatisfactory arrangement where very sick or unconscious patients were concerned, for it was impossible for a nursing staff limited in numbers to supervise all these at one time.

There were no staircases or lifts—merely a sloping ramp, winding upwards from the ground floor to the seventh.

The battle for Walcheren and beyond was at its height, and the hospital staff were kept overwhelmingly busy; but everything was soon reduced to a system.

There was much to do on the administration side also. The building was filled with unnecessary furniture, and the place was filthy, following the German evacuation. Fortunately civilian labour was available for cleaning purposes, thus releasing every available man for ward duties.

And assuredly all these men were needed, for the flow of patients at this time was continuous, since the hospital for some weeks had to discharge the functions of a casualty clearing station, no patient staying for more than forty-eight hours if he was fit to travel. Its largest intake on one day was 1,048 cases, and more than one Sister could say that some of her beds had been filled and emptied three times in twenty-four hours.

Fortunately the Belgian population were more than willing to help, and the Belgian Red Cross and Boy Scouts did invaluable work as stretcher-bearers. Some indication of the need for their services may be gathered from the fact that in the first four weeks 1,634 operations were performed. The theatre staffs worked all round the clock; the maximum number of cases dealt with in one period of twenty-four hours was 120. By the inclusion of part of the University buildings, the number of beds was increased to 1,531.

After a month, as other hospitals began to arrive in the area, the strain was relaxed, and the hospital itself was able to resume its normal status and routine as a British General Hospital.

This was important, for two reasons. In the first place, it was possible to give fuller and more elaborate attention to each patient, especially 'dangerous' cases; and in the second it gave great satisfaction to a Sister to be able to get to know her patients and watch their recovery. It conferred a benefit on the patient himself, for an invalid finds it easier to get well when he is attended throughout by one who is no longer a stranger, but has become an understanding friend.

Mention has already been made of the fact that at this hospital the majority of the patients were 'major cases'.

> The busiest ward [we are told] was the Maxillo-Facial and Neuro-Surgical Ward, containing 100 beds, with an emergency expansion of twenty more. The majority of these patients were unconscious and 'dangerously' ill, which made the ordinary nursing points, such as feedings, attention to backs, and (in the case of the Maxillo-Facial patients) the syringing of mouths, a herculean task in itself.

This report ends with the usual tribute to the virtues of penicillin.

> In some cases the results of its use were little short of miraculous, the patient's condition improving hour by hour. The drug was used either by the 'drip' method or by injection.

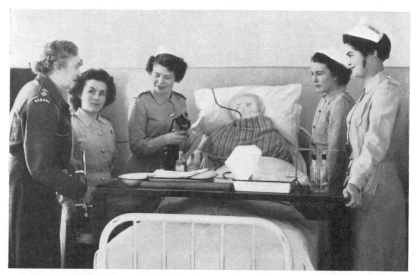

Captain O'Neill, Q.A.R.A.N.C., Sister Tutor at Hanover B.M.H., giving instruction to the newly arrived other ranks with a dummy patient
(*Rhine Army Official Photo*)

Pistol type ionisation chamber detector demonstrated by Inst. Lt. Alabaster to four nurses of Q.A.R.A.N.C. (*The Nursing Mirror*)

Officers on parade at Anstie Grange. Khaki service dress

The Jubilee Parade at Alexandra Camp, Q.A.R.A.N.C., Depot and T.E. Other
ranks in new No. 1 Dress

Progress was greatly assisted at this time by the high morale of the patients themselves. They were winning the war, and nothing else mattered. What they had gone through had been worth while after all.

> I remember on one occasion [a Principal Matron tells us] going round a ward and coming to a patient on the 'Dangerously Ill' list. He had a head and a hand wound, his left eye was enucleated, and his right leg amputated. In his injured right hand he was clutching a pencil.
>
> I asked him how he was feeling. He laughed, and told me that he was trying to write to his wife. 'I'm fine,' he added: 'I've lost an eye, of course; but I'm not worrying about that: I've got the other one!'
>
> I then asked after his leg. 'I've lost one,' he replied, 'but then again I've got the other one.'

A military Mark Tapley, in fact. And in those days the British Army was full of them.

Convalescence too was a pleasant business in this period of dawning victory, for the inhabitants of those countries which our men had helped to deliver from the burden of enemy occupation were anxious to show their gratitude.

Patients who were fit enough to go out received many offers of hospitality, while to those who remained in bed came visitors bearing fruit and flowers. Later, towards Christmas, fruit having become scarcer, the gifts took the form of toys. These particular gifts gave the men more pleasure than anything else, for they could be sent home to their children—children for some of whom a real toy had become a forgotten luxury. To the very youngest a toy was a complete novelty.

CHAPTER 22

VICTORY AND BEYOND

By November 1944 the Scheldt Estuary had been passed, and the Allies had advanced into Holland, closely followed by their medical services.

Just before leaving Belgian soil one hospital had had an ominous experience.

> On two Sundays in succession we heard two mysterious explosions somewhere in our neighbourhood. They puzzled us: there was no enemy artillery anywhere near, no aircraft in the sky, nothing at all—just two big explosions. We afterwards learned to our horror that these were caused by V.2 rockets, of which we had already heard rumours. The Germans had been testing their range-finding apparatus, preparatory to beginning the systematic bombing of England, by V.2 rockets in place of the V.1 bomb.

On arrival in Holland this particular hospital was allotted quarters in a theological college six miles from Eindhoven. It was occupied by a body of French monks, known as the White Fathers.

> It was strange at first to find these white-robed figures drifting in and out, giving a helping hand, with a word here and there. They were all linguists, and could speak English quite well. They also acted as interpreters between us and the German prisoners, which was a great help. These White Fathers were kind to us in another way: they took upon themselves to give us all, including the orderlies, lessons in

German, so that when we eventually crossed into Germany we could have a little knowledge of the language.

Contact with Thomas Atkins, incidentally, seems to have enlarged the English vocabulary of the White Fathers considerably, sometimes with interesting results. One Cockney soldier in this unit was an expert in what is known as rhyming slang, of which 'Trouble and Strife' for 'wife', and 'Gawd Forbids' for 'kids' are familiar examples. He communicated this accomplishment to his own particular tutor, who one evening announced to the startled Sisters that he was about to go up the 'Apples-and-Pears' to 'Uncle Ned', to get some 'Bo-Peep'. The reader should have no difficulty in interpreting this intriguing pronouncement for himself.

It was about this time, just before Christmas 1944, that Rundstedt launched his great counter-offensive against the Allied line. It was his very last attempt, and it nearly succeeded.

His handling of the earlier stages of the operation was masterly. He had selected for his point of attack a sector on General Bradley's 12th United States Army Group, somewhat lightly held owing to heavy American concentration in the Aachen area farther north. The surprise was complete, and the four divisions guarding the position were swept away. The Group was split completely in two; and General Bradley, in his headquarters south of the break, found himself cut off from all control of the U.S. Ninth Army, and of most of the First.

General Eisenhower, now in supreme command, acted promptly. He immediately placed these two armies under the temporary command of General Montgomery, who was operating in this area. The situation was critical, for a breach had been created some forty-five miles wide and thirty deep, with the result that the whole line of the Meuse was threatened, and with it the road to Liège and Antwerp.

This was the beginning of the famous 'Battle of the Bulge', which continued with the utmost fury through Christmas and after. The enemy penetrated at one time to within three miles of the hospital of the White Fathers, to the natural concern of its inmates and the sad disruption of their modest Christmas celebrations.

> We began to wonder just what was going to happen. 'Do we stay put, or shall we have to move back?' To our great joy we heard that the 15th Scottish Division had gone in to the attack. Then we knew we should stay put.

This, the reader will have realized, is something of an *ex parte* statement, for many other formations besides this particular Division participated in that fateful battle. The American troops within the salient, many of them cut off from outside aid, put up a most gallant and resolute defence, especially round the vital road-centre of Bastogne; while the American First and Ninth, and the British Second Army combined successfully to reduce the northern shoulder of the Bulge.

In the end the German attack failed, with enormous losses; the position was restored, and Rundstedt's bolt was shot. He was succeeded by Kesselring, who had achieved distinction by his able defence of the German line in Italy.

II

The final phase of the liberation of Europe, so far as the B.L.A. was concerned, began with a pitched battle of great intensity— one of the bloodiest of the war—on the western bank of the Rhine during January and February 1945, which filled the hospitals in Holland and Belgium to overflowing, and kept our medical and nursing staffs busy once more all round the clock.

By the beginning of 1945 the Allied forces faced squarely east, with the enemy between them and the Rhine. The general lay-out was as follows:

On the extreme left, and farthest north, came the First Canadian Army, still engaged in clearing the Scheldt Estuary and the Island of Walcheren. Then came the (British) Second Army, then the Ninth (U.S.) Army, which had been left by General

Eisenhower under General (now Field-Marshal) Montgomery's operational command. These formations comprised the 21st Army Group, with a front extending as far south as Dusseldorf, just above Cologne. American and French troops continued the line right down to the Swiss frontier.

Field-Marshal Montgomery had long determined to bring the enemy into action on the western (or left) bank of the Rhine, thereby ensuring that the great river should act as an obstacle to retirement in the hoped-for event of enemy defeat; whereas if the enemy was permitted to cross without fighting, the position would be reversed and the British advance seriously impeded.

In this project he was completely successful, though resistance was severe and the conditions could not have been more unfavourable.

> The keynotes of the Battle of the Rhineland [says Field-Marshal Montgomery] were the intense and fanatical opposition of the enemy and the appalling weather conditions.

Here is General Eisenhower's tribute to the achievement of the 21st Army Group in this operation.

> The weather conditions could hardly have been more unfavourable. January had been exceptionally severe, with snow lying on the ground through the month; and when the thaw set in in February the ground became extremely soft and water-logged, while floods spread far and wide. The men sometimes had to fight waist-deep in water; but their spirit was indomitable, and they overcame their personal hardships with great gallantry, to inflict a major defeat upon the enemy in some of the fiercest fighting of the whole war.

After that came the Allied crossing of the Rhine itself. The Americans had the good fortune to discover an unguarded railway bridge at Remagen, and exploited their opportunity to the full. They had secured a footing on the farther bank by March 7th.

Farther north, Field-Marshal Montgomery had planned, with his usual methodical thoroughness, to be across the river by March 24th. As usual he was more than punctual, actually crossing a day earlier.

The first British Hospital Unit to follow him on to German soil was the 81st General.

III

Before arriving at the scene of ultimate victory—now not far distant—it will be appropriate to summarize the achievement of our Army Medical Services throughout the B.L.A. campaign.

Firstly, sickness among the troops, owing partly to the preventive measures employed and partly to the superb physical condition of the men themselves, was almost halved compared with that of the First World War. In sweeping through conquered Germany, liberating and tending such notoriously unhealthy prison-camps as Belsen and Sandbostel, where thousands of people were dying of typhus, only twenty-four British soldiers contracted this disease. There will be more to say about Belsen later.

Secondly, we have to note the inestimable aid rendered by air transport in the swift and comfortable evacuation of casualties; and thirdly, by the extensive and highly successful employment of blood-transfusion methods. A co-ordinated service of air transport and refrigerator trucks was constantly available.

In particular, the devotion of the Field Surgical Units, both Surgeons and Sisters, operating as they did right up to the line, was responsible for a most gratifying reduction in the number of deaths from intestinal wounds. In the First World War two out of every three men wounded in the abdomen died; in the Normandy campaign of the Second World War two out of every three men so wounded recovered.

The net result of this phenomenal progress in medical and surgical practice, coupled with the increased 'expectation of life' afforded to all ranks by the elimination of unwieldy and wasteful attacks in mass across a no-man's-land swept by machine-gun fire, was a marked decrease in the casualty lists as compared with those of the First World War. In that war, as the reader will remember, we lost a million dead: in the Second the losses of the British Army in killed, missing, and died of wounds in six years came to 177,850. Of these 27,000 died in fighting the Japanese; some 20,000 others died as prisoners of war.

Of the final stages of the victorious Allied campaign in Germany there is no need to speak in detail here, except to note the sudden and general collapse of enemy resistance.

> Our plan [Field-Marshal Montgomery tells us in his final Dispatch] for outflanking Hamburg by a manœuvre similar to that employed at Bremen, was actually under way when, on May 2nd, the Germans came out to negotiate its surrender.
>
> Across the Elbe the countryside was packed with a mass of German soldiers and refugees fleeing from our advance and that of the Russians, with whom we established contact on May 2nd.

Less than a week later the war against Germany was over. On May 4th General-Admiral von Friedenberg, Hitler's more or less self-appointed deputy, signed the Instrument of Unconditional Surrender of all German naval, land and air forces opposed to the 21st Army Group. Three days later a General Instrument was signed at General Eisenhower's Headquarters, and the Surrender was complete, for it covered not only the German forces opposing the Americans but the Germans in Italy as well.

Three months later the 21st Army Group became the British Army of the Rhine, with duties involving, for the time being, the government of the British Zone, and the rehabilitation of its inhabitants.

In this task our Army Medical Services played a notable part. Their duty was now twofold—to continue to operate all Army Hospital Services in the British Zone until the last casualty had been evacuated, and to take over the local German prison camps and attend to the crying needs of those confined there.

IV

Of our own Army Hospital Services in Germany there is no
need to say more. The tale of their devotion and achievement
has already been told. Let us turn instead to their post-war
preoccupations, especially in the Concentration Camps. As an
outstanding example we will select Belsen.

Evidence as to conditions in that camp in 1945 is available to
us from two especially interesting sources. The first is a narrative, written in the form of a personal letter to a Q.A.I.M.N.S.
Sister (in not very good English), by a former inmate of this
camp. His name was Willy Lubba, and by his own account his
only crime had been that of anti-Naziism and the fact that he
had fought against Franco in the Spanish Civil War.

His troubles seem to have begun early. At the outbreak of
the Second World War he was resident in France, and as a
German subject was confined in an internment camp. Upon the
invasion of France by the Germans in 1940 the Vichy Government handed him over to the Gestapo, who transferred him
to a concentration camp at Sachsenhausen, where the treatment
of the prisoners appears to have been harsh, though not actively
sadistic. Work was hard—twelve hours a day—and the feeding
arrangements were totally inadequate. Consequently there was
a great deal of sickness.

A sick man is of no use in a forced labour camp, so in February
1945 Lubba, in company with a number of other invalids, was
transferred to Belsen, which he was assured was 'a lovely
sanatorium'.

When we arrived there we found that we had been sent
to Belsen Camp (No. 1) to die! By this time it was being
called by the inmates the Camp of Death.

The first day we had to stand for three hours in the rain
and cold. The S.S. tried to count us, but it was impossible.
Hundreds lay on the wet ground completely exhausted from
the wet march and from starvation.

The camp was overcrowded with peoples, and when the barracks were completely full, the rest had to stay outside. Every day, in the morning, there were hundreds dead. These we had to carry out of the barracks into the square.

For the last six weeks before the English liberated the Camp we had 35,000 deaths from ill-treatment, typhus and starvation. During the night people had to sleep with those who died. There was nothing else to be done: you simply pushed the dead bodies on one side, so that one could occupy their places and have a little more room.

Then follow many lurid details. The inmates, we are told, lived like animals, the stronger taking away the food of the weak and helpless.

Cannibalism was not infrequent. It was no unusual occurrence to find the bodies of those who had died during the night—or possibly had not yet died—cut open, with their livers removed and eaten raw. There are other and even more revolting details.

Lubba himself was suffering from typhus when the moment of liberation came. The effect was electric.

Everyone who could rise from his miserable bed went to see and cheer them, and those who could not go wept, kissing and shouting for joy.

We were all evacuated to hospital, first the women and children and then the men. We have now clean beds, good food, and are treated with so much kindness by our English Sister and the Orderlies.

I wish to express here my most heartfelt thankfulness to that Sister. She was our Mother, never too tired to help us and glad to see us happy. I will never forget her, and will remember always what she has done for us, representing the noble, worthy, and gallant English.

That Willy Lubba's grim narrative was not an overstatement of the facts is more than borne out by the Report of a Q.A. Nursing Sister who worked in Belsen Camp No. 2 during the weeks following the German surrender. She was accompanied by a contingent of British medical students who had volunteered to serve in the work of relief. They were replaced later by Belgian students, who proved most efficient.

v

At the present day, when some years have elapsed and the British people, after their invariable habit, are inclined lazily to forget and forgive and let bygones be bygones, it may be as well to jog the memories of the too-forgiving by putting and keeping on record the story of Belsen Camp. Our Sister's Report, then, is here given *in extenso*, unabridged and unexpurgated.

Next day, with a V.A.D., I was detailed to find Square 10, Block 61, in an enormous compound. Each square was surrounded entirely by high barbed wire, to which were attached large notices, reading 'DANGER—TYPHUS'. Every building was the same, dull-looking, of grey stone with small windows. Some had iron bars across, and a centre door. One had previously been used to house the German S.S. Panzer Division, and I was not surprised to see a large Red Cross painted on each roof. The Germans had made full use of this sign to protect themselves.

Passing through the door of Block 61, I was astonished to hear sounds of hundreds of various tongues; and the dreadful smell, only to be associated with Belsen, was indescribable. A British medical student and I, with Nurse, were able at last to overcome the feeling of nausea.

No one had been able to compile a register of patients. Many, of course, had forgotten their identity. However, with Nurse, I visited the human remains lying on the straw palliasses, covered with filthy blankets. At first glance we were unable to define their sex. Several were lying on top of the blankets, their heads shorn. The agony of their suffering showing clearly in their expression, with eyes sunken and listless, cheek-bones prominent, too weak to close their mouths, with arms extended in an appealing manner. 'Essen—essen!' was the general cry.

There was not an open window, the floor was filthy, straw littered with human excreta. Thousands of flies were re-creating the Typhus circle, by settling on potato peelings picked from the garbage-bins. Broken cups and plates held pieces of black bread, turnip tops and very sour milk.

The working personnel consisted of five Hungarian soldiers. About 100 of these men had been left when the S.S. Panzer Division moved out. There were also two Poles, four Czechs and six Hungarians, all young girls, themselves in a convalescent stage from Typhus. A Hungarian surgical specialist, Dr. Sachs, was a charming woman. She also had had Typhus, had twice been removed from the gas chamber, had left-sided paralysis of the face, and a deep scar extending down her neck to the left shoulder, the result of an experiment carried out by the Germans. She was an amazing woman, working amongst the patients day and night. She was delighted to have the opportunity of speaking English again, and said she had heard no kind word for six years. Her husband was a doctor and, with their two children, was 'removed' by the enemy. She had since heard that they were dead.

With the aid of a British medical officer every patient was examined. Ninety per cent were suffering from Tuberculosis, in addition to other specific fevers and Post Typhus conditions. The seriously ill T.B. girls were placed in a large ward, where supervision of special diets and rest was possible.

Gradually I felt the air of fear and suspicion fading away, and with regular meals one could see a gradual improvement. A smile would flicker across a pale, thin face, a hand would try to rise in salute. 'Guten Morgen, Schwester!' was becoming quite usual.

After seven days writing paper and pencils were distributed. Several patients hesitated, their names temporarily forgotten, while tears poured down their faces. The letters they wrote were sent to the Red Cross, and in due course replies were received. One husband met his wife after a separation of five years.

Clothes had been collected from German families, and 'Harrods' was born. Every day several patients from each block were given slippers. As supplies were received, soap, towels, tooth brushes, combs, mirrors and cosmetics were distributed, amid great excitement. The task of supplying nearly 17,000 was no small matter. Several girls could not recognize their own reflections, not having encountered a mirror for years.

My patients improved, step by step, until they could be allowed to be clothed and so get into the sunshine. By this time the prison-like appearance of the Camp had disappeared; to my joy the barbed wire was removed. I heard snatches of laughter and the singing of National songs.

The last three weeks of our stay were used to evacuate patients to Sweden, where they hoped to recuperate in more congenial surroundings. The British Red Cross used a large loud-speaker van to announce the names on their lists. Many friends were thus united, after long periods of separation: I saw husbands and wives with children, all of whom had thought the others dead, brought together again.

Most of the internees were young girls, arrested for some so-called political offence. One girl told me she was on a tram when S.S. removed everyone on board to this Camp. I heard many stories of trains being stopped and people removed. Whole districts were awakened at 2 a.m. and the inhabitants marched off in their night attire. Many experiments had been tried on young girls aged fourteen to twenty-one years: their food was drugged for the purpose. Thereafter many had adopted an animal-like existence.

Many times did I thank God that I am British and the enemy are defeated.

Part Four

RETURN TO NORMAL

CHAPTER 23

THE ADMINISTRATIVE SIDE

Army Nursing, as we today understand the term, began in 1854, with the departure of Florence Nightingale and thirty-eight nurses to the Crimea. In 1856, by Royal Warrant, as a result of the success of that historic expedition, the enrolment of female nurses was authorized for *all* military general hospitals, and in 1884, on the recommendation of Miss Nightingale, the Army Nursing Service came into formal and official existence.

A further step was taken ten years later, when Queen Victoria's third daughter, H.R.H. Princess Christian, who may be regarded not only as the forerunner of Queen Alexandra, but the lineal successor of Miss Nightingale herself in the matter of Army nursing development, put forward a scheme for the formation of a 'war reserve' of nurses, and sought the advice and help of Florence Nightingale in the matter. Miss Nightingale, though she welcomed the project warmly, was by this time eighty years of age and a confirmed invalid; and the ultimate success of this timely and far-seeing project was due entirely to the indefatigable labours of Princess Christian herself. And she was well rewarded, for when the South African War broke out in 1899, an organized Reserve of Nurses, bearing Princess Christian's name was ready to set out with the Expeditionary Force to augment the Army Nursing Service.

Finally, in 1902, at the end of the South African War, the Army Nursing Service, which up to this time had been a purely civilian body attached to the Army for nursing purposes, ended its valuable if somewhat anomalous existence, and its place was taken, as we know, by Q.A.I.M.N.S. Applicants for enrolment in the new Service, both from the A.N.S. and the A.N.S.R., were given priority of admission.

At the same time a Q.A.I.M.N.S. was formed in India, on the insistence of Lord Roberts, then Commander-in-Chief in India, and Lady Roberts. Lord and Lady Roberts even raised a fund for the nursing of officers, until such time as the Government of India recognized the need for it.[1]

In 1902 also we witness the beginnings of a scheme for ameliorating the health conditions under which soldiers' wives and children had so far existed, by committing these to the care of Army nurses. It was a makeshift scheme, and the conditions under which it worked were never satisfactory, especially with regard to the position of the nursing staff. It was not until 1921 that matters were finally adjusted by the formation of Q.A. Military Families Nursing Service. Conditions of service, pay, and the like were the same as for members of Q.A.I.M.N.S.

In 1926–27 all distinctions between the various Q.A. Nursing Services were abolished, and Q.A.I.M.N.S. both at home and in India, together with Q.A.M.F.N.S., were amalgamated into a homogeneous whole.

In 1941 Q.A.I.M.N.S. and T.A.N.S. were commissioned into the temporary Women's Forces and this arrangement lasted until 1949, when the final and decisive step was taken, and Q.A.I.M.N.S. was reorganized to form a corps of the Army, under the title of Queen Alexandra's Royal Army Nursing Corps. From now on Nursing officers were granted regular commissions in the Women's Forces.

As a natural corollary to these important developments, the T.A.N.S. was in 1950 disbanded, and became the Q.A.R.A.N.C. (T.A.). At the same time Q.A.I.M.N.S. (R.), was merged into the Q.A.R.A.N.C. (Regular Army Reserve of Officers).

---

[1] See Chap. 23, pp. 339–341.

Q.A.R.A.N.C. Depot. Drumhead service in the presence of Queen Mary at a Passing-Out Parade at Anstie Grange

(*The Nursing Mirror*)

Five members of Q.A.R.A.N.C. before leaving for Korea, October, 1950
(P.A. – Reuter)

1902   1939   1912   1854   1952
Uniforms of the Army Nursing Service *(Depot and T.E., Q.A.R.A.N.C.)*

II

Mention has frequently been made in these pages of the Territorial Army Nursing Service. Here is an appropriate moment to study its origin and history in greater detail.

The T.A.N.S. was founded in 1908, for the purpose of maintaining an establishment of nurses willing to do service in general hospitals in the event of mobilization of the Territorial Force, which had come into existence (in place of the old Volunteers) as part of Lord Haldane's great scheme of Army Reform in 1909.

Its establishment was considerable, and consisted of:

Matron-in-Chief	1
Principal Matrons	23
Matrons	23
Sisters	506
Nurses	1,564
Total	2,117

During the First World War the number was increased to 7,117, of whom 2,280 served in hospitals overseas.

After the First World War, in which the Territorials had played a most gallant part, the Force was reconstituted, in 1920, as The Territorial Army. The Territorial Force Nursing Service was accordingly reorganized in 1921, as The Territorial Army Nursing Service.

Between the two World Wars the numbers fluctuated between 3,460 and 4,764.

In 1939 came an important change in the status and administration of the T.A.N.S. Up till this date this Service had always been administered separately. It was now decided that, since the Territorial Army had been merged into the Regular Army, the T.A.N.S., as was only logical, should follow suit. It was therefore merged into, and became an integral part of, Q.A.I.M.N.S., and served with it thereafter in all theatres. Conditions of ser-

Y

vice, pay and the like, were in all respects identical with those of Q.A.I.M.N.S. The T.A.N.S., however, retained its old title. Its administration was in the hands of a joint board, known as Queen Alexandra's Army Nursing Board. The same Board administered Q.A.I.M.N.S., but each of the two Services was controlled by its own Committee. This body framed rules for the admission of nurses, and made such recommendations as seemed necessary for the administration of the Service, and for the promotion of Matrons and Sisters. It also selected ladies for appointment to the post of Matron-in-Chief and Principal Matrons.

The Matron-in-Chief, T.A.N.S., was appointed for five years, or alternatively until she reached the age of sixty-two. She was provided with an office and clerical staff, but not unnaturally had to spend much of her time touring. She visited Principal Matrons and Secretaries of the Territorial Army Association all over Britain, and even large civilian hospitals, where she was usually given an opportunity to speak to sisters and nurses on the aims of the T.A.N.S.

Eighteen Principal Matrons were appointed, and were detailed as follows:

Eastern Command . . .	5
Southern Command . .	5
Western Command . .	4
Scottish Command . .	4

Principal Matrons were selected and offered the appointment by the T.A.N.S. Committee. It is interesting to note that their appointment was that of Matron in one of the large *civilian* hospitals in the Command concerned. They thus played a double *rôle*, combining the appointment of Principal Matron, T.A.N.S., with that of Matron in their civilian capacity.

The Principal Matrons also undertook to recruit nurses for enrolment, and forwarded the names of candidates to the Committee for consideration.

The nurses themselves were enrolled for duty with specific

Territorial hospitals: in most cases the majority of sisters and nurses in these were drawn from the same civilian hospital. In this way the T.A.N.S. was built steadily up during the years of peace, so as to be ready at any time, in the possible event of war, to be in complete readiness for general mobilization.

During the First World War, it should be noted, the Principal Matrons were called up for duty, and were required to devote to that duty such time as they could spare from their civilian occupation. But they were not asked to leave their own hospitals. Their duties during this period included the inspection of nursing arrangements in Territorial Force hospitals, giving advice on nursing matters, and enrolling additional nurses as required.

These public-spirited ladies received no pay from Army Funds, and were often put to considerable expenses personally. They did, however, receive a gratuity, according to the length of their war service, and £5 per annum for clerical assistance.

So much for the position of the Principal Matrons, T.A.N.S., during the First World War. By 1939 the situation was different, for the T.A.N.S. had now been merged into Q.A.I.M.N.S., and both Services were brought together under the Matron-in-Chief.

In 1950, as a result of the formation of Queen Alexandra's Royal Army Nursing Corps, the T.A.N.S. was disbanded as such, and reborn as Q.A.R.A.N.C. (T.A.).

Such is the story of the embodiment of Q.A.R.A.N.C. (T.A.). from the point of view of its internal and administrative history. To its actual service and sacrifice in every theatre of war, its own Roll of Honour renders abounding testimony.

III

Let us next enlarge upon the activities, during the Second World War, of the Nursing Services in India.

During that war these Services were composed of Q.A.I.M.N.S. and its Reserve, the T.A.N.S., the Indian Military Nursing Service, and its temporary Service, together with the Army in

India Nursing Service Reserve and the Auxiliary Nursing Service.

Members of the British Nursing Services served in both British and Indian Military Hospitals. There were also a number of Combined Military Hospitals, where British and Indian patients were admitted. Nursing staff of both nationalities were employed.

Of the above-mentioned units, the record of the Army in India Nursing Service Reserve is particularly interesting, for this body was formed at the outbreak of war and was composed of British trained nurses who were at this time domiciled in India. Many of the women who joined this Service had been members of Lady Minto's Nursing Association, formed when Lord Minto was Viceroy of India. These nurses, we are told, were of great assistance in the war effort, serving as they did both in British and Indian Military Hospitals, and also in the Families Wings of such hospitals.

The Auxiliary Nursing Service replaced the Voluntary Aid Service and was constituted to provide a reserve of nursing staff sufficiently instructed to be of immediate use when called up for duty during the War. But that was not the end of these activities. In 1943 further training schemes were put into operation designed to have more far-reaching effects in India where the status of nursing and consequently the supply of nurses left much to be desired. Two military hospitals were staffed and equipped as nurse training schools for the Auxiliary Nursing Service under an agreement which permitted the period there to count towards training for the recognized nursing qualification for the country, with added concession of reduced civil training time for all periods of military service. Training and examination schemes were set up in all Commands for Indian male nurses as well. Administrative courses were sanctioned for Sisters of the Indian Military Nursing Services. These took place at the College of Nursing, Delhi. Practical instruction and experience for the senior nursing members of the Indian Service was provided by posting as many as possible in turn to the Nursing Department at G.H.Q. Delhi.

The Chief Principal Matron in India was a senior appointment of the Regular Q.A.I.M.N.S. She was responsible for the nursing administration both in British and Indian Military Hospitals throughout the whole of India: Ceylon and Burma were added during the war. At the outbreak of war the Chief Principal Matron was Miss E. E. O'Connell, R.R.C. She was succeeded early in 1942 by Mrs. L. J. Wilkinson, who held the appointment until 1944, when she left India for the United Kingdom, to take up the appointment of Matron-in-Chief, War Office (A.M.D.4). Mrs. (later Dame Louisa) Wilkinson was followed as Chief Principal Matron in India by Miss J. Patterson, who was succeeded in due course by Miss A. Thomson, the last member of Q.A.I.M.N.S. to hold that post. (Miss Thomson, later Dame Anne, succeeded Dame Louisa Wilkinson as Matron-in-Chief.) With the departure of the British from India, these duties were handed over to the Indian Military Nursing Service.

IV

We pass now to a brief survey of the history of Q.A.R.A.N.C., especially in the matter of its evolution from the date of its founding in 1902, through various vicissitudes of composition, administration, status and responsibility, to its present officially recognized position as a Regular Corps of the British Regular Army, ranking equally with the R.A.M.C., and R.A.D.C.

From 1902 to 1939 Q.A.I.M.N.S. were a body of professional women attached to the Army for the purpose of nursing the sick men, women and children of that Army, and for the training and teaching of the R.A.M.C. Nursing Orderlies; and although much of the general organization of the Army, as a way of life, was cheerfully accepted, Q.A.I.M.N.S. maintained its own particular code of pay and promotion, based upon civilian conditions, which of course made no allowance for the regimental aspect superimposed upon the profession of nurse.

This attitude remained unchanged until 1939, when something happened which made it incumbent upon Q.A.I.M.N.S. to take stock of the new situation and revise its previous views as to its status and prestige within the British Army. This was the enrolment in the Army of hundreds of women-soldiers of the A.T.S. whose way of life was aligned at every stage with that of their male counterparts. This being so, Q.A.I.M.N.S. found itself at a serious disadvantage, for whereas the A.T.S. enjoyed full official recognition as members of the British Army, Q.A.I.M.N.S., with a distinguished record of thirty-seven years' service to the Army behind it, occupied no established military position within the Army structure at all. A.T.S. and the Nursing Services were commissioned in 1941 under an emergency scheme, but because of the difference in uniform and conditions, the Sisters' status was not generally recognized and led to many anomalies. Therefore in 1945 Q.A.I.M.N.S. set to work, employing its experience gained during two wars, to reorganize and to establish itself within the Army structure. With the certainty of Regular Women's Forces from now on, there could be no return to pre-1939 conditions, nor could Q.A.I.M.N.S. hope to make secure its future unless its outmoded and now most unfavourable terms of service were brought up to and in line with those of the Army generally.

Total warfare had made it plain that women could no longer remain 'in' but not 'of' the Army, and that members of Q.A.I.M.N.S. who accompanied the soldier into the firing-line, and even found themselves actually in the midst of battle, must be protected, not from the hazards of modern warfare—those they were perfectly prepared to face—but by becoming an integral part of the Army, not only wearing a recognized uniform which they had done since 1944. Rank markings they had worn since 1941. As an integral part of the Army, they would be known and accepted by a belligerent and treated accordingly.

Such protection was especially to be desired if a member of Q.A.I.M.N.S. should become a prisoner of war. There were many cases during the Second World War in which, since the enemy declined to recognize the uniform she wore, the unhappy prisoner had no means of establishing her identity, and with it the immunity from ill-treatment to which she was justly entitled, e.g. the Japanese refused to give Q.A.I.M.N.S. the rations and prisoner-of-war pay of a member of the British Army. (Strangely enough, within the precincts of P.O.W. camp hospitals, Sisters who possessed them found the wearing of the scarlet cape ensured some attention at least to their requests for their patients, though not necessarily anything further than that.)

Today after years of careful consideration and planning the following results have been achieved and made public both to friend and potential foe:

(1) Queen Alexandra's Royal Army Nursing Corps is a self-contained, self-administered corps—the third corps in point of fact of the British Army Medical Services—of equal standing with the R.A.M.C. and R.A.D.C. and, like them, complete with Other Ranks cadre. The Matron-in-Chief is Director of the Army Nursing Services and is responsible to the Director-General Army Medical Services.

(Dame Anne Thomson was the first Matron-in-Chief to be appointed Director of the Army Nursing Services, and incidentally to hold the honour of being King's Honorary Nursing Sister.)

(2) Q.A.R.A.N.C. takes precedence as the Senior Corps of the Women's Forces, with pay, promotion, conditions and regulations aligned in general to the male equivalent, rank for rank, in the same manner as the Women's Royal Army Corps.

Her Majesty Queen Mary, lately President Q.A.I.M.N.S., is Colonel-in-Chief Q.A.R.A.N.C. A Colonel Commandant Q.A.R.A.N.C. has been appointed, Dame Louisa Wilkinson being the first.

The Corps flag, it should be added, now comprises the old Q.A.I.M.N.S. colours, with the new Q.A.R.A.N.C. badge superimposed.

The Corps also has its own Q.A.R.A.N.C. march 'Grey and Scarlet', arranged by Captain Brown, Director of Music,

R.A.M.C., from suggestions furnished by Professor A. Lewis, of the Barber Institute of Fine Arts, Birmingham University, and members of the Q.A.R.A.N.C. Depot staff. It opens with a brisk martial theme of Purcell's *King Arthur*, followed by the tranquil, peaceful note of the traditional air, 'The Gentle Maiden' —a truly happy and expressive combination, denoting the dual role of the 'Q.A.' in the Army.

V

All British regiments maintain their own Regimental Association, and Q.A.R.A.N.C. has not been long in following suit. The Q.A.I.M.N.S. Association was formed on December 5th, 1947. Dame Louisa Wilkinson, Matron-in-Chief at that time and less than a year from retirement, generously undertook the organizing work in connexion with its establishment.

Prior to that date, benevolent and social activities on behalf of both past and present members of the Service, had been carried out by the Matron-in-Chief's Department at the War Office. The Association was formed to bring the Nursing Service into line, in this respect, with other corps and regiments of the Army, especially in view of the projected change in the Corps' own military status.

The object of the Association is to foster and create friendship among those who have at any time served in the Army Nursing Services, and to help those who may be in need. An Association Gazette is published quarterly. Re-unions are regularly held, and several branches have been formed, three overseas in Australia, East Africa and New Zealand.

The name of the Association has now, as is only appropriate, been changed from Q.A.I.M.N.S. to Q.A.R.A.N.C. Association, since February 1st, 1949, when the service became Queen Alexandra's Royal Army Nursing Corps by Royal Warrant.

Her Majesty Queen Mary, Colonel-in-Chief of Q.A.R.A.N.C., is Patron of the Association.

VI

We will conclude the present chapter with a full account of the origin and growth of one of the most important adjuncts of Queen Alexandra's Royal Army Nursing Corps, the Depot and Training Establishment, created as recently as 1944.

Previous to this, the majority of Nursing Sisters were drafted directly overseas with their units, and thus had little or no time for thorough basic training. But the need for a permanent Depot and Training Establishment had been fully recognized for some time, and a beginning was made by the setting up of such a Depot at Anstie Grange, Holmwood, Surrey.

This Depot was concerned at first with but two duties only—that of receiving newly commissioned Nursing Officers (as they were called) into the Service, and dispatching serving Officers overseas. The Depot had already established an important precedent by becoming the first unit with a female Commanding Officer entirely responsible for the male Other Ranks of which the staff was composed.

The newly-joined Officers were given medical inoculations, fitted out with uniforms, and given a brief course of lectures on the type of duties they would undertake on their posting to military hospitals. This drafting of Officers overseas filled a long-felt want, for by this time units no longer travelled as such; Officers now travelled overseas as individuals, thus relieving hospitals in the United Kingdom of much extra work.

With the coming of final victory and the end of hostilities, a fresh duty was imposed upon the Depot—that of re-posting surplus Officers to other theatres overseas. This was undertaken by a sub-unit, formed at Netley, and itself the forerunner of the Holding and Drafting Unit. Original overseas postings, however, were still undertaken by the Depot at Anstie Grange.

With the end of 1945 came a further commitment—that of releasing Officers on completion of their service. This had originally been fulfilled through the Q.A. Military Hospital at Millbank, but was now taken over by the unit at Netley.

By 1945 it was realized that the time had now come to convert
Anstie Grange into a more compact unit, absorbing the Unit at
Netley and thus coming more into line with other regimental
depots. Several Officers, not only from the existing staff but
from outside it, were selected to attend courses at the A.T.S.
Officers' School at Windsor, and so acquire some very necessary
knowledge of regimental procedure, drill, and the many and
various duties of the company officer. Eventually, in April of
that same year, the first Officers' Training Course of the Depot,
Queen Alexandra's Imperial Military Nursing Service, came into
being.

Such was the origin of the Regimental Depot which is today
responsible for such diverse duties as military basic training, for
Officers and Other Ranks, basic nurse training for Other Ranks;
running courses in administration for serving Officers; the release
of those Officers who have completed their period of service;
the drafting of others for service overseas; and the administration
of the unposted strength of the Service.

By August 1948 it had become obvious that the premises at
Anstie Grange were no longer adequate for their purpose. The
Depot was therefore transferred to 'A' Block of the Army
School of Health at Mytchett. By this time, too, in addition to
the basic and administrative courses already in existence, another
course was set up for the training of Assistant Sister Tutors.

In the following year a further step forward was achieved,
with the admission of six Officers to the Commanders' Courses,
conducted by the School of Military Administration at Beacons-
field. This again was a break with precedent, for no woman
had as yet been included in such company; and this privilege
proved to be of particular value at this time, when the change
of status to 'Officers of Queen Alexandra's Royal Army Nursing
Corps', was coming into operation. By February 1949, the
Service had become a Corps of the British Army, with the prospect of administering its own Other Ranks. Four more Officers
were sent on such a course early in 1950, making a total of ten
in all.

The Depot itself, all this time, was steadily increasing in size;

and this circumstance, together with added experience and training now being gained, enabled the unit to shape itself on truly regimental lines, with separate wings, each with its own clearly defined functions.

In February 1950 another landmark was reached, for the unit was transferred from Mytchett to premises of its own at Ontario Camp, Hindhead. At the same time its title was expanded to 'Depot and Training Establishment' to show clearly the dual *rôle* of the unit.

At first, incidentally, the accommodation at Mytchett had proved insufficient, and the Training Wing was housed *pro tem.* at Fernhurst Camp, near Midhurst, in West Sussex. Within a few months, however, it was found possible to bring the unit together again, though still under somewhat cramped conditions; for the Royal Engineers were still in possession of much of Ontario Camp. Some time had to elapse before the presence of road-making gangs, bricklayers, carpenters and concrete-mixers had ceased to be a feature of the amenities of the camp.

So much for what may be called the pioneer work—the housing, training and administration of the Commissioned Officers. The time had now arrived for the recruitment of Other Ranks. To facilitate this undertaking the step was now taken of sending an Officer to learn, 'behind the desk', how other Corps dealt with the initial training of recruits.

For their sympathetic attitude and practical aid at this time, a deep debt of gratitude is owed both to the R.A.M.C. and W.R.A.C. Plans were worked out and initiated for dealing with accommodation, kitting, payment, welfare, and other requirements of the new venture. The planning of a training syllabus, we are told, was a 'monumental task' in itself.

Another step was to establish a course for N.C.O.s desiring to transfer from the A.T.S. and W.R.A.C. This included instruction both at the Depot and Training Centre and at the W.R.A.C. School of Instruction. Out of this small band of volunteers were chosen the first 'Squad N.C.O.s' for the training of the recruits, which was to begin in July 1950.

This was the military side, but plans had previously been put into effect to meet the Nurse training aspect which would form the larger part of Other Rank training. Specially qualified Sisters were necessary for this purpose if the training was to be approved by the General Nursing Council of England and Wales and to provide opportunity for State Registration as nurses. A certain number of Q.A.I.M.N.S. had been seconded by the Army to take a two-year course and had become qualified Sister Tutors. Now, concurrently with other strenuous activities at the Depot, the Sister Tutor Section was expanded into a Preliminary Nurse Training Centre on the same lines as those in civilian hospitals. At the same time arrangements were made to augment the staff with R.A.M.C. Sergeant Instructors.

By July 1950 the organization of the Regimental Depot was complete. There was a Headquarters Wing, responsible for policy and the broad administration of the unit. It comprised three companies, one for the permanent staff, one for the holding and drafting wing, and one for the recruits. There was also an Officers Training Wing, for basic and administrative courses, together with the Preliminary Nurse-Training Centre.

Nothing now remained but to declare the Depot open in due and ceremonial form. This occurred on September 13th, 1950. The Adjutant-General took the salute at a march past of representative detachments of Officer Students and male and female Other Ranks. A drumhead service was conducted by the Chaplain-General. Finally, it was intimated that the camp was to be renamed Queen Alexandra Camp.

Colonel E. M. B. Dyson was the officer to whom was given the tremendous responsibility of planning and putting into being this feat of organization, the formation of the Q.A.R.A.N.C. Depot and Training Establishment. She had been one of the Q.A.I.M.N.S. Prisoners of War in Hong Kong and on her return was posted to the Matron-in-Chief's Department at the War Office to take part in the work of re-organization. She became the first Commandant of the Depot.

CHAPTER 24

TO SUM UP

It is now close on a century since Florence Nightingale and her sturdy following set out for the Crimea, there to establish petticoat (or crinoline) rule for the first time in a British military hospital.

It should here be remembered, however, that female nurses had already been employed in military hospitals since 1800, but only upon home service.[1] They were almost entirely untrained, and their pay was one shilling a day. In other words, they were Sairey Gamps.

Then, in 1854, came the Crimean War, and Florence Nightingale, and the day of Sairey Gamp was over. The Crimean War was followed, as seems to be inevitable in our military history, by a searching *post-mortem*. This led to an immediate and sweeping campaign of Army Reform in which the Army Nursing Services participated, with Florence Nightingale unanimously accepted as guiding spirit.

As a result of the unceasing activities of her party of reform, the South African War, when it broke out in 1899, found the Army Nursing Services prepared to meet the emergency without hasty improvisation or *ad hoc* expedients. There was no lack of trained nurses now, for official opinion had at last been converted to the view that in a military hospital the actual nursing 'must be entrusted to women and not to hospital orderlies'. Netley Hospital could now boast a staff of one Lady Superintendent, nineteen Supervising Sisters, and sixty-eight Sisters. These too had at their disposal the resources of the large Princess Christian's

---

[1] At the instance of Elizabeth Fry, famous as an eighteenth-century prison reformer and philanthropist in general.

Army Nursing Reserve. In the course of the war no less than 1,800 trained nurses were sent out to South Africa.

These nurses were mostly young, keen and of a very different walk of life from that of their predecessors of half a century ago. Very different too were the conditions under which they worked —chiefly in great base hospitals, whither the wounded were conveyed from the casualty clearing stations, swiftly and without undue discomfort, by well-appointed hospital trains. The nurses who served in these trains enjoyed the distinction and excitement of being carried to within sound, though there was no suggestion as yet that they should be allowed within range, of the guns.

Hospital uniform too had been modernized. The crinoline, white nightcap, and apron of Florence Nightingale's Nurses had long been superseded. The Nursing Sister in South Africa took her walks abroad in a grey dress and a 'boater' straw hat, encircled by a scarlet ribbon. The famous scarlet cape too was by this time in universal use.

Early in 1902, with the South African War practically at an end, 'Queen Alexandra's Imperial Military Nursing Service', headed by a Matron-in-Chief at the War Office, came into being. Q.A.I.M.N.S. enjoyed no official rank or status; they were merely trained nurses employed by the Army, and it was as such that they served throughout the First World War.

In that tremendous conflict no less than 10,000 Nursing Sisters were enrolled, and served all over the world, under conditions already rendered familiar to the reader of these pages. They were still precluded from venturing nearer the Line than a casualty clearing station, and these at that time lay some distance in rear of the trenches. But for all that, 195 of them lost their lives.

Army Nursing was no longer in any sense a sheltered profession. The U-boat had added a new terror to transport by sea, and many Nursing Sisters perished by mine or torpedo action, too often in hospital ships theoretically immune from such dangers. Hospitals, too, as we have seen, were frequently bombed.

The same conditions applied during the Second World War, and owing to the progress of scientific research in the art of mutual extermination, upon a highly increased scale. Between 1939 and 1945, 220 Nursing Sisters gave their lives.[1] There was no distinction between the sexes now in any theatre of war: a nurse on active service during the Second World War took many of the same risks as a Regular soldier.

This being so it was obviously high time that Q.A.I.M.N.S. should be elevated to the status and distinction of Regular members of His Majesty's Forces. True, this anomaly had to a certain extent been corrected between the two wars[2] though in somewhat grudging fashion: in 1926 Q.A.I.M.N.S. were granted 'equivalent rank' as Regular Army Officers, ranging from the rank of full Colonel, conferred upon the Matron-in-Chief, to that of Lieutenant held by a Sister or Staff Nurse.

In other words this status was purely honorary and carried no particular weight or authority with the Army itself beyond the confines of the wards of military hospitals. In 1941, however, Regular Emergency Commissions were granted.

In February 1949, a woman's right to hold a Regular Commission in any branch of the Women's Forces of the Crown was recognized by Parliament. Under its provisions the Commission of the Sisters of Q.A.I.M.N.S. became permanent and regular, and the style and title of the Service was amended to Queen Alexandra's Royal Army Nursing Corps, or Q.A.R.A.N.C.

Finally, it should be said that Army Nursing has kept pace with the development of the profession in civilian life. All its officers up to the present time have been trained in civil nurse training schools, though with the introduction of other ranks, some of the future officers may complete their nurse training within the Army.

Short service commissions bring a constant flow of nurses from civil life into the Corps and vice versa, thus maintaining a closer knowledge and relationship than might otherwise have been possible between military and civil nursing because of the long

[1] These casualties arose chiefly from two causes—submarine warfare, and the fact that the casualty clearing stations were pushed much farther forward than in the First World War.

[2] As more fully explained in the previous chapter, p. 341.

stretches of service overseas which is part of the life of the Army Nurse.

The post-graduate professional courses, Public Health, Nurse Tutor and many others necessary to fit the Army Sisters for the diverse demands made upon the Corps in all parts of the world, are taken with other students from varying nursing spheres, at the Royal College of Nursing or certain special civil hospital or centres.

It is worth mentioning that two Matrons - in - Chief Q.A.I.M.N.S. have had the honour of being elected President of the Royal College of Nursing—Dame Sidney Browne and Dame Louisa Wilkinson.

II

Having briefly summarized the steps by which, under stress of war service, the Army Nursing Sisters achieved the final recognition which it had awaited so long, let us proceed to review its present activities in the more tranquil atmosphere of peace-time, so called. This will involve us in a visit to one or more of our great military hospitals.

We will begin with the Royal Herbert Hospital, Shooter's Hill, Woolwich.

The first and outstanding impression of the lay visitor is that the personnel of a military hospital in peace-time contains a surprisingly small percentage of Sisters. This is possibly due to the general shortage of State Registered Nurses in the country. The Nursing Orderlies are men of the R.A.M.C. with a proportion of Q.A.R.A.N.C. women.

The hospital contains 450 beds, nearly all of them occupied all the year round; for Thomas Atkins is as subject to the common ills of the flesh as the next man. The doctors and surgeons are either regular R.A.M.C. officers or qualified doctors and surgeons, undergoing their National Service training.

A Sister has charge of one or more wards, according to size. Her duties are by this time familiar to the reader and need not be particularized unduly: one of the most important of them in peace-time is the training of Nursing Orderlies, by lecture and demonstration. A Sister Tutor is now in charge of these activities at most hospitals, with her own lecture-room, furnished with anatomical charts and other educational paraphernalia. It contains one or two standard hospital beds, each occupied by a pyjama-clad dummy, for purposes of instruction, for instance in correct bed-making without disturbing the patient—an art in itself and a most important one.

I am told that the Nurse Training Scheme throughout the Army is laid down with due regard to the requirements of the General Nursing Council, the statutory body dealing with the training and registration of nurses—R.A.M.C. men and Q.A.R.A.N.C. women can become Army Trained Nurses which qualification permits them to sit for the examination for State Registration as a nurse.

Each ward has attached to it two small rooms. The first of these is the Sister's duty-room, which she occupies when not engaged in the ward. Here she conducts general ward business in consultation with the medical staff. The second is the ward kitchen—or servery. Here special 'feeds' only are prepared; the normal meals have to be conveyed from the central kitchen.

The Royal Herbert Hospital, like others, has its own personal and particular features. There is a chapel, which can be adapted to the requirements of Anglican or Roman Catholic churches. There is a cinema, equally popular both with convalescents and orderlies.

The convalescents, too, have their own recreation-room, where they can enjoy ping-pong and other remedial exercises. A special room is set apart for the entertainment of patients' visitors: its privacy is specially prized by courting couples.

The Royal Herbert was the first military hospital built on the 'pavilion' plan. It is now one hundred years old, though from its trim appearance and up-to-date equipment, it might have been built yesterday. The main staircase is adorned by three busts—of Queen Victoria, Florence Nightingale, and the hospital's own patron saint and eponymous hero, Sidney Herbert.

z

III

Aldershot, well-remembered and well-loved by every elderly soldier, has now been shorn of much of its former prestige, chiefly owing to the mechanization of warfare, which calls for widely extended training grounds; and also to the undesirability, in these days of concentrated bombing, of keeping all one's military eggs in one basket. So Catterick, Salisbury Plain, and other roomier and more distant areas have now usurped much of its authority.

But Aldershot is still an important hospital centre. First comes the great Cambridge Hospital—so called in honour of George, Duke of Cambridge, first cousin of Queen Victoria and Commander-in-Chief of the British Army for nearly half a century. It stands high above the town, with its big clock-tower facing four-square, a familiar landmark for miles around. It is a 600-bedded hospital, and, like the Royal Herbert, is designed upon the pavilion plan, with a wide and seemingly endless corridor cutting right across each building and giving access, right and left, to the wards, theatres, offices and kitchens.

Its activities, as usual, fall into two groups, medical and surgical. There is also a Serious Accident Ward: as previously noted, peacetime conditions are no guarantee against physical disaster. In the Serious Accident Ward I conversed with two newly arrived sergeants, both prostrate with ruptured kidneys—the result of being suddenly brushed off by a passing vehicle while sitting on the edge of a lorry. In a veranda attached to another ward lay four patients undergoing open-air treatment for tuberculosis of the spine, well wrapped up and apparently quite warm, despite the wintry conditions prevailing at the time.

The Cambridge Hospital always seems to be full, though some of the cases are comparatively light. Each patient on entering presents himself at the Reception Office, carrying from his Medical Officer a chit which indicates the nature of his malady and is passed on to the appropriate department. Everything is a matter of routine today: there is none of the enforced high pressure, none of the desperate moments of emergency inevitable under active service conditions.

There are also Officers' Wards, both for seniors and juniors, for Millbank cannot accommodate everybody. The seniors are usually accorded the privilege of a bedroom to themselves. There is also a ward for women Other Ranks.

The training of orderlies is carried out upon the same lines as at the Royal Herbert. Upon the occasion of one visit to the Sister Tutor's class-room I observed an interesting variation in the routine of bed-making: this time her pupils were being instructed in the art of giving an injection—as usual, to an unresisting dummy.

Not all of these orderlies achieve the grade of N.O. Class I, and go on to study for Army Trained Nurse. There is plenty for the lower grades to do other than actual nursing—the handling of hospital equipment, for instance, especially linen, a perpetual labour in itself. Hospital laundry, one is informed, is a 'nightmare', for every single article—and their name is legion —has to be checked and handed in, in exchange for a clean one.

All patients are encouraged to take a pride in the appearance of their own particular ward. This is part, and a by no means unimportant part, of a regular and unobtrusive scheme of occupational therapy. A prize is given for the best decorated ward at Christmas, and each patient participating is presented with fifty cigarettes. In most of the beds too you may behold a man knitting, or carving, or even embroidering.

A further step in the process of moral rehabilitation, as well as of ensuring quiet for less advanced cases, is to get patients out of bed as soon as possible and send them to take their meals in a dining-room. These convalescents, clad in hospital blue, help themselves, *cafeteria* fashion. The spacious dining-room can on occasion be employed as a place of entertainment for concerts and the like. Last Christmas the staff even achieved a pantomime.

IV

The most interesting hospital in Aldershot, and perhaps, for many Sisters, in the whole of the Army, is the Louise Margaret Military Families Hospital, adjacent to the Cambridge, and so called in honour of the Duchess of Connaught, Queen Victoria's daughter-in-law.

Soldiers' wives and children have long been the special care of our Army nursing services, but it was not until the Nursing Sisters so employed were regularly absorbed into Q.A.I.M.N.S. proper that this service assumed regular and official status. The Military Families Hospital is highly popular, for it affords the Sisters a welcome alternative to the nursing of men only.

The hospital is divided into the usual surgical and medical wards, with a special ward for maternity cases. Adjoining this is an apartment exclusively reserved for newly-born babies, all carefully numbered and ticketed. Here one may behold no less than twenty-four of these recent arrivals, each wrapped up in its own cocoon and slumbering peacefully in one of a series of wooden trays set round the walls. An oxygen tent stood in one corner, available against emergency.

Opening out of the babies' dormitory is their bathroom, an establishment equipped with various and most ingenious labour-saving devices. The baby bathing basins in the Louise Margaret Hospital are fixed at a convenient height, while the water supply is controlled by the nurse's foot, thus leaving both hands free to cope with the wrigglings of a resisting and slippery infant.

In addition to the Maternity Ward and its appurtenances there is a ward for small children. It offers to the visitor two interesting and indeed romantic exhibits. One is a small brass cot—all the others are of regulation iron—in which Prince Edward of Wales, afterwards King Edward VIII, enjoyed some of his earliest slumbers. It was presented by his mother, Her Majesty Queen Mary. Close by stands the second exhibit, the gift of the same Royal hand—the Prince's rocking-horse.

The Families Hospital has always been a special object of

Queen Mary's well-known thoughtfulness and generosity. To realize that, we have only to visit the Queen Mary Wing, opened in 1926, for the wives and families of military officers. The necessary funds were subscribed by the Aldershot Command Charities Trust, and were accompanied by a most generous donation by Her Majesty, of plate and linen. Her crest may still be observed upon the silver presented by her.

Queen Mary's active interest in the Louise Margaret Hospital has been maintained for many years, as may be gathered from the frequent appearance of her signature in the Visitors' Book.

As we are aware, Time has recently been Marching On in no uncertain fashion, and our Hospital Services have now been taken over in great measure by the Government. This has brought about certain changes in the control and administration of the Louise Margaret Hospital, including the Queen Mary Wing.

The officers whose families made use of the private wards in the wing were accustomed to pay for the privilege, and the money thus derived was paid back to the Trust. Since the extension of National Health Insurance, however, it is no longer always legal for any hospital to take fees; with the result that this accommodation is now free, and is available, in special cases, for the dependants of Other Ranks.

The hospital as a whole still enjoys the services of one or more Welfare Officers contributed by the Red Cross—St. John Joint Committee. These render valuable aid in occupational and recreational therapy; help with library books; write letters to patients' relatives in the wards; and are of considerable assistance to the ward Sister.

In the wards themselves the patients, as in the Cambridge Hospital, are encouraged to take a pride in their surroundings and enjoy the cheerful amenities provided for their comfort and healing. In one ward I was particularly interested to note that one girl had assembled upon her bridge-like bed-table a varied assortment of miniature toys—china dolls, jumping frogs, tin soldiers, ivory elephants, and the like. My interest arose from the fact that I had only once set eyes on such a motley collection before—and that was along the edge of the desk of Franklin

Roosevelt, President of the United States, in the White House in Washington, the only time I ever met him. These little gadgets were a special hobby and distraction of his, and were sent to him by friends from all over the world, to be passed on in due course to local hospitals.

V

One other visit must assuredly be paid before we leave the Aldershot district. This is to Queen Mary's House at Fleet—a large and comfortable country mansion standing in its own pleasant grounds. It is occupied by a company of a dozen or so elderly Nursing Sisters and Matrons, honourably retired from the stress and strain of their lifelong vocation.

The service of the majority of these was rendered during the First World War, concerning which I listened to many an interesting story. One Sister actually lent me her personal diary of experiences on the Western Front, excerpts from which figure in some of the earlier pages of this book.

The service record, however, of the Senior Sister present went back much further, for she had served through the South African War, and had actually been a member of a nursing unit which had followed Lord Roberts in his triumphant march to Pretoria fifty years ago. Though well over eighty years of age, her memories were still crystal-clear.

Each lady has her own bed-sitting-room, furnished according to her own individual taste, with a pleasing variety of design as a result. The basic idea throughout is to enable each separate member of this little community to preserve her own individuality, and so avoid one of the obvious drawbacks of communal life. Each, for instance, has her own table at meal-times—a wise custom habitually observed in Catholic monasteries, where the Brothers in the Refectory are accustomed to sit well apart from one another, to be free of the tedium of repetitious small-talk. (One sometimes wishes that the custom could be extended to more portentous social functions in the world without.)

As its name implies, the House owes its inception, and a great part of its furniture and equipment to the gracious thoughtfulness of Queen Mary. Her Majesty still maintains her interest in the establishment, and is constantly devising new methods of adding to the comfort of its residents. Her most recent gift was a large refrigerator.

Queen Mary's House is essentially a tranquil establishment, a real home of rest within their means for those whose life's tour of duty has been faithfully accomplished. The more energetic residents have many hobbies and outside contacts, but as a rule the older members retire to bed for an hour or so each afternoon, to rise refreshed and ready to entertain visitors in the big drawing-room downstairs—an entertainment of which one visitor at least has carried away the happiest and most grateful of memories.

A second and larger Queen Mary's House has been established at St. Leonards-on-Sea. This house was opened in July 1948 and many visits are exchanged between the residents of these two houses.

Both houses have guest rooms where friends of the residents and past and present members of the Army Nursing Services may stay.

VI

Our tale is all but told, but one reminder may not be out of place. As the reader will long have realized, that tale has not been primarily concerned with the administrative services of the Q.A.R.A.N.C., important and indispensable though these have proved themselves. Its true and almost sole purpose has been to place on record, in the simplest and least technical language possible, the service and sacrifice of thousands of devoted women, whether gentle or simple, rendered to our sick and wounded in every theatre of warlike operations. Not so much a military history, perhaps, as a human document.

For the same reason few names have been mentioned. Where so many thousands have given of their best, to particularize would be an ungrateful and invidious task: and the members of the Army Nursing Services one feels will be well content to allow the individual merits of each act to be merged in the common record.

We must always remember, too, that in any and every war, some of the bravest deeds must go entirely unrecorded, for the simple reason that no one was present to observe them—and we all know how hard it is to be brave when nobody else is looking. If everything were known, the long tale of Awards and Decorations to be found at the end of this volume would be longer still.

Of the war diaries and personal narratives available for our purpose, it is impossible here to offer more than a selection; but that selection is fully representative of the story as a whole—a story that cannot be too widely known.

That is why it is set down here—partly as an actual record of our Army Sisters' valour and achievement, but above all as an abiding tribute to the gallant memory of those who did not return. One hopes that a study of what they did and dared may bring a certain measure of pride and consolation to those who remember and honour them today. *Sub Cruce Candida.*

APPENDICES

APPENDICES

(A) ORDERS AND DECORATIONS TO Q.A.I.M.N.S. AND
    Q.A.R.A.N.C. (1914–18 AND 1939–45)
(B) Q.A.I.M.N.S. MATRONS-IN-CHIEF
(C) LADY SUPERINTENDENTS, Q.A.I.M.N.S., ETC.
(D) LIST OF RANKS, ARMY NURSING SERVICE (1884–1950)
(E) AUTHORITIES CONSULTED

APPENDIX A

LIST OF DECORATIONS AWARDED TO Q.A.I.M.N.S.
AND Q.A.R.A.N.C.

Orders and Decorations (1914–18)

	Q.A.I.M.N.S.	T.A.N.S.
R.R.C.[1]	138	65
Clasp to R.R.C.[1]	39	4
A.R.R.C.[1]	105	3
G.B.E.	3	1
C.B.E.	5	1
O.B.E.	9	—
M.B.E.	1	1
M.M.	8	—
Order of St. Sava	2	2
Greek Medal for Military Merit .	2	—
French Silver Medal for Epidemics .	1	—
French Silver Gilt Medal for Epidemics	3	—
French War Cross	2	—
Belgian Medal of Queen Elizabeth .	4	—
Order of Christ	—	1

[1] R.R.C. by Royal Warrant, 1883. Bar to R.R.C., and A.R.R.C. by Royal Warrant, 1931.

Awards from 1939 to 27th October, 1952

D.B.E. 3
C.B.E. 6
O.B.E. . . . . 17 (including 1 for service in
                                      Korea and Japan).

M.B.E. 33
R.R.C.[1] . . . 219 (including 2 posthumous, 3 for
                                      service in Korea, Japan and
                                      Malaya).

Bar to R.R.C.[1] . . 11
A.R.R.C.[1] . . . 531
B.M.E. 31
G.M. 1
Mentions in Despatches . 528 (including 5 posthumous, and
                                      2 for service in Malaya).
Commendations . . 4 (including 2 posthumous).

Total 1,369 (9 posthumous awards).

APPENDIX B

MATRONS-IN-CHIEF—T.F.N.S. AND T.A.N.S.

Dame Sidney Browne, G.B.E.,
    R.R.C.   } 1908 to February 2nd,
    ex-Matron-in-Chief, Q.A.I.M.N.S. 1920

Miss Riddell,
                        } March to July 1920
    Acting Matron-in-Chief

Dame Maud McCarthy, G.B.E.,
    R.R.C.   } July 1920 to September
    ex-Matron-in-Chief, Expeditionary 22nd, 1925
    Force, Q.A.I.M.N.S.

Dame Ann Beadsmore Smith,
    D.B.E., R.R.C. and Bar   } September 22nd, 1925 to
    ex-Matron-in-Chief, Q.A.I.M.N.S. December 31st, 1930

---

[1] R.R.C. by Royal Warrant, 1883. Bar to R.R.C., and A.R.R.C., by Royal Warrant, 1931.

Miss R. Osborne, C.B.E., R.R.C.
ex-Matron-in-Chief, Q.A.I.M.N.S. } January 1st, 1931 to January 1st, 1936

Miss A. M. Phillips, R.R.C.
ex-Chief Principal Matron, India,
Q.A.I.M.N.S. } January 1st, 1936 to May 1940

The appointment of Matron-in-Chief, T.A.N.S., was terminated in May 1940.

APPENDIX C

LADY SUPERINTENDENTS—ARMY NURSING SERVICE

AND EARLIER

Lady Jane Shaw Stewart, Lady
Superintendent . . . October 30th, 1869
Mrs. Deeble, Lady Superintendent November 1st, 1869–1889
Miss Norman, Lady Superintendent 1889

MATRONS-IN-CHIEF, Q.A.I.M.N.S.

Dame Sidney Jane Browne, G.B.E.,
R.R.C. 1902–1906
Miss Caroline Helen Keer, R.R.C.
and Bar 1906–1910
Dame Ethel Hope Becher, G.B.E.,
R.R.C. and Bar . . . 1910–1919
Dame Ann Beadsmore Smith,
D.B.E., R.R.C. and Bar . 1919–1924
Miss Florence May Hodgins, C.B.E.,
R.R.C. and Bar . . . 1924–1928
Miss Rosabelle Osborne, C.B.E.,
R.R.C. 1928–1930
Miss Marguerite Elizabeth Medforth, C.B.E., R.R.C. . . 1930–1934

Miss Daisy Maud Martin, C.B.E.,
     R.R.C.   1934–1938
Miss Catherine Murray Roy,
     C.B.E., R.R.C., M.M. .   .   1938–1940
Dame Katharine Henrietta Jones,
     D.B.E., R.R.C. and Bar   .   1940–1944
Dame Louisa Jane Wilkinson,
     D.B.E., R.R.C. .   .   .   1944–1948
Miss A. Thomson, C.B.E., R.R.C.   1948–January 31st, 1949

Q.A.R.A.N.C.
MATRON-IN-CHIEF AND DIRECTOR OF ARMY NURSING SERVICES

Brigadier Dame Anne Thomson,
     D.B.E., R.R.C., K.H.N.S.   .   February 1st, 1949–1952

MATRON-IN-CHIEF
Brigadier H. S. Gillespie,
     M.B.E., R.R.C., Q.H.N.S.   .   1952–to date

APPENDIX D

LIST OF RANKS—ARMY NURSING SERVICE

1884   Lady Superintendents
          Superintendents
          Nurses, Classes 1, 2 and 3

          Q.A.I.M.N.S.
1902   Matron-in-Chief   Regarded as having officer status
          Principal Matrons   ,,   ,,
          Matrons .   .   ,,   ,,
          Sisters .   .   ,,   ,,
          Staff Nurses .   .   ,,   ,,

1926   Granted equivalent ranks
          Matron-in-Chief   .   .   .   Colonel

| Principal Matrons | . | . | . | Lieut.-Colonel |
| Matrons . | . | . | . | Major |

Sisters
Staff Nurses $\Big\}$ . . . . Lieutenant

1941 Granted emergency commissions in the Women's Forces with equivalent ranks.

Matron-in-Chief	.	.	Brigadier
Chief Principal Matron	.	.	Colonel
Principal Matrons	.	.	Lieut.-Colonel
Matron .	.	.	Major
Senior Sister	.	.	Captain
Sister .	.	.	Lieutenant

1949 With the formation of Q.A.R.A.N.C. nursing officers were given rank titles in use by the Women's Forces.

Matron-in-Chief	.	.	Senior Controller
Chief Principal Matron	.	.	Controller
Principal Matron	.	.	Chief Commander
Matron .	.	.	Senior Commander
Senior Sister	.	.	Junior Commander
Sister .	.	.	Subaltern

1950 The rank titles were changed to those in use for Army officers.

Senior Controller	.	.	Brigadier
Controller	.	.	Colonel
Chief Commander	.	.	Lieut.-Colonel
Senior Commander	.	.	Major
Junior Commander	.	.	Captain
Subaltern .	.	.	Lieutenant

APPENDIX E

LIST OF AUTHORITIES CONSULTED

Florence Nightingale and the Crimea:
> *Life* (2 Vols).   Sir Edward Cook.
> *Eminent Victorians.*   Strachey.
> Reports of Various Royal Commissions *re* The Crimean War.

South African War:
> *Official History.*
> *The Great Boer War.*   Conan Doyle.
> *Experiences of an Army Surgeon in South Africa, 1899–1900.* G. H. Makins.
> Personal Narratives, derived from Letters Home.

The First World War:
> *Official History.*
> *History of The European War.*   John Buchan.
> *The Great War and the R.A.M.C.*   Brereton.
> *Medical History of the War.*   Gen. Sir W. G. Macpherson.
> *The Ship of Remembrance.*   Ian Hay.
> *Reminiscent Sketches by Members of Q.A.I.M.N.S.* (1914–1919).
> *Gallipoli.*   John Masefield.
> Numerous Official Reports.
> Many Personal Narratives, Diaries, and Letters.

The Second World War:
> *The British Nurse in Peace and War.*   Elizabeth Haldane.
> *A Short History of the R.A.M.C.*   Col. Fred. Smith, R.A.M.C.
> *Women in Uniform.*   D. Collett Wadge.
> *Nursing in the Army.*   H.M.S.O. (Official).
> Numerous Official Pamphlets and Orders.

NOTE TO APPENDIX E

The Second World War (cont.)

Comparatively little historical research has been called for in this section of the book, since abundant information has been available at first hand, in the form of personal narratives contributed by Nursing Sisters from every theatre of war, by land and sea. The author has been privileged to study at least one hundred of these, and has been deeply impressed by their high standard of narration.

INDEX

INDEX